CW01081389

ROPE & CHAIN HAULAGE

THE FORGOTTEN ELEMENT OF RAILWAY HISTORY

COLIN E. MOUNTFORD

INDUSTRIAL RAILWAY SOCIETY 2013

Published by the INDUSTRIAL RAILWAY SOCIETY
at 24, Dulverton Road, Melton Mowbray, Leicestershire. LE13 0SF

© INDUSTRIAL RAILWAY SOCIETY 2012

ISBN: 978 1 901556 84-1

Visit the Society at www.irsociety.co.uk

Details of the other titles published by the Society and currently available can be obtained
by sending a stamped, self-addressed envelope to Mr.S.Geeson, Hon. Sales Officer, 24,
Dulverton Road, Melton Mowbray, Leicestershire. LE13 0SF

British Library Cataloguing in-Publication Data. A catalogue record
of this book is available from the British Library.

All rights reserved. No part of this publication may be reproduced, stored in a retrieval
system or transmitted in any form or by any means without prior permission in writing
from the Industrial Railway Society. Within the UK, exceptions are allowed in respect
of any fair dealing for the purpose of private research or private study or criticism
or review as permitted under the Copyright, Designs & Patents Act 1988.

Designed and printed by **hpmgroup**, Prime House, Park 2000,
Newton Aycliffe, Co.Durham, DL5 6LR,
0191 300 6941.

Front cover:
*An incline undertaking its normal work on a normal day. A set of six full coal wagons ascends the top section
of the Black Fell Incline on the Bowes Railway in Co.Durham on 27th May 1970. The incline was opened in
1842 and was 1¼ miles long, mostly on a gradient of 1 in 15. It was latterly worked by a 500 h.p. electric
hauler on the skyline in the distance. It brought the Railway's traffic from underneath the East Coast Main
Line between Newcastle and London part way up the eastern side of the valley of the River Team. The second
rope on the right shows that the descending six empties have passed. Note the rollers needed both to separate
and to accommodate the two ropes on the curve. The incline closed on 4th October 1974.*

Back cover:
*Not only did rope haulages survive into the second half of the twentieth century and the days of colour
photography, so did a few top endless chain plateways. This example was operated at Old Meadows Colliery
near Bacup in Lancashire and was recorded in May 1968. It closed on 14th March 1969.*

Contents

Introduction

I came to the University of Durham as a student in 1961, and being from a railway background, I was soon starting to explore the area's railways. These were very different from my previous experience, in two main aspects. Firstly, there were private railways, operated by the National Coal Board, with their own locomotives and workshops. Then there were the rope inclines, mostly on the NCB lines but with a handful on British Railways; I had no idea rope inclines existed. Some were self-acting and operated using gravity; some were powered and used stationary engines. I was fascinated, and began to collect information about them. They were all over a hundred years old and didn't seem to have changed much. Many of the men who operated them had been there for years, and their fathers before them. When they saw that I was genuinely interested, they were friendly and helpful, even putting me in touch with elderly men who had retired but who could tell me some of the history. On the Bowes Railway in north Durham there were six inclines in succession, totalling six miles, and the Railway Manager kindly gave me an official pass to ride anywhere on the Railway, including the inclines; one sunny day I remember getting the bus to Marley Hill loco shed, then catching a loco up to Birkheads on the western side of the Team valley, before riding five of the inclines across to Springwell. Another time I remember riding the empties up from Springwell Bank Foot, to find they went so slowly up and over the kip at Springwell I wondered if they were going to make it!

I had written small railway articles for the local county paper while I was still at school. Then whilst exploring the Bowes Railway, I was loaned two beautiful old nineteenth century photographs of locomotives which I paid to have copied - no digitisation in those days, copies meant having negatives made – and then sent them in to the editor of the *Industrial Railway Record*. They were returned with a request for more information, which eventually resulted in *The Bowes Railway*, my first book, published in 1966 when I was a postgraduate student. I was honoured to present a copy of the 2nd edition to Queen Elizabeth The Queen Mother when she opened the Bowes Railway preservation scheme in 1976. I continued to edit books and write articles during my subsequent career in teaching, mainly for the Industrial Railway Society and the magazine *Archive*.

Then in 1998 I received a copy of the programme planned for the First International Conference on the History of Early Railways. It did not contain any reference to rope haulage. I wrote to the organising committee, to be told that it was a fair point, but that it was too late to rectify it. Then six weeks before the conference I received a letter saying the committee had decided the omission was too serious and would I be willing to present a paper? So I offered a very basic paper, close to the title of this book, and I gave papers on other aspects of rope haulage at the succeeding Conferences in 2001, 2004 and 2008. All of these papers were included in the subsequent books of the Conferences, and I hope that they helped to raise the general awareness of the place of inclines in railway history.

Remarkably, in the whole history of railways, across now more than 200 years, it would seem that there has never been a book devoted solely to rope haulage. Many people said that this was a major gap and that it ought to be filled, and they thought that I was the person who should tackle it. For quite a while I was able to say that I was too busy with the books on the industrial railways and locomotives of Durham. The third of these was published in 2009 and there was one more to do, but again people pressed for a book on rope inclines. So after getting the support of the two friends who would also be committing to a lot of work, and also getting the support of the committee of the Industrial Railway Society, who promised to publish the book when it was ready, I set out.

I was soon overwhelmed by people I had never heard of writing to me asking if I had heard of 'this incline/haulage/haulage system', not only in Britain but in India, Brazil, Australia, New Zealand and Japan. I had originally intended to confine the scope of the book to Britain, but when I began researching, I began to feel that some of these inclines abroad deserved to be included if only as a contrast with those here; and in any case nearly all of them had British engineers and/or British equipment. It was quickly obvious that I needed to make several important decisions. The first was to decide exactly how to define the 'rope haulage' I was going to include. This became 'a haulage where either the vehicles or their contents could be transferred to another means of haulage'. I decided to exclude funicular railways, as historical booklets have been published about most of them. Secondly, it became clear that I would have to include haulage by chain as well as haulage by hemp or wire rope, as the first powered inclines in 1803 were operated by endless chains, and a chain haulage was still being operated in 1980. Finally, although the term 'inclines' is in common use, it seemed to me that it implied a gradient, whereas on the level this was not the case; so I have used 'haulage' as a general term.

I realised from the beginning that the search for information and illustrations would take me well beyond those who knew me from previous work to those who had never heard of me. I am so very grateful to all the people who have so willingly helped me, not just with suggestions but with information, with illustrations, with names of contacts and by kindly reading sections of the draft with which they were expert. I knew too that I, as an economic historian, could well face problems with interpreting the engineering which such a wide range of haulages involved, and I am very grateful indeed for the help of Malcolm Young, a qualified National Coal Board engineer, in explaining so much engineering to me and 'keeping me right' in so many ways. The book would have far less merit without his input. So many people have helped me, but I would especially like to thank Michael Bailey, Ainsley Cocks and John Smith of Cornwall Council, John Cowburn, Peter Darley, Eric Foulkes, Colin Goodwyn, Andy Guy, Philip Hammon and Philip Pells in Australia for so much help with the Katoomba Incline, David Kitching, John Liffen, David Moores and Robin Weywell. Everyone has so willingly helped me and shared their research and knowledge, and I am sincerely grateful. David Butler and Rob Pearman have carefully read the proof pages. But the final text here is mine, and I take responsibility, and apologise for, the errors and imperfections which I am sure the reader may still find.

Diagrams and maps

The majority of these have been superbly drawn by Roger Hateley, to whom I am especially grateful for his skill and patience; the quality of his work is outstanding. I am also very grateful to those who have allowed their diagrams to be re-drawn, in order to standardise the icons used for self-acting and powered haulages. I am equally grateful to those who have allowed me to use their own diagrams and maps. All will I hope enable the reader to understand better the haulages and locations that they illustrate.

Illustrations

These have been acquired from over a hundred sources. They range from oil paintings and lithographs made before photography had been invented to digital photographs taken towards the end of 2011. I am especially grateful to the owners of illustrations and photographs, from all parts of the world, who so very generously have not only allowed me to use their material but had it scanned at a high resolution and without exception waived any reproduction fee for it. I hope when they see the book they will be pleased. Very many of the illustrations have needed work to present them at their best for publication, and for that I am again heavily indebted to my friend Malcolm Young, who has used a wide range of digital techniques, We were very conscious of the ethical issues in undertaking this work, and our prime aim was to do nothing that would alter the view that the original photographer saw. We have therefore cropped, corrected tilt, repaired creases and scratches, removed hair marks, spots and similar marks and we have altered the brightness and contrast and corrected the colour balance where necessary; but the final result is still the picture which the original photographer saw in front of him. I am very grateful to Malcolm for all his skill and patience, which I hope will be conveyed to the reader in the superb range and quality of photographs here, many of them never previously published.

The illustrations are credited as follows:
G.H.Anderson/D.G.Charlton collection: 6-30, 6-33.
J.W.Armstrong/Armstrong Railway Photographic Trust: 1-21, 5-5, 5-36, 6-24, 7-22, 9-20.
E. Ashton collection : 8-6.
B.Bater/Manchester Model Railway Society collection : 2-7, 2-8.
Beamish, The Living Museum of the North : 250, 6-13; 627, 6-12; 17678, 7-12; 23515, 9-6; 80866/Philipson ?, 6-41; 80870/Philipson H2920, 6-32; 80871/Philipson H5293, 6-42; 80872/Philipson H2921, 6-31; 80873/Philipson H2922, 6-40; 80876/Philipson H2923, 6-38; 80877/Philipson H5296, 6-39 (all Philipson Collection photographs by courtesy of J. Morelees); 17678, 7-12; 168228, 7-19; 25756 : 7-26.
courtesy of the Regional Resource Centre, Beamish, The Living Museum of the North : 1-14, 3-15, 5-1.
Bedfordshire and Luton Archives and Records Services : 9-5, 9-9, 9-10, 9-11.
From T and P Berg, *R R Angerstein's Illustrated Travel Diary, 1753-1755* : 1-1.
Bradford Museums : 2-9.
Bradken UK Ltd : 7-50.
Camden Local Studies Centre : 5-42.
Camden Railway Heritage Trust : Fig.24, Fig.25, Fig.65, 10-40, 10-41, 10-42, 10-43.
I.S.Carr/Armstrong Railway Photographic Trust : 1-13, 5-2, 5-3, 5-6, 6-26.
I.S.Carr/Tyne & Wear Museums & Archives, Newcastle upon Tyne : J18392, 6-14.
D.G.Charlton : 1-4, 9-15.
D.G.Charlton collection : Fig.33, 6-17.
L.G.Charlton/D.G.Charlton collection : 1-11, 1-12, 3-10, 5-4, 6-21, 6-22, 9-16.
J.Clewley/D.G.Charlton collection : 5-7.
A.Cocks : 8-3, 8-5.

A.Cocks collection : 2-11.
John Cook collection : 3-17.
Anthony Coulls : 10-8.
John Cowburn : 9-58, 9-59, 9-72, 9-73, 9-74, 9-75.
Geoff Cryer : 9-50.
Peter Darley : Fig.26, Fig.65.
Peter Darley collection : 5-41, 5-43.
Roger Darsley : 9-60, 9-61, 9-62, 9-63.
Courtesy of Darlington Central Library : 2-17, 5-10.
Hugh Davies : 7-32.
Alan Denney : 10-45.
Derbyshire County Council : Fig.28.
Derbyshire Record Office : 3-21, 5-17, 5-19, 5-20, 5-21, 5-22, 5-24, 5-29, 9-22.
T.Dolan/C.E.Mountford collection : 1-19.
Chris G. Down : 9-23, 9-26, 9-43, 9-44, 9-46, 9-49.
John Dunn collection : 6-18, 6-20.
Robert Dunn collection : 9-7.
Peter Excell : 9-40.
Jack Faithfull/Industrial Railway Society collection : 9-68.
H.Forster/J.M.Bentley collection : 2-19, 5-23.
H.Forster : 9-17, 9-18.
Robert Forsythe : 1-22.
Gateshead Libraries : 9-1.
Greymouth *Evening Star* collection, New Zealand : 8-15.
Frank Grimshaw : 7-5.
Gwynedd Archives, Caernarfon : L0001196, 7-29; 1077.12.11, 7-31; 0000372, 7-36; 1077.12.10, 7-37; L0000149, 7-39.
H.Guersching, C.S.Small collection, per John Agnew, New Zealand : 8-20.
C.Hahmann, C.S.Small collection, per John Agnew, New Zealand : 8-23, 8-28, 8-30.
after Thomas Hair, Hatton Gallery, Newcastle University/Tyne & Wear Archives & Museums : 1-15, 3-23, 3-26, 5-39, 6-15.
Mark Hambly collection : 7-41.
Copyright of Harris Museum & Art Gallery, Preston : 2-1, 2-2, 2-3.
Geoffrey Hill collection : 8-8.
Philip Hindley 7-47, 7-48, 7-49.
John Holroyd : 9-21.
The Hunslet Engine Co Ltd : 8-26, 8-27.
Paul Jackson collection : 7-24, 7-25.
Basil Jeuda collection : 1-2.
E.H.Jeynes/C.E.Mountford coll : 2-18.
N.Jones/J.M.Bentley collection : 3-7, 6-1, 6-3, 6-4, 6-5.
The Kauri Museum, Matakoe, New Zealand, Tudor Collins collection : 8-19.
Leeds City Library : 2-14, 2-16.
S.A.Leleux : 7-10, 7-16, 7-40, 7-44, 9-13, 9-14, 9-66, 9-67, 9-76, 9-77.
S.A.Leleux collection : 1-7, 1-8, 1-9, 1-10.
Locomotion, The National Railway Museum at Shildon : 2-6.
John Liffen collection : 5-44, 5-45, 5-46, 5-47.
S.Linsley collection : 6-25.
David McAlone : 9-65.
John Marshall collection : 5-18, 5-26, 5-27.
C.Midgley : 7-46.
R.Mason/C.E.Mountford collection : 3-12; 3-19.
David Moores : 9-24.
C.E.Mountford : Front Cover, 1-20, 3-3, 3-4, 3-14, 3-20, 3-22, 3-25, 6-36, 6-43, 7-20, 7-21, 7-23, 7-24, 8-1, 8-2, 8-4, 9-2, 9-3, 9-4, 9-27, 9-28, 9-29, 9-30, 9-31, 9-32, 9-33, 9-34, 9-35, 9-36, 9-37, 9-38, 9-39, 9-45, 9-47, 9-48, 9-51, 9-52, 9-53, 10-1, 10-2, 10-3, 10-4, 10-5, 10-13, 10-14, 10-16, 10-17, 10-20, 10-21, 10-22, 10-23, 10-24, 10-44, 10-46, 10-47.
C.E.Mountford collection : 2-16, 3-16, Fig.9, 5-16, 5-25, 5-28, 5-34, 5-35, Fig.27, 6-34, 6-35, 6-37, 7-6, 7-7, 7-9, 7-11, 7-14, 7-15, 7-17, 7-27, 7-30, 7-45, 8-12, 8-13, 8-14, 8-21, 8-22, 8-24, 8-29, Fig. 51, Fig.53, 9-12, 9-41, 10-18, 10-19, 10-25.
George Nairn collection : 1-16, 1-17, 1-18, 2-5, 3-13, 3-18, 7-18, 9-5,
National Library of New Zealand, Wellington, Alexander Turnbull Library, W. Humphreys collection : 7-13.

National Library of New Zealand, Wellington, Alexander Turnbull Library, Henry Thomas Lock collection : 8-18.
National Library of New Zealand, Wellington, Alexander Turnbull Library, John Pascoe collection : 8-16.
National Library of New Zealand, Wellington, Alexander Turnbull Library, photographer unknown : 8-17.
National Railway Museum, York : Fig.29, Fig.30, 10-7.
National Railway Museum, Derby Collection, 12325/Science & Social Picture Library : 6-6, 6-7.
New South Wales Library, Sydney, Australia, Mitchell collection : 8-31.
Newcastle University, Robinson Library Special Collections, Archive 11/5/2, by permission of the Librarian : 3-23, Fig.31, Fig.32, 6-10.
Alan Nicholson : 10-15.
North of England Institute of Mining & Mechanical Engineers, Newcastle upon Tyne : Fig.37, Fig.38, Fig.39, 7-1, 7-2.
D.J.Norton : 3-8.
C.J.Osborne/Tyne & Wear Museums & Archives, Newcastle upon Tyne : K54, 6-28; K55, 6-27; K57. 6-29.
courtesy of Philip Pells, New South Wales, Australia, Paulette Myers' album, Belmont, NSW : 8-32.
Ian Pope collection : 1-3; 3-9, 8-10 (almost certainly an official GWR photograph).
Railway Magazine : 3-11, 5-37, 5-38.
W. Rawstron collection : 7-3.
David Ripley collection : 4-1, 4-2, 4-3.
Brian Rumary : 9-25.
John Ryan collection : 7-4, 7-8.
David Sallery : 7-28, 7-33, 7-34, 7-35, 7-38, 7-42, 7-43, 10-39.
Bruno Sanches : 10-26, 10-27, 10-28, 10-29, 10-30, 10-31, 10-32, 10-33, 10-34, 10-35.
Science & Social Picture Library, Science Museum, J.B.Pyne : 2-10.
Science & Social Picture Library, Science Museum : 3-6, 5-11, 5-12, 5-13, 5-14, 5-15, 5-30, 5-31, 5-32, 5-33, 5-40.
Peter W. Semmens : 9-42.
Cliff Shepherd : 9-78.
C.S.Small collection, per John Agnew, New Zealand : 3-2, 8-25, 8-30.
Somerset Record Office : A-BAZ 4-15-4 33; original taken by Herbert Hole, Williton), 2-12; A-BAZ 4-15-4 58, 2-13; A-BAZ 4-15-4 38, 3-24.
John Titlow : 9-69.
Michael Tolich : 10-37, 10-38.
Eric Tonks (?)/C.E.Mountford collection : 7-10.
Tyne & Wear Archives & Museums, DT.BEL/2/287, 1-5; 3-1.
University of London, Senate House Library, Special Collections : 3-5, 5-8, 5-9.
W.A.Potter/Ian Pope collection : 8-11.
courtesy of Railway Magazine : 3-10.
R.C.Riley/www.transporttreasury.co.uk : 8-7, 8-9.
Courtesy of Scenic World and Philip Hammon, New South Wales, Australia : 8-33, 8-34.
Elliott Simpson : 10-6.
A.Temple collection : 1-6.
H.Townley/J.M.Bentley collection : 6-2.
C.H.A.Townley/Industrial Railway Society collections : 6-16, 6-23, Fig.34, 9-19.
B.K.Twigg collection : 1-23.
Tyne & Wear Archives & Museums, Newcastle upon Tyne : DT.BEL/2/287, 2-4; 3-14; 4-4; H19001, 3-1, J18392, 6-14; J18395, 6-10; J18396, 6-9.
George Watkins collection, National Monuments Record Centre : WAT 378A, 6-17, WAT 378B, 6-19.
James Waite : 9-70, 9-71.
Russell Wear collection : Frontispiece.
Robin Weywell : 9-64.
John K.Williams : 9-54, 9-55, 9-56, 9-57.
Malcolm Young : 10-9, 10-10, 10-11, 10-12.

In commending my efforts to the reader, I can only say that I have done my best to tackle this gap in published railway history and hope that I will stimulate the interest of others to undertake further research.

31st January 2013

Colin E. Mountford
27, Glencoe Avenue
Cramlington
Northumberland
NE23 6EH

Maps and Diagrams

Inclined Plane on the Railway from South Hetton to Seaham Harbour, showing the manner in which a Loaded Train of Waggons pulls an empty one up the declivity.]

Frontispiece

In the spring of 1835 the Monthly Supplement of THE PENNY MAGAZINE of the Society for the Diffusion of Useful Knowledge published consecutive editions (February 28 to March 31 and March 31 to April 30, 1835) devoted to the coal trade of North-East England, concentrating specifically on South Hetton Colliery in County Durham, then recently opened. Various lithograph views were included, amongst them this one in the second issue, illustrating one of the two self-acting inclines on the railway between the colliery and Seaham Harbour. There is a degree of artistic licence, as the route did not have the mountainous background seen here. Nevertheless, this is one of the first illustrations of a self-acting incline. Nearly a century and a half later this incline and its partner were to be the last self- acting inclines to operate commercially in North-East England, closing in March 1984.

Chapter 1 Self-acting (gravity) inclines

The principle that the weight of a load descending a gradient could be used to raise a lighter load up the same gradient was probably discovered in the mists of time. The early inventors undoubtedly also discovered that the system worked much better when their wooden-wheeled waggons ran on wooden rails.

For the early developments of rope haulage on wooden waggonways in Scandinavia and in Europe, the best book remains *Early Wooden Waggonways* by M.J.T.Lewis, published in 1970 by Routledge & Kegan Paul. Lewis describes early haulages in Sweden and Austria powered by water wheels and the first self-acting incline in Germany. There were also inclines constructed on canals in Flanders to lower boats down between two levels as early as the twelfth century, as there were to be later in Britain.

The first written English reference to what clearly was rope haulage on a waggonway occurs at the very beginning of the history of wooden waggonways. James Clifford, the lord of the manor of Broseley in Shropshire, opened out a coal mine on his land at Calcutts, from which a short waggonway ran down to a wharf on the southern bank of the River Severn between Coalbrookdale and Coalport. Nearby one of Clifford's tenants, Richard Wilcox, also opened a mine and built a waggonway down to the same wharf. Relations between the two men soon deteriorated so badly that violence broke out between their employees; full details of the dispute can be read in *The First Shropshire Railways* by Dr. Peter King.[1] The criminality was referred to the Court of Star Chamber in London, whose records survive in the National Archives. Violence erupted again in October 1606. On 26th October William Wells, Wilcox' son-in-law, took some men and went to the 'rayles.....where Robert Prescott with others was then carrying coals to Severnside at which time [Thomas Cruxon, one of Wilcox' employees].....did there offer to cut the roope that the coals were let down withall to Severnside.'[2] On 3rd November the 'tilting rails' were 'pulled down' and removed, one man admitting that he pulled out 'the pynnnes of the tilting rails.'[3] New tilting rails were fitted, but they in turn were removed three days later.

King argues that Clifford's 'transport device', with its rails, tilting rails secured with pins and a rope, was a rope-operated inclined plane, with the tilting rails being points at a loop where ascending and descending waggons could pass.[4]

A full wagon descending must have pulled an empty wagon up, perhaps with the rope wound around a drum at the top. King's assertion would thus place a self-acting incline at the very beginning of wooden waggonways in Britain, perhaps even on the first-ever waggonway.

As the Industrial Revolution began to develop in Britain, so there developed the need to move raw materials, and this stimulated technological invention. Significantly, Michael Meinzies, a Scotsman, was granted a patent, No.653, on 9th February 1750 for what was clearly a self-acting incline. However, it was of a type specifically adapted for use underground in mines and rather more complicated than Meinzies might reasonably be expected to have seen in operation on a surface railway. This strongly suggests that, although his actual design may have been novel, the general principle was not. One example usually quoted to support this was on Ralph Allen's Prior Park tramway at Bath, connecting his stone quarries at Combe Down with the River Avon. Bertram Baxter, in his *Stone Blocks and Iron Rails* (1966), states that the incline was built in 1755 by Richard Jones, Allen's clerk of works. However, others since have disputed both the incline and its date.

Interestingly, it is another example from Shropshire that was definitely in use in the 1750s, when its brakeman demonstrated it to Reinhold Angerstein (1718-1760), a Swedish industrialist travelling around Europe. About October 1754 Angerstein was somewhere near Coalbrookdale and came upon this incline: he subsequently wrote in his diary:

> 'When the waggons approach the river Severn, they are hooked on to an iron chain that is wound on to a drum provided with spikes, and in this way very slowly lowered down the steep slope, whilst an empty waggon is pulled up, as shown in the drawing [1-1]. If the waggons start going too fast the winding man has a brake in the form of a wooden lever that is pressed against the drum to slow it down. However, when I was viewing the operation of the incline he let the speed get out of hand and the loaded waggon accelerated so fast that the chain broke and the waggons ran down the hill out of control and were smashed to bits'.[5]

1-1. 'Coal wagon way' near Coalbrookdale in Shropshire, drawn by R.R.Angerstein in 1754. The arrangements at the bottom seem improbable; it is more likely that the waggon was unhooked from the chain and taken on to a wharf to be unloaded.

Tyneside also had quite an extensive system of waggonways by 1750, but nothing is known about whether they included any rope-worked inclines. The first record of these here was made by a French geologist, Faujas de Saint-Fond (1741-1819), who visited Britain in 1784; he noted that 'when the local circumstances have permitted, the weight of the load and the accelerated movement have been combined in such a manner that files of loaded waggons run down the inclined plane and at the same time cause empty waggons to re-ascend without the assistance of horses, along another road parallel to the first.' This would suggest that rope working was not uncommon and that they were operated using parallel tracks with more than one waggon ascending and descending, different in detail from what Angerstein saw.

The first self-acting incline on Tyneside recorded in detail was that operated by Thomas Barnes at Benwell, west of Newcastle upon Tyne, built in 1798. This was 864yds long and the waggons took 2½ minutes to travel. But its design was unlike anything known before. Alongside the bank head was a shaft 144yds deep in which was suspended a cast iron weight of 16½ hundredweights (20 cwts = 1 ton). This was wound round a drum on the same shaft as another drum for the incline rope,

the drum over the shaft having a circumference one sixth of the other. The descending full waggon raised the weight, and when the empty waggon at the bottom had been attached to the rope, the now-heavier weight descended its shaft, hauling the waggon up. Presumably the track was single line, with a full and empty waggon being worked alternately.

Barnes' incline appears to have been unique. As more and more self-acting inclines were built, all over Britain, two basic designs came to predominate, those with one drum or two and those with a wheel. If the rope was wrapped several times around the drum, sufficient friction occurred to prevent the rope from slipping. However, whilst on a self-acting incline the load on the descending side needed to be greater so as to produce a gentle start, the rope being paid out added weight to the descending load, while the rope being wound in reduced the weight of the load coming up. Therefore the speed of the descent gradually increased and some kind of brake had to be fitted to control it – not an easy task, as Angerstein saw.

With a drum two strong wooden A-frames were erected, often on either side of the track initially, supporting a horizontal wooden shaft. The drum

1-2. The single rope drum at the top of the Froghall Incline in Staffordshire, photographed about 1904. This was one of three inclines on this 3ft 6in gauge line, just over three miles long, which was opened in 1849 to bring limestone from huge quarries at Caldon Low to Froghall Wharf at the end of the Caldon Canal. Here, about ten miles east of Stoke-on-Trent, the stone was either loaded as quarried or calcined into lime. Note the very large brake lever held by the man in the centre beyond the drum, and the absence of any protection from the weather for the drum or the men. The railway was closed in 1920.

1-3. In 1873 the Kirkleatham Iron Stone Co built a 3ft 0in gauge railway approximately five miles long between its newly-sunk ironstone mine and the also-new Coatham Iron Works, owned by Walker, Maynard & Co, near Redcar in the North Riding of Yorkshire. About ¾ mile from the mine a ¾ mile self-acting incline was needed to bring the line down from the moor on to the coastal plain. This photograph of its bank head is believed to date from the summer of 1874. The drum is supported by two thick stone walls, and the brakeman clearly controlled the drum from 'up aloft'. It has been suggested that here too only one rope was used, but the raised section in the middle of the drum would suggest that there were two ropes, with the left one coming off the top and the right-hand one coming off the bottom. A careful examination of the picture suggests that there is a central kip for the empties, with roads for the fulls on either side. The lever in the foreground probably operated catch points just below the bank head, to derail any full tubs if they ran away. The 0-4-0ST locomotive, waiting to return to the mine with empties, is KIRKLEATHAM No.1, built by Henry Hughes of Loughborough in 1874 and thus only a few months old. The railway closed with the exhaustion of the mine on 31st December 1886.

was then mounted on the shaft, which was always square in section at this period to prevent the drum from revolving on the shaft. If only one drum was used, it was often almost the length of the shaft between the frames in order to accommodate both ends of the rope. One of the ends would come off the top of the drum and the other off the bottom, so that as the drum revolved, one end would pay out as the other wound in. The wooden disc at one end of the drum would be widened a little to accommodate a band brake, initially made of wrought iron, which would be applied by hand. Two drums could also be used, with a rope on each, but used in the same way. With this system the drum shaft could be extended out beyond the frame on one side to allow for a wheel to be fitted, on which the brake was mounted.

Angerstein's drawing shows a passing place, universally called 'a meetings', in the middle of the incline for the descending and ascending waggons to pass each other. Above and below the meetings single track is shown. This layout created the problem of both ends of a rope, moving in opposite directions, occupying the upper section at the same time. Occasionally engineers would construct an incline with two tracks all the way

1-4. An example with two small drums on the same shaft - at the bank head of the short incline down to the East Holywell staith (coal shipping point) on the north bank of the River Tyne, in 1955, after closure. Note that the drum shaft is square in section, as were many nineteenth century drum shafts; this prevented the drum from revolving on the shaft. The brake is on the end of the shaft in the stone brake cabin, so that the brakeman does have some protection from the weather.

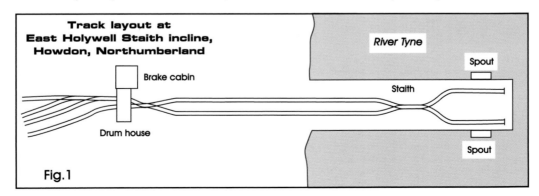

down, but gradually a 'normal' layout evolved, with three rails at the top, four at the meetings and two on the bottom section. At the meetings, the descending wagons automatically altered the lower points so that they were correct for the next ascending set, while the ascending wagons altered the upper points similarly for the next descending set. Engineers soon found that it was necessary to make provision to reduce the tension on the rope as the

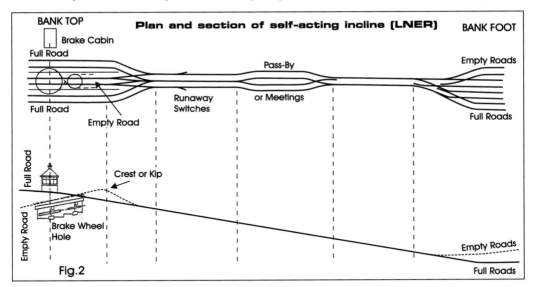

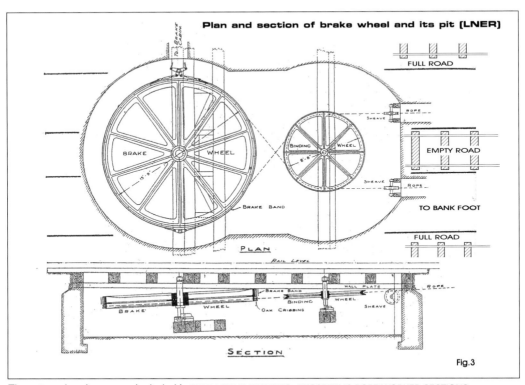

These two drawings were included in SELF-ACTING INCLINES : DESCRIBING ROPE-WORKED SECTIONS OF MINERAL BRANCHES IN THE NORTH EASTERN AREA OF THE LONDON & NORTH EASTERN RAILWAY, *written by an un-named author and published in* THE RAILWAY GAZETTE *on 14th April 1933, 514-517.*

1-5. A small section of the pen-and-ink drawing forming the title page of the OUSTON COLLIERY – ITS WAGGONWAY AND FARMS, surveyed by John Bell in 1820, and showing a set of four full waggons, with their set-rider, leaving Ouston Colliery.

waggons reached the top of the incline in order for the men there to take the rope off. If the incline was at the top of a hill, then the slopes of the hill itself could be used; but if not, an artificial hump, which became commonly known as a 'kip', was built. On reaching the 'bank head' or 'bank top', as the top of an incline became known, the waggons, usually known collectively as a 'set' or 'run', ran up one side of the hump and then as they descended the other side, the rope would go slack and could be taken off. It became the practice to detach the rope while the waggons were still moving, so that they could be run down away from the bank head and so make room for the next set to ascend. Various different layouts were used at the bank head, but some in the nineteenth century had only one track, or 'road', for fulls and one kip for empties, which meant that the ropes had to cross on alternate sets (see the pictures below).

At the bottom of an incline, which became known as the 'bank foot', either the rope would go slack when its other end at the top did the same, or the set ran into a man-made depression called a 'dish', where the waggons stopped and the rope could be detached. A man, or even a boy, known as a 'set-rider', 'waggon-rider' or 'bank-rider', rode on each set, partly to assist in detaching the rope (see chapter 3) but also to ensure the set 'ran

safe'. If an emergency happened, he was expected to jump off and pull a wire alongside the track to warn the men at the top so that they could stop the set; it was not an easy job to jump from moving wagons in rain, ice, snow or darkness. Such men were used from the early days, for a set-rider is shown on a set of four waggons on the title page of *Ouston Colliery – Its Waggonway and Farms* (see 1-5), surveyed by John Bell in 1820.[6] Ninety years later set-riding was one of the first jobs undertaken by boys of 13 when they started work on the inclines (1-6).

Drums mounted above the track suffered from several inherent disadvantages. The worst of these were the stresses and vibration created when the drums revolved, severely shaking the structure. This became worse on standard gauge inclines when the old $4\frac{1}{2}$ ton chaldron waggons commonly used from the second half of the nineteenth century were replaced by 10 ton wooden hopper wagons from the end of that century onwards. The construction involved lifting the drums up on to their frame. The braking of the drum was primitive and there was often no protection for the brakesman, although these problems could be tackled by enclosing both the drums and the brakesman inside a specifically-designed building which became known as a 'drum house'.

[This FORM of REQUISITION is furnished gratuitously. The applicant must fill in the required particulars, sign his or her name at the foot, and either take the form to the SUPERINTENDENT REGISTRAR of the DISTRICT in which the Birth occurred, or send it to him, together with the fee of 6d. and 1d. for postage.]

The Form must NOT be sent to the Registrar-General.

The Certificate is not available for purposes of Secondary Education.

SCHEDULE.

THE FACTORY AND WORKSHOP ACT, 1901.

REQUISITION for a CERTIFIED COPY of an ENTRY of BIR for the purposes of the above-mentioned Act, or for any purpose connected with the EMPLOYMENT in LABOUR or ELEMENTARY EDUCATION of a Young Person under the age of Sixteen years, or of a Child.

To the **Superintendent Registrar** or **Registrar of** and **Deaths** having the custody of the Register in which the Birth of the under-mentioned Young Person or Child is registered.

I, the undersigned, hereby demand, for the purposes above-mentioned, or some or one of them, a Certificate of the Birth of the Young Person or Child named in the subjoined Schedule.

Christian Name and Surname of the Young Person or Child of whose Age a Certificate is required.	Names of the Parents of such Young Person or Child.		Where such Young Person or Child was Born.	In what year such Young Person or Child was Born.
	FATHER.	MOTHER.		
Thomas Arthur Temple	Thomas Temple	Mary Ann Temple	3rd Incline Hetton Railway nr Silksworth	1896

EXAMINED
DATE 25 OCT 1910
DISTRICT CLERK
SCHOOL No.

The Certificate is required for the following purpose, namely:— *To leave School to start work. to satisfy the education authorities*

Dated this __15th__ day of __October__ 1910

Signature __Thomas Temple__

Address __3rd Incline Hetton Railway__

Occupation __Waggon Rider__

WHEREAS by Section 134 of the Factory and Workshop Act, 1901, it is enacted as follows:—" Where the age of any young person under " the age of sixteen years, or child, is required to be ascertained or proved for the purposes of this Act, or for any purpose connected with the " employment in labour or elementary education of the young person or child, any person shall, on presenting a written requisition, in such " form, and containing such particulars as may be from time to time prescribed by the Local Government Board, and on payment of a fee of " sixpence, be entitled to obtain a certified copy under the hand of a registrar or superintendent registrar, of the entry in the register, under " the Births and Deaths Registration Acts 1836 to 1874, of the birth of that young person or child; and such form of requisition shall on " request be supplied without charge by every superintendent registrar and registrar of births, deaths, and marriages." NOW THEREFORE, We, the Local Government Board, in pursuance of the powers given to Us by the Statutes in that behalf hereby Order as follows:—

ARTICLE II.—The requisition to be made to entitle any person to obtain a certified copy of an entry of a registry of birth under the section above-cited shall be in the Form set forth in the Schedule to this Order.

ARTICLE III.—This Order shall come into operation on the Fifteenth day of April, One thousand nine hundred and ten.

GIVEN under the Seal of Office of the Local Government Board, this Fifteenth day of March, in the year One thousand nine hundred and ten.

(Signed) JOHN BURNS, *President.*
(Signed) WALTER T. JERRED, *Assistant Secretary.*

1-6. After 1901 a child could leave school before his/her fourteenth birthday if he/she had a job to go to, but a certificate was required. This was the certificate for Thomas Temple, who left school in October 1910 at the age of 13 to become a waggonrider on the inclines of the Hetton Railway in Co.Durham. Note his address - '3rd Incline, Hetton Railway'; his father was the brakesman for the 3rd Incline and lived in one of the houses at the bank head.

1-7. From the huge limestone quarries at Crich in Derbyshire, owned by the Clay Cross Co, a metre gauge line built in 1847 took the quarried stone down to Ambergate, where it was either loaded direct into main line wagons or calcined in kilns into lime. To overcome the problems of stress and vibration, the single large drum wheel was mounted horizontally and inside a strong wooden frame which was itself supported by two thick stone walls. Note that the waggons passed underneath the frame and drum, and also note the narrow vertical guides for the ends of the rope.

1-8. The bank head of the Ambergate Incline, with the immediate change to a gradient of 1 in 4, hence its nickname of 'The Steep'.

1-9. Looking down the Ambergate incline, which was 550yds long. Two tracks were used on the top section, narrowing to one just before the bridge in the distance for the remaining section. Allowing workmen to travel in the waggons to avoid a tiring uphill walk was the least a company could do, albeit at the men's own risk.

An interesting 'change of mind' at this period is recorded in Scotland. About 1819 Charles Landale (1764-1834), the Agent for the 7th Earl of Elgin, began the rebuilding of the Earl's 6-mile long railway between collieries north-west of Dunfermline and a harbour at Charlestown on the north bank of the River Forth, using edge rails. This work involved the construction of two short self-acting inclines, the Pittencrieff Incline, 360yds at 1 in 12, and the Colton Incline, slightly shorter, with a gradient of 1 in 14.4. Landale originally proposed to use a horizontal wheel at the top of both inclines, but after visiting Tyneside he was persuaded to install drumhouses instead, housing a horizontal shaft fitted with two drums, each 6ft in diameter and 4ft 6in wide and each fitted with a hemp rope 570yds long.

Landale also included an interesting innovation between the inclines. The western track was so engineered that loaded waggons ran downhill from the Colton Incline on a gradient of 1 in 192 to the head of the Pittencrieff Incline. Similarly, the eastern track was arranged so that the top of the Pittencrieff Incline was higher than the foot of the Colton Incline, allowing the empties to run down by gravity on a gradient of 1 in 165. This innovation seems not to have been adopted anywhere else, possibly because of the cost of construction or because it was found to be unnecessary. The line opened on 15th May 1821, with the inclines running sets of six waggons.[7]

Despite the disadvantages of drumhouses, one of the last standard gauge self-acting inclines to be built in Britain included a drum house. In 1890 The Consett Iron Co Ltd, one of the largest iron and steel manufacturers in North East England and also extensive coal owners, acquired a largely-undeveloped coal royalty from the Marquis of Bute in north-west Durham. This had only one colliery on it, which was served by a waggonway just over 4½ miles long down to the River Tyne at Derwenthaugh, operated by a mixture of inclines and locomotives. This line was completely inadequate for the greatly-increased output envisaged, and the new owners planned to replace the inclines with a new locomotive-worked line. But the gradients that would have been involved made the cost prohibitive, and the company finally decided on a line of half the length, but including a self-acting incline 1½ miles long, perhaps the longest ever built. This would take the line down from 506ft above sea level to only 46ft above sea level, with gradients of 1 in 15 on the upper section, 1 in 21 around the meetings and 1 in 19.4 on the bottom section. The brief given to the consulting engineers required that

1-10. Looking up the Ambergate incline from the bank foot. Note the two additional safety chains on the waggons to give added protection from runaways caused by the breaking of the central coupling. The incline closed in 1957 after 110 years' service.

the incline should be capable of running sets of six 10½ ton wagons and of handling up to 3,000 tons of coal in a 10½ hour shift. The consultants decided that using a braked return wheel would not provide sufficient braking power, and went back to a drum house containing two drums, 15ft in diameter and 6ft wide, with two brakes on each drum.[8]

The Garesfield Incline was opened in July 1899, with the journey time for sets being between twelve and fifteen minutes, including the time needed to attach and detach the rope. However, as photograph 1-11 shows, the drum house came to need heavy buttressing on both sides, although this was partly because of mining subsidence. The incline, latterly known as the Thornley Incline, was closed on 22nd October 1960.

1-11. The rear of the drumhouse at the top of the Thornley Incline in Durham on 28th October 1959, showing the heavy buttressing needed latterly to strengthen the building against vibration and subsidence. The fulls went underneath the building, while the empties came up the kips on the far left and right. The incline closed on 22nd October 1960.

1-12. The front of the drumhouse at the bankhead of the Stargate Incline in Durham in 1960, with its two drums visible. The incline was ¾ mile long and took coal down to sidings at Hedgefield on the British Railways' line between Newcastle and Carlisle. The fulls are being run through by gravity on to the middle and right hand rails of the three-rail section, while the rope is manhandled out of the way. Note the different designs of wagon, including the 21-ton steel hoppers owned by BR. The incline closed in August 1961.

The alternative to using a drum or drums at the top of an incline was a wheel, and indeed some of the early descriptions mention a drum when clearly what was used was a wheel; where this is known, the term 'drum wheel' is used here. When two Prussian engineers, Karl von Oeynhausen (1797-1865) and Ernst Heinrich von Dechen (1800-1889) visited Durham in July 1827 and inspected the self-acting inclines of the Hetton Railway, opened in 1822 (see chapter 5), they reported that the rope on each incline went round a brake wheel which lay beneath the rails.[9]

1-13. The rear of an older and rather tired drumhouse at the top of the Randolph Incline near Evenwood in Durham on 7th August 1966. The incline was 1260yds long and was opened in 1895, linking Randolph Colliery to the NER Butterknowle branch. The drumhouse was probably unique on the standard gauge, because in 1962 it was converted from a self-acting incline to be fitted with a 70hp electric hauler to enable coal to be hauled up for the Randolph Coke Ovens here. The 0-4-0ST is WINSTON, built by Robert Stephenson & Hawthorns Ltd at Newcastle upon Tyne in 1944, works No.7159. The incline was closed in September 1968.

However, contemporary visual evidence elsewhere would seem to suggest that at this period it was more common to mount the wheel in a roofed building above the track. The earliest known example of this is found in the water colours of the Middleton Railway at Leeds,[10] painted in 1825 by the American architect William Strickland (1788-1854), who was visiting England like the Prussians to gain information for his sponsors back home. Strickland added detailed notes about the incline on his paintings.

The Middleton Railway at Leeds, serving Middleton Colliery, had been built in 1758, much of it now a heritage railway, the world's oldest continuously-working railway. The gauge when built was 4ft 1in. In 1807 its wooden rails began to be replaced with iron edge rails and five years later it was laid with iron rack rails to accommodate the steam locomotives designed by its manager, John Blenkinsop (1783-1831) and the engineer Matthew Murray (1765-1826). When Strickland saw the railway in 1825 the rack locomotives worked on two levels, one a mile long and the other two miles, separated by an incline 350yds long on a gradient of 1 in 24.

The section of the painting showing the brake wheel house has on it detailed descriptions of the main components:

'A Is a horizontal wheel 16ft in diam, the rim of which is about 9in broad made of wood, the edge grooved to receive the rope. The lower edge of the rim is hooped with iron.'

'B Is a flexible rim made of several thicknesses of lath lined on the inside with thin Iron, surrounding the rope wheels and suspended at a small distance from them. The rim is made to colapse upon the rope wheel so as to check the velocity of the descending load at any time, and ultimately to stop the wagons at the head and foot of the inclined plane. This is done in a moment by pressing upon the lever C. It is a very simple and ingenious contrivance by which 10 tons of coal and 8 wagons are perfectly controled and transported to the distance of 1000 ft in 60 seconds of time.'

The wheel would appear to be mounted about 10ft above ground level. Note the stove provided for the brakesman, and indeed the attractive design of the building.

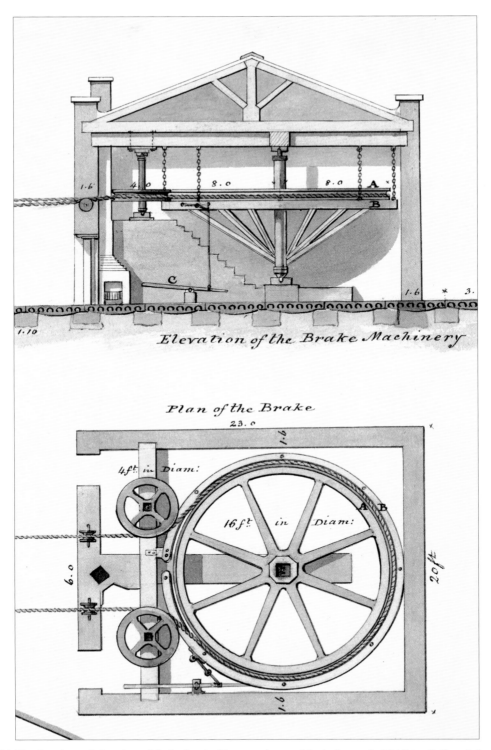

1-14. The elevation and plan views of the brake wheel house at the top of the incline on the Middleton Railway in Leeds, painted by William Strickland on 30th April 1825. Note that in the bottom left the railway passes the building at an angle, thus keeping the rope ends clear of the waggons.

THE CHURCH PIT, WALLSEND.

1-15. A lithograph of a water colour painted by Thomas Hair (c1810-1875) in 1838, showing the Church Pit at Wallsend on the River Tyne, with a brake wheel house basically similar to that painted by Strickland. The Church Pit was sunk in 1802. Note the waggonway from Killingworth Colliery, under different ownership, crossing immediately behind the wheel house. The original painting is now in the Hatton Gallery of Newcastle University.

1-16. One of the self-acting inclines at Pelaw Main Staiths at Bill Quay on the south bank of the River Tyne, taken about 1905. As explained in the text, because there is only one fulls and one empties/kip road at the bank head, the rope on the next set of empties to come up must cross the rope of the descending fulls. Note in the foreground the slots in the rails to accommodate the rope.

1-17. The later conventional layout of a self-acting incline bank head at Whitehill Bank Head on the Heworth Incline of the Pelaw Main Railway, again taken about 1905. A set of fulls, with its set-rider, is leaving the centre road, with the rope emerging from the return wheel underground. The tall brake cabin stands alongside the elevated 'rapper' (see chapter 3).

1-18. A few minutes later the ascending set of eight empties arrives on the eastern kip. At the appropriate place, known as the 'mark', the set-rider would release the rope, which would then fall out of the way into the centre road. Note all the 'sprags' to thrust between the spokes of the poorly-braked chaldron waggons, and the 'gallows' for the fire basket illumination, superceded by the gas lighting. Note too the telegraph pole, with all the insulators for the 'omnibus' telephone system.

There was clearly a major disadvantage in mounting the wheel above the track which took the wagons through to the bank head, as the ends of the rope got in the way, as can be seen in picture 1-15. Another problem is illustrated in picture 1-16 – that of having only a single road for the fulls and one kip for the empties. In that picture the empties have just arrived on the kip and the 'long end' of the rope can be seen down the right-hand side of the three-rail section. This means that the next set of empties will come up that side, while the next set of fulls will descend down the left-hand side. On reaching the top of the three-rail section the empties must cross over the other rope to reach the kip, causing all the difficulties arising from crossed ropes.

The best layout to solve all these problems was first of all to put the return wheel in a brick-lined pit, even if rails had to be put over the top of it when it was not possible to locate the wheel in an offset position. As was noted above, this seems to have been the system adopted on the Hetton Railway from its opening in 1822, but it is far from clear when it became more common. Rope slippage was reduced by wrapping the rope round the wheel 2½ times, thus increasing the friction, and this was increased further by introducing a 'binding wheel' in front of the brake wheel and then routing the rope in a figure of eight around the two wheels, as shown in Fig.3.

The method of applying the brake changed over time too. The system of braking the Hetton Railway's return wheels in later years involved the brakesman sitting on a seat which pressed a lever down a toothed rachet and thus applied increasing pressure to a band brake (Fig.4). It may be that this method went well back into the nineteenth century. The application of the brake by turning a wheel which operated a worm gave a more precise application, quite apart from allowing the brakesman to stand up. In addition, the brake cabins themselves were built higher, allowing the brakesman a better view down the inclines, at least during daylight. This method was used on the North Eastern Railway's Pontop & South Shields branch inclines and on the self-acting inclines latterly operated by the National Coal Board in North East England. Both improvements made the inclines safer to operate.

Figs.5 and 6 give a detailed breakdown of the bank head on the Hetton Railway's No.3 self-acting incline. The brake cabin was old-fashioned by the 1940s in having 'living facilities' included in the operating area, and also in having a second section serving as a store. Every men's cabin had a large stove with usually an adjacent oven, the coal for which was removed from passing wagons. The brakesman was not allowed to go off duty when there was a lull in traffic, but the Hetton cabins were unusual in containing a bed, shielded

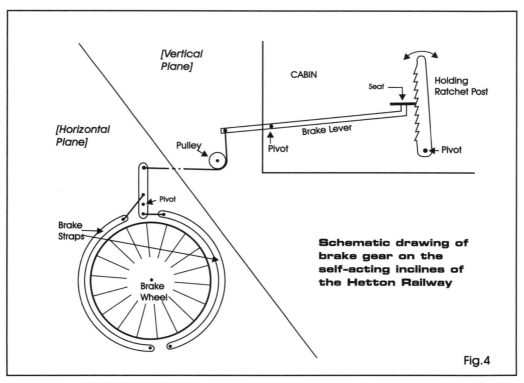

Schematic drawing of brake gear on the self-acting inclines of the Hetton Railway

Fig.4

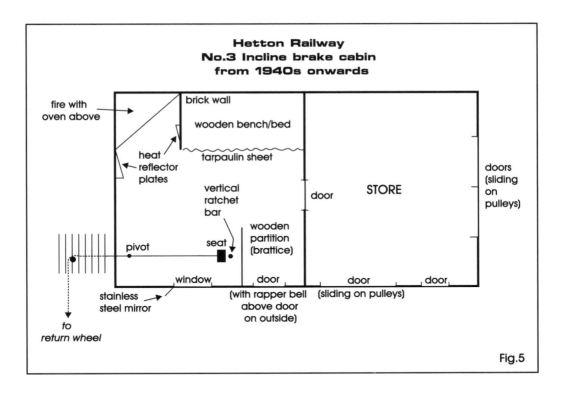

Hetton Railway
No.3 Incline brake cabin
from 1940s onwards

Fig.5

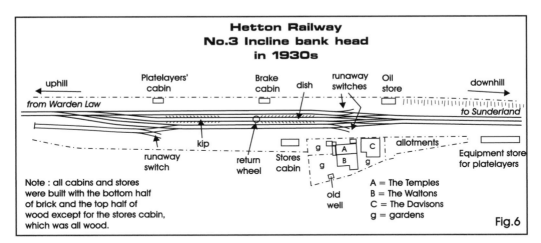

Hetton Railway
No.3 Incline bank head
in 1930s

Note : all cabins and stores were built with the bottom half of brick and the top half of wood except for the stores cabin, which was all wood.

A = The Temples
B = The Waltons
C = The Davisons
g = gardens

Fig.6

by a tarpaulin sheet, with a rapper bell over the door to wake him up when he was needed. Note on Fig.6 that the workmen's houses and their gardens lay adjacent to the railway. As none of the houses had a well, a 3,000-gallon water tank wagon was worked through to them regularly. This stood alongside the houses overnight for the women in the family to hand-pump water into the tanks next to the fire for hot water and into the cold water tank outside. From 1882 the brakesman on this incline was Thomas Temple, who was succeeded by his son, Thomas Arthur Temple, in 1922. As the latter had nine children, an 'extension' built from railway sleepers was added to one corner of the house to provide sleeping accommodation for the younger children.

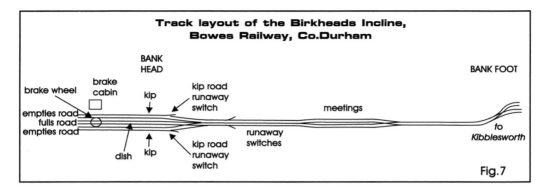

**Track layout of the Birkheads Incline,
Bowes Railway, Co.Durham**

BANK
HEAD

BANK FOOT

brake wheel
brake cabin
kip
kip road
runaway
switch
meetings
empties road
fulls road
empties road
to
Kibblesworth
runaway
switches
dish
kip
kip road
runaway
switch

Fig.7

1-19. An empty set arriving on the northern kip of the Birkheads Incline on the Bowes Railway on the western side of the Team Valley on 21st October 1968. The three rails on the top section can be clearly seen. There were catch points just above the distant bridge.

1-20. The bank head of the Springwell Incline on the Bowes Railway on 29th September 1974. The wheelpit lies to the left and slightly behind the brake cabin. Note the 'bull' (see text) on the kip and the 'chocks' on the nearer fulls road. To the left of centre are the Railway's Wagon Shops, while beyond lie the Engineering Shops.

THE FORGOTTEN ELEMENT OF RAILWAY HISTORY

Even in the later years of self-acting inclines there was no standard design of bank head. As noted above, to avoid the problems caused by crossing the ropes three roads were needed at the bank head. The commoner layout was to have two kips for the empties on the outside roads, with a road between for the fulls, with the wheelpit located at the uphill end of this road. This system allowed the ascending rope from the wagons climbing on to a kip to fall into the fulls road when it was knocked off. This system can be seen on the Birkheads Incline at the western end of the six inclines on the main line of the Bowes Railway in County Durham (picture 1-19). Yet at the eastern end of the same series of inclines, at Springwell Bank Head, the fulls roads were on the outside with a single central kip. However, because the railway changed direction at the bank head, the wheelpit could be offset to the line and so keep the rope ends in line with the fulls roads.

Although some standard gauge self-acting inclines were built with gradients steeper than 1 in 15, most gradients were between 1 in 15 and 1 in 30. The first inclines were quite short, between 350 and 500 yards, but longer inclines soon followed, with the Whitehill Incline near Gateshead, opened on 18th March 1810, being 1,337yds. The Springwell Incline, down the same ridge but further east and part of the Springwell

Colliery Railway, was 1¼ miles long on a gradient averaging at 1 in 24 and was opened on 17th January 1826. From an operational point of view, it was clearly an advantage if such a distance was straight, as then the ends of the rope descended and ascended effectively in straight lines. But straight inclines were not always possible, and where inclines included curves, engineers faced problems, for not only did the rope curve horizontally, it also rose vertically from ground level up to the drawbar hook of the wagon, whilst the severity of the gradient also affected the route of the rope. Sometimes curves could be accommodated by quite low-level sheaves and conical vertical rollers, as in picture 1-21. In other places quite substantial wooden frames had to be built to house quite large vertical rollers or curved steel plates, as on some of the Hetton Railway's inclines.

If the descending gradient was quite lengthy, then more than one self-acting incline was used in succession. The maximum seems to have been four, from the summit of the Hetton Railway at Warden Law, between Hetton-le-Hole and Sunderland, down to the southern outskirts of Sunderland. Combined, the four inclines were 2 miles 624yds, with the longest 1,302yds and the shortest 716yds.

1-21. The problem of curves on inclines. A set of three 21-ton British Railways' wagons leaves the bank head of the Lobley Hill Incline on British Railways' Tanfield branch in Durham, probably in the 1950s. Note how a long line of vertical rollers, initially conical and latterly parallel sided, is needed to keep the ascending end of the rope clear of the descending wagons. Note the angled parallel roller protecting the kip wall, one of a series on the inside of the curve to accommodate the descending rope.

1-22. The return wheel in its pit at the bank head of the Swine Lodge Incline at Dawdon in County Durham, on the National Coal Board line between South Hetton, Hawthorn and Seaham Harbour on 9th August 1983. The rope is wrapped round the wheel 2½ times, with the brake shoes top and bottom.

1-23. Locomotives were allowed on rope inclines more often than one would think, either on their own or balanced against a set of wagons. Here, in about 1895, 'the oldest locomotive in the world' stands on the 3-rail section of the self-acting incline from Elemore Colliery down to Hetton on the Hetton Railway in Durham. Not one of the original Hetton engines from 1822, she was almost certainly built at Hetton in or about 1852.

In his history of the North Eastern Railway, Tomlinson states that in 1841 there were 17 self-acting inclines in North East England alone[11] - 6 on the Stanhope & Tyne Railway, 4 on the Brandling Junction, 2 on the Hartlepool Dock & Railway and the West Durham Railway, and one each on the Whitby & Pickering, Durham & Sunderland, Stockton & Darlington and Seghill Railways, though it should be noted that this list excludes the colliery railways, which would probably have doubled the total. As has been seen, there were a number of self-acting inclines in Scotland by this date, and also in other parts of Britain. Indeed, ten years earlier the first railway in Australia had included a self-acting incline. In 1831 the Australian Agricultural Company took over the sourcing of coal from the New South Wales Government, sank the 'A' Pit at Newcastle and built a railway down to the harbour there which included a self-acting incline, with two 1-ton wagons being run simultaneously. It would seem quite likely that the equipment used was imported from Britain.[12]

What of the hours, working conditions and wages of the men who worked on the inclines? Inclines were almost inherently dangerous. At 6.15am on 11th January 1893 one of the bank-riders on the self-acting Waldridge Incline on what was then the Pontop & South Shields branch of the North Eastern Railway died from the injuries he received whilst attempting to detach the rope from an ascending set at the bank head, and Major F.A.Marindin (1838-1900), an inspector with the Board of Trade (Railway Department), carried out the subsequent enquiry.[13] He did not confine his investigation simply to the circumstances of the accident, but unusually also collected a range of statistics about the work of the incline and the men employed there, which were included as an appendix to his report. This information is rare for inclines in the nineteenth century.

He reported that, starting at 6am, the men had for many years worked for 12 hours a day, but 'some time since' the men had made application for the working day to be 11 hours, which the company had granted. However, this also gave the men a wage increase, for in practice the arrangement was that work should cease at midnight [that is, an 11-hour day plus 7 hours' overtime], but should only go on this long on three days a week, ceasing at 9pm if it was necessary to go on so long on the other days. Saturday work finished at 2pm and 4pm on alternate weeks. The men took three periods of 20 minutes each for meals and could get other rest when there were no wagons to run. Marindin included statistics for the ten weeks between the week ending 3rd December 1892 and 4th February 1893, which he described as falling during the busiest period of the year,[14] and he commented that the stoppages could vary

between a few minutes and 1½ hours, most caused by waiting for full wagons. Marindin took evidence that the men were paid weekly, as follows:

Brakesman	£1 8s 6d	[£85.34][15]
Bank head man	£1 6s 0d	[£77.86]
Bank-riders	£1 8s 6d	[£85.34]
Bank foot man*	18s 0d	[£53.90]

* described as 'a young man of three or four years' service'.

The overtime was 6d per hour, except for the bank foot man, who received 4d per hour. The incline would also have employed a teenage boy to oil the sheaves. It is known from other sources that on the NER the incline men were not employed by the Traffic Department but by the Engineering Department, and that they also carried out all incline maintenance, including permanent way repairs and changing the ropes.

Marindin commented that the work performed by the bank-riders 'has the appearance of a dangerous character....., but that these men have a very long training, commencing when quite young, and many of them, I understand, succeeding to their fathers or other relations....' This close-knit family community amongst incline men continued to be true forty years later, even to sons helping with the work whilst still at school and men spending a working lifetime on the inclines. Marindin also found that the men had rejected a company offer to operate with two shifts, and although he thought that 'a better and safer mode of uncoupling [the rope] might easily have been devised, the men saw no need for that either;[16] the men expressed themselves contented with their lot, and so he felt it would be undesirable to propose anything which might 'disturb the harmony' on this portion of the NER.

Some equally interesting and almost contemporary statistics were given by the NER Chief Engineer, Charles Harrison (1848-1916), in an article in *Railway Magazine* in December 1898.[17] Harrison took the Stanley Incline, further west on the Pontop & South Shields branch, as his example of a self-acting incline's carrying capacity and economy of working, and stated:

> 'This incline is 2,250 yards long, on a gradient of 1 in 17. The rope measures 2,300 yards, and the number of wagons [carrying 10½ tons of coal and weighing 16 tons loaded] attached is six at either end. The average number of sets per week over a period of three years has been 428, equal to 26,838 tons of coal, amounting to nearly 1,400,000 tons per annum. Coal and coke are almost the only articles carried.'

Harrison went on to state that at full pressure, the incline had handled 55,000 tons of coal in a week.

> 'The cost of working this incline amounts to £1,050 [£62,883] per annum. This comprises the wages of six men, including overtime, £520 [£31,142]; maintenance of ropes, sheaves, etc., £350 [£20,961], and maintenance of permanent way and interest of first cost of incline, £180 [£10,780]; total £1,050. The carriage per ton of coal over the mile and a third of this incline will be found to work out at 0.18d [5p], or nearly half a farthing per ton per mile.'

Harrison added that 'the brakesmen judge the speed of the travelling wagons entirely by ear; and so accustomed are they to the different sounds made by increased or normal velocity that they apply the brake accordingly.' He continued 'the drum wheel...has a very long life, but the brakes on it, which are made of thin iron, require to be renewed every three months, and it is necessary to have a jet of water constantly playing on them, as the friction is at times very great.'[18]

Anyone looking at picture 1-15 would understandably draw the conclusion that the operation of self-acting inclines was slow. Whilst that might have been true in the 1830s, it was far from true 130 years later. In the early 1960s the Bowes Railway inclines were handling 1½ million tons of coal per year. With the Railway using a combination of 10-ton wooden hopper wagons and 13 or 14-ton steel hoppers, the average tonnage per set of six was 65-70 tons, close to the tonnage required of the Garesfield Incline fifty years earlier. Operating demands required the Springwell Incline to handle six sets of fulls and empties per hour, or approximately 420 tons of coal, with the sets being run at about 25 m.p.h. Every hour a locomotive brought to the bank foot a further 36 empties to go back to the collieries and collected 36 fulls to take to the coal washery at Wardley or for shipment at Jarrow Staiths. The incline started work at 7am each weekday and apart from a 30 minute break for lunch at 12.30pm, it continued working until the day's requirement for coal was satisfied, rarely stopping before 4.00pm. This was serious railway work by any standards.

1   *The First Shropshire Railways,* P.King, in *Early Railways 4,* ed. G.Boyes, Sudbury, 2010, 70-84.

2   The National Archives, records of the Court of Star Chamber (TNA, STAC) 8/109/8, examination of Thomas Cruxon [m39].

3   TNA, STAC 8/109/8, examination of Thomas Wakelam [m38].

4   King, p.82.

5   *R.R.Angerstein's Illustrated Travel Diary, 1753-1755,* Torsten & Peter Berg (trans), London, 2001, 337-8.

6   Deposited with Tyne & Wear Archives & Museums, Newcastle upon Tyne, DT.BEL2/287.

7   For details of other self-acting inclines in Fifeshire at this period, see *Early Railways of West Fife* by A.W.Brochie & Harry Jack, Catrine, Ayrshire, 2007.

8   For a full description see *The Garesfield Railway and Incline,* presented by J.R.Gilchrist of The Consett Iron Co Ltd to the Institution of Mining Engineers on 17th September 1902 and published in Vol.XXIV of the Institution's *Transactions, 1902-1903.* To permit the upward haulage of loaded wagons of materials, a steam stationary engine was included in the original design, but in the event it was found that the incline could handle these amongst the ascending empties, and so it was never installed.

9   *Railways in England, 1826 and 1827: Observations collected during a journey in the years 1826 and 1827,* K. von Oeynhausen and E.H. von Dechen, trans E.A.Forward, ed C.E.Lee and K.R.Gilbert, Cambridge, 1971, 39.

10 *General Plan & Elevation of Mr.Brandling's Railway from Middleton Collieries to the Town of Leeds, Yorkshire.* All of these paintings are now held at the Regional Resource Centre at Beamish, the Living Museum of the North.

11 *The North Eastern Railway – Its Rise & Development* by W.W.Tomlinson, Newcastle upon Tyne, 1914, 376.

12 *Uncovering & Understanding Australia's First Railway* by D.Campbell, J.Brougham & R.Caldwell, Newcastle, New South Wales, Australia, 2009.

13 TNA, RAIL 1053/82.

14 Because the collieries were working flat out to meet the increased winter demand.

15 Conversion figures as at March 2011, using The National Archives' conversion tables.

16 For a description of the rope couplings used on this incline forty years later see chapter 3.

17 *Self-Acting Inclines* by Charles A.Harrison, *Railway Magazine,* December 1898, 523-527.

18 In later years the brake shoes were fitted with brake linings, and so did not require to be cooled in this way.

Chapter 2 Powered Inclines

As many railway historians have recorded, the second half of the eighteenth century saw a considerable growth of waggonways, together with an increasing use of self-acting inclines for moving heavy loads downhill. But such inclines were limited to this simple movement, and for the movement of heavy loads uphill, entrepreneurs saw canals as the answer, using either locks or tunnels to overcome hilly areas. From the first evidence of a self-acting incline in 1606, over a century passed before the invention by Thomas Newcomen (1663-1729) of the atmospheric steam engine in 1712. The first engines were used for pumping, but gradually they were put to other uses. One of these was to power inclined planes on canals in Shropshire, raising and lowering canal boats on rail-borne cradles; the Hay Inclined Plane, now part of the Ironbridge Gorge Museum and restored, is the best surviving example. The engines used on these planes established their practicality for hauling loads uphill.

Almost certainly the earliest application of steam power to tramroads was on the Lancaster Canal tramroad. The chief engineers for the Canal were John Rennie (1761-1821) and William Jessop (1745-1814), although their resident engineer was William Cartwright. The tramroad was built as a temporary measure to link the northern and southern ends of the canal across the Ribble valley (although a permanent canal link was never built) and came into use late in 1803. It was a double track iron plateway (with the flange on the rail rather than the wheel), five miles long, and was built to a gauge of 4ft 3ins. With coal being conveyed in one direction and limestone in the other, the inclines had to be steam powered. There were three of these, all worked by continuous chains. The first was the Walton Summit Incline, where waggons were hauled up to the canal basin at Walton on a gradient of 1 in 13. This had been replaced by 1813 by a different route using horses, with the engine being moved to Preston to pump water. The second was the Penwortham Incline, which ascended the southern side of the Ribble valley for 232yds on a gradient of 1 in 9. This too had been replaced by a longer route using horses by 1818. The final incline ran for 115yds northwards from the bridge over the River Ribble on a gradient of 1 in 6. This was the Avenham Incline, worked by the Avenham Engine, described as a 'Boulton & Watt

2-1. The Avenham valley of the River Ribble at Preston in Lancashire in 1862, taken by the early Preston photographer, Robert Pateson. The chimney of the Avenham Engine marks the top of the 115-yard incline, while the bottom of the incline was located on the bridge across the river.

engine',[1] and, as it lasted very much longer than its companions, rather more is known about it. The incline was double track, and to house the drum wheels for the continuous chains, there was an upper drum house next to the engine house and a lower drum house actually sited on the bridge which carried the tramway across the River Ribble. Both of the drum wheels were mounted horizontally below a pitched roof but open to the weather. As a pioneer of its type, its early operators soon discovered the problems of operating powered inclines.

2-2. The Avenham Engine, also taken by Pateson, almost certainly in 1862, the year in which its operation probably ceased. The drum wheel for the endless chain can be seen on the left. Note that, unusually, the engine house buildings are made of brick; possibly they were rebuilt when the engine was replaced in 1822.

2-3. The lower drum wheel house, standing on the wooden bridge over the River Ribble. The double track of the 1 in 6 incline can be seen rising steeply to the right. Today a replica footbridge crosses the river at the same point.

The chain stretched a sixth of its length in the first three years of use. It broke altogether in 1826, causing the first of various serious accidents, with waggons ending in the river. The engine proved underpowered, and was replaced in 1822. The engine's buildings survived to be photographed (photo 2-2), as did the foot of the incline (photo 2-3). The site of the engine house was subsequently re-used to erect the Belvedere when it was moved from a nearby park, while the route of the incline is now a footpath in a public park.

Given the widespread development of tramways in North East England in the eighteenth century, it was almost inevitable that it was here that the next recorded example was built. Here the economic pressures were different and perhaps more compelling. Most of the early waggonways in this area took the coal to the rivers Tyne and Wear, because the main market was London. In the west of the area the coal was close to the surface, which meant the waggonway to a river could be quite short. With coal always going downhill, a self-acting incline could be used where appropriate, and horses did all of the other work. But having the shipping points, called staiths, well upstream meant loading the coal on to small boats called keels, which then took it downstream to the places where the sea-going colliers moored. As the demand for coal increased, pits had to be sunk

further away from the rivers, making longer waggonways necessary. With the wars against Napoleon, the cost of horse fodder rose considerably from the mid 1790s, whilst the leading coal owners sought to cut out the keels by shipping much further downstream, which meant even longer waggonways, often running across country, with all the geographical problems that presented. In this combination of circumstances, coupled with the introduction of iron edge rails, it was inevitable that, with the need to haul coal uphill, coal owners should decide that the solution to this was to use a stationary steam engine.

About 1805 a waggonway built from the Birtley area of County Durham to the River Wear at Fatfield is believed to be the first in North East England to incorporate a steam stationary engine to haul waggons. It was located on Black Fell, on the eastern side of the valley of the River Team, which the line had to climb before then descending to Fatfield via a self-acting incline. Interestingly, its construction in 1805 happened in the same year as a Trevithick steam locomotive was being built at John Whinfield's foundry in Gateshead, only a few miles away. This line was subsequently rebuilt in 1809 and re-routed to the River Tyne. It was further rebuilt and opened as the Ouston Waggonway on 17th November 1815.

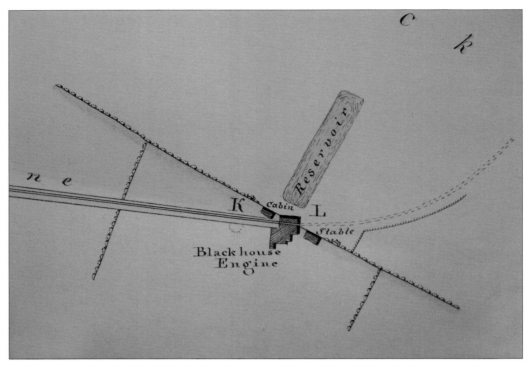

2-4. The Blackhouse Engine, built in 1805, as shown on the plan of the Ouston Waggonway drawn by John Bell in 1820. Note the reservoir, to supply the boiler(s). The engine hauled uphill from the left.

The earliest known survey of the Ouston Waggonway, undertaken by John Bell in 1820, survives in Tyne & Wear Archives & Museums,[2] and shows three stationary engines on the route. Assuming that all three were the originally-installed machines, then the oldest was that at Black Fell. It seems likely that it was a single vertical-cylinder condensing beam engine, with a flywheel and probably two drums, inside a stone engine house. The incline had been divided into two by 1820, and a second stationery engine, called the Birtley Engine, was installed for the lower section. The original engine, known as the Blackhouse Engine, had been replaced by a new engine by the mid-1890s. A little more is known about the Ayton/Eighton Engine, as its replacement after exactly 100 years' service was reported in the local press; but how much of the original engine survived then is unknown.

On these inclines almost certainly a single hemp rope was used, rather than an endless chain, as at Preston. This in turn meant drums, often called 'barrels' in early references, could be used, rather than wheels. Almost certainly inclines operated with hemp ropes ran sets of waggons alternately. The engine would haul a full set up and then it was put out of gear to enable an empty set to be lowered by gravity, controlled by a hand-operated brake on the drum. This method of powered haulage was later commonly known as 'direct haulage'. In the 1820s a set in this type of haulage seems to have been between four and six waggons, of the chaldron design carrying 4½ tons. As with self-acting inclines, most early powered inclines seem to have been no more than 300-500 yards, although the original Blackhouse incline was nearly a mile long. Whilst single line inclines continued to be built, and to be used well into the twentieth century, the increasing demand to carry more traffic saw inclines and their engines rebuilt to run fulls and empties simultaneously, passing at a meetings in the middle of the incline, as on self-acting inclines. To accommodate this sometimes a single drum was divided by a board in the middle; sometimes two drums were fitted. Either way, with two ropes in use, one had to come off the top of its drum while the other came off the bottom, so that when a single drum rotated, or two drums rotated in the same direction, one rope was wound in while the other was paid out. The engine was reversed, and then the opposite happened. If the drums were on separate shafts, then both ropes might come off the top of their drums, but one came out of the rear of the engine house, went 180 degrees round a large vertical return wheel and came back underground to the bank head. An example of this was the Black Fell Engine, built about 1840 on what was to become the Pontop & Jarrow Railway, later the Bowes Railway.

2-5. When fulls and empties were run simultaneously, a 'meetings' was needed in the middle of an incline, a four-rail section where the sets could pass. This picture shows chaldron waggons passing at the meetings at Birtley on the Blackhouse Incline of the Pelaw Main Railway, formerly the Ouston Waggonway, in Durham about 1905.

2-6. A modern watercolour of the final development of the Brusselton Engine on the Stockton & Darlington Railway, looking towards Etherley after its closure in 1858. There are some differences of detail with photograph 5-10 in chapter 5.

It might be thought that such an operation of an incline, with a stationary engine at the bank head, was a straightforward matter, but it was not so in every instance. A report into the Newbottle Waggonway in central east Durham by the mining engineer George Hill, dated 26th May 1818 and recommending the extension of rope haulage on the line, includes a description of the West Herrington Engine, which worked the West Herrington incline, 1,308yds on a gradient of 1 in 72. The engine, a 30 h.p. machine, hauled sets of 12 waggons up, 'but a horse must be employed to assist the return of the empty waggons, the descent of the Plane not being enough to enable them to descend with the rope attached to them'.[3]

It soon became common to site a stationary engine at a summit, so that it could work inclines on either side of it. This was cheaper than installing a self-acting incline on the downhill side. The simplest version of this saw only one drum and one rope used. The engine would haul up one side, the waggons would be detached and run past the engine house by momentum and then the same rope would be attached to the rear of the set to lower it by gravity down to the bank foot on the other side, with the drum being braked. Almost certainly the first engine designed to do this was the Brusselton Engine on the Stockton & Darlington Railway, opened in 1825. Whilst its eastern section was famous for the first passenger train in the world hauled by a steam locomotive, the section west of Shildon was worked by rope haulage. The engine was designed by Robert Stephenson (1806-1859) and was unusual amongst engines on railways in being based on marine engine practice, with the beams mounted at floor level. It has been stated that the original drum was mounted vertically,[4] but there seems to be no evidence to support this, nor to support the claim that it was replaced by a two-part

2-7. This shows the view down the top 3-rail section of the Warden Law Incline on the Hetton Railway, with the 'long' rope end showing where the last empties descended. Note the rail slides for the rope to slide up on to the rollers. Directly ahead of the photographer, between the rails with its raised end facing him, is the 'bull' here, which caught each of the wagon axles as it passed over the top of it; if the rope broke, the wagons would run back and the nearest axle to the bull would lock up against it, stopping the set. On the right, running along the posts, is the wire which operated the white disc at the bank head, which was raised by the bank foot men to show that the set was ready to run.

horizontal drum in 1826. When Oeynhausen and Dechen saw the engine in the spring of 1827 it had a single parallel drum mounted horizontally over the track,[5] which seems more likely to have been how it was built. Having been hauled up one side, the rope was slipped, the waggons were run past and then the same rope was attached to the rear of the set for it to descend the other side, with the drum being controlled by a hand-applied brake. Other engines which also worked inclines on either side of a summit with a single rope were the Barlowfield or Spen High Engine on the Garesfield Waggonway and the Urpeth Engine on what was latterly the Pelaw Main Railway, both also in Durham.

Interestingly, another summit in Durham did not see this solution adopted. This was at Warden Law, north of Hetton-le-Hole, on the Hetton Railway.

A series of stationary engines hauled coal up to Warden Law, but the descent to Sunderland was much longer than could be accommodated by one incline, and this was almost certainly why the Warden Law Engine remained a standard engine, latterly working fulls and empties simultaneously. Instead to the north there were no fewer than four consecutive self acting inclines to bring the line down to the more level section south of Sunderland. The juxtaposition of the two different types of haulage resulted in a fascinating intermesh of ropes travelling in opposite directions as well as the need for careful gradients to ensure that the sets ran downhill by gravity to their next rope. This would seem to be an attempt to speed up the traffic and so increase the capacity of the inclines.

2-8. This is taken from the upper window on the front of the Warden Law Engine House, showing an interchange between powered and self-acting haulage. In the distance is the bank head of the Warden Law Incline, which the engine operated, with a central kip, over which the ascending fulls came, with an empties road on either side. The Warden Law Incline was a standard powered incline, with direct haulage used to run fulls and empties simultaneously. The engine had two drums and thus two ropes, with one hauling up and the other lowering down. Because the track was curved here, both ropes from the engine had to go underground beneath the track in order to reach the bank head. The engine was stationary when this picture was taken, as the rope can be seen attached to the set of six empties standing at the bank head. Don't be misled by the angle of the rope on to the wagons; when these had left the bank head, the left hand rope in the foreground would become straight. There are two cabins for the men. On either side of the right hand one, with its little toilet, can be seen the two white discs, or indicators, which slid up and down the poles to which they were fixed. They were once used by the men at the bank foot, the disc being raised to tell the men at the top that the set at the bottom was ready to run. Beyond the left hand cabin is the fenced-off wheel pit of the No.1 self-acting incline; the four inclines down to Sunderland were numbered from 1 to 4. One end of the rope can be seen coming out from the pit, and because it is taut, it must be working a set. The other end of the same rope comes through an underground gully beneath the kip and emerges through a boarded entrance, passing in front of the man standing there to reach the road on the far side, where it can clearly be seen. The rail cross-over in the bottom right corner led to the boiler house siding and was used to bring a full wagon of coal into it. When the wagon was empty it was run out into the left hand empties road for return to Hetton. A fascinating picture.

However, over time most, though not all, stationary engines working two inclines from a summit were rebuilt with two drums so that both inclines could be operated simultaneously, either by hauling on one side at the same time as using gravity to lower a set on the other side, or by using gravity on both sides. Interestingly, all of the known examples of this involved single line track only, so that fulls and empties had to be run alternately.

The next major development in the use of stationary engines was to use them in a system which became known initially as 'reciprocating haulage'. This was installed on more level terrain where normally horses had previously been used. The foremost advocate of reciprocating haulage was Benjamin Thompson (1779-1867), who became a minor figure nationally as railways developed in the 1820s and 1830s. On 24th October 1821 he took out a patent for 'a method of facilitating the conveyance of carriages along iron and wood railways, tramways and other roads', in which 'fixed engines....at such a distance from each other as the nature of the line shall render most convenient....shall be interchangeable and reciprocal'.[6] In 1821 he adopted this on part of the Ouston Waggonway, replacing the ten horses working the 1,992yds between Blackfell bank head and Eighton bank foot, together with the Eighton Incline itself, by fitting the Blackfell and Eighton Engines with 'rope wheels', which hauled sets of six waggons between them, fulls and empties alternately. This produced considerable savings in costs, but did not prove entirely satisfactory, so within a short time the Eighton Incline was re-instated and a new stationary engine was installed at Eighton bank foot to operate the straight, level section to Blackfell. This continued until 1869, when the boiler of the engine at Eighton bank foot exploded and it was decided to replace the system here with locomotive working.

Thompson subsequently added to his control the management of the Fawdon and Brunton Collieries, to the west of Newcastle upon Tyne, and between 1822 and 1826 he engineered the Brunton & Shields Railway, a line 9¾ miles long between the collieries and the northern bank of the River Tyne at Howdon. Here too he introduced his reciprocating haulage, although whether the whole of the line was worked in this way is uncertain. The line incorporated at least six stationary engines and, unusually, used half-size chaldron waggons, holding 26½ hundredweights; the gauge was 4ft 6in. John Rastrick (1780-1856) visited part of the line in January 1829 and described the visit in his notebook.[7] From the river the first engine was the Percy Engine, built by R. & W. Hawthorn of Newcastle upon Tyne, works no.75/c1825, only 8 h.p., with a cylinder 11¾in by 36in. This drew up 16 empty waggons 95yds in 2½ minutes, with 16 fulls descending with the rope in 3¾ minutes. Also using

direct haulage, the 24 h.p. Flatworth Engine, RWH 59 or 60, with a cylinder 19¼in by 48in, hauled up 16 empties over 2,068yds in six minutes, the fulls descending in 5 minutes. Note that the engines are hauling empties and that the inclines are much longer than fifteen years earlier. Then came the Shiremoor, Holystone and Killingworth Engines, illustrating Thompson's principles more directly. The Shiremoor Engine was 12 h.p, although the engineman told Rastrick that with the boiler pressure increased it was now 'equal to 18 h.p.'; this had a cylinder with a 14in diameter and a 84in stroke. The Holystone Engine, later called the Backworth Engine, was RWH 84/c1825 and very small, only 6 h.p. with a 10¾in by 32in cylinder, and had two barrels, while the Killingworth Engine, called later the Hillhead Engine, was RWH 59 or 60 and 24 h.p. It was identical with the Flatworth Engine except for also having two barrels. The Shiremoor Engine, at a summit, drew 16 empties up the Murton Plane, 1,760yds on a gradient of 1 in 123, in four minutes, the fulls taking the same time to run down with the rope. On the other side, the Shiremoor Plane, 1,562yds at 1 in 172, hauled 16 fulls bringing after them a 'tail rope' - here meaning a rope attached to the rear of a set - from the Holystone Engine in six minutes. The Holystone Engine used this rope to haul back 16 empties 1,680yds up to itself, whilst on its northern side a second tail rope was used on the Backworth Plane in conjunction with the Killingworth Engine. This hauled up 16 empties in 8 minutes, dragging the Holystone Engine's second tail rope, which then helped to haul down 16 fulls; however, when Rastrick visited it on 27th January 1829, the Holystone rope was not being used, as there was no wind and the gravity of the fulls was sufficient to run down the incline and pull the Killingworth rope after it. Rastrick noted an unusual operating feature, that both the Shiremoor and Killingworth Engines drew both the empty and full sets up to the top of their planes before running both of them downhill at the same time, saying that 'by this arrangement these engines work just some of their time'.

This was a similar system to that installed on the Etherley Inclines of the Stockton & Darlington Railway in 1828 by the line's resident engineer, Timothy Hackworth (1786-1850). These were worked by the Etherley Engine, whose initial operation may well have been similar to the Brusselton Engine. Taking the lengths of the inclines and different sized drums, Hackworth calculated a system whereby as a set was lowered down one side it helped to haul up another set on the other side; a detailed description of this is included in chapter 5.

A main-and-tail system was also installed in 1827 on part of the Hetton Railway, between the bottom of No.4 self-acting incline south of Sunderland, and the top of the incline down to the shipping staiths on the River Wear, a distance of just over

2-9. 'Near Atherstone', by Edmund John Neimann, R.A., (1813-1876). This oil painting now hangs in Bradford 1 Gallery and has been dated to about 1845. A very similar view hung in Merevale Hall near Atherstone in Warwickshire, the home of the Dugdale family who owned the nearby Baddesley Colliery. Output from mine workings near Baddesley Ensor was originally taken to the Coventry Canal by a route which apparently included two inclines. Although the painter is believed to have used some artistic licence, the railway detail may be accurate. Note the tall, narrow, engine house, obviously housing a vertical-cylindered engine. Its flywheel is mounted outside the building and a small section can be seen, as can the top of the low pressure, 'haystack' boiler. The two drums seem to lack brakes and are much too large for the rope, which is made of hemp; a wire rope would lie differently. What kind of incline(s) the engine worked is unclear; nearest to the painter there appears to be a rope ending at the waggon and another beyond it draped over the rollers above the gulley, which might suggest there was a return wheel away behind the painter. On the other hand, there are two sheaves beyond the waggon, suggesting there was an incline here too. The 'apparatus' beyond is also a mystery; there seems to be a man sitting at the top of a pole, having reached there via a ladder, and the pole in front of him could be some kind of signal. The implement lying across the track in the foreground is a wooden jack on its side; the circular wooden block would be placed on the ground vertically and using this as a fulcrum, the long handle would provide the leverage to put a waggon back on to the rails.

2½ miles; but as this is a rare example of stationary engines replacing steam locomotives, it deserves to be described in full. From its opening in 1822 locomotives of the basic Killingworth design, designed and supplied by George Stephenson (1781-1848), were used here, but within months this was one of the areas of the railway causing concern to the Hetton directors, and they commissioned another leading engineer of the period, William Chapman (1749-1832), to investigate. In July 1823 he reported that the steam-hauled trains normally travelled at five miles an hour, but that their speed on the final 1,533yds up to the foot of No.4 Incline fell to 2½-3 mph, due to the curves and gradients (between 1 in 109 and 1 in 139).[8] The locomotives were hauling sets of sixteen waggons, here making ten round trips totalling fifty miles in fourteen hours, a considerably stiffer task than faced Stephenson's locomotives at Killingworth in Northumberland.[9] Chapman concluded that the situation could be managed given the existing traffic, but that if that increased, it would be essential to acquire an additional locomotive or to re-model the track.

With a second colliery commencing production in February 1827, the directors decided to replace the locomotives with three stationary engines. The first, situated at the foot of No.4 Incline and thus known as the Fourth Incline Engine (single cylinder, 22in by 60in), worked the first 2,602yds by direct haulage. When John Rastrick saw this incline working on 22nd January 1829,[10] the engine drew up twenty-four empty waggons in nine minutes, while twenty-four loaded waggons ran down, taking the rope with them, in ten minutes. The other two engines, the Winter's Lane Engine (single cylinder, 16in by 48in) and the Staith Engine (single cylinder 22in by 72in), worked the remaining 1,748yds by reciprocating haulage, using one rope each, attached to each end of the set of waggons. When Oeynhausen and Dechen saw all this working, some two months after its introduction, the Fourth Incline Engine was hauling sets of sixteen, but at 10 mph, while the other two engines were working sets of twenty four, and even twenty eight or thirty, again at 10 mph and in about seven minutes,[11] and of course both sections were working simultaneously, a

2-10. The winding engine and gearing at the top of a temporary incline serving the construction of Belsize Tunnel on the extension of the Midland Railway between Bedford and St.Pancras, which was begun in 1863. Belsize was the third of three tunnels between Kentish Town and West Hampstead stations in London. The engine was used to bring rubble, loosened by dynamite, to the surface. Note that the engine house is made of wood, to make it easier to dismantle at the end of the work.

marked improvement on the performance of the locomotive haulage. By about 1830-31 the Fourth Incline Engine was working sets of twenty four, lowering in 11½ minutes, with 2½ minutes for changeover and then raising twenty four in ten minutes. On the neighbouring system the Winter's Lane Engine took 2½ minutes to give signals to the Staith Engine, which then ran twenty-four full waggons in seven minutes; it took one minute for the signal to be given and then the Winters Lane Engine drew twenty-four empties in another seven minutes, giving a total of 18½ minutes to haul approximately 200 tons.[12]

Although the system described above became called 'main-and-tail haulage', this term was later also used to describe a variation of this, much cheaper because it only needed one stationary engine and one rope. At the opposite end of the length of track involved, a 'return wheel' was installed. The rope went from the engine out to the return wheel, round it and back again. The end of the rope nearest to the engine was known as the 'main' end, the other end as the 'tail' end, and with both rope ends attached to opposite ends of a set, the waggons could be hauled in or out as necessary. Probably the earliest example of this was installed for the opening in 1834 of the

Stanhope & Tyne Railway on the section across the moors north-west towards what became Consett. The section between the Weatherhill Engine (see chapter 6) and the Meeting Slacks Engine (40 h.p.) was divided into approximately two halves. Horses worked the first half, bringing the waggons to the Park Head wheel house (NZ 008445 approx), where the tail rope of the main-and-tail system worked by the Meeting Slacks Engine was attached to haul them over gradients mostly about 1 in 80 to the engine house. The Engine also worked the incline on its eastern side, 1 mile 453 yards, lowering the waggons down over gradients from 1 in 26½ to 1 in 58. In 1844, after the Railway had passed to the control of the Stockton & Darlington Railway, the horses were replaced by a second main-and-tail system worked by the Weatherhill Engine, presumably with a second return wheel at Parkhead.

Knowledge of standard gauge main-and-tail haulage is, perhaps understandably, very scanty, but new information can come to light, especially now most Record Offices make their catalogues available on the internet. Amongst the Londonderry Papers in the Durham County Record Office is a detailed survey of the cost of operating the Rainton & Seaham section of the Londonderry Railway between Pittington and the Jane Pit at Newbottle in 1839. The whole of this length was worked by rope haulage, and near Pittington village the Flatts Engine worked by main-and-tail haulage both the branch from Broomside Colliery, 1,377yds on a rise of 1 in 288, and the next section of the main line, 726yds on a rising gradient of 1 in 576.[13] Another section of this railway is also said to have been worked by main-and-tail haulage at this time; whether this involved two stationary engines or one with a return wheel remains to be discovered.

One example at least survived into the 1870s. On 22nd April 1871 the supplement to the *Mining Journal* described Frankland Colliery, to the north of Durham City, and included a description of the railway running from it: 'the haulage beam engine for the pit is used to haul the waggons on the branch railway for ¾ mile by main-and-tail, to the top of a self-acting incline'. It might seem incredible that a stationary engine used for winding in a shaft could also be used to operate main-and-tail haulage along ¾ mile of railway, but colliery engineers in the 19th century were often inventive, resourceful and keen to save money. A similar engine was used not far away at Pittington Colliery. Here a horizontal engine with two 13¼in by 24in cylinders hauled waggons over 1,007yds of the

Railway, replacing seven horses, while ropes from two other drums went down the shaft into the Main Coal seam to haul tubs, the only powered haulage underground at the pit at that time.[14] The engine here had a chequered history: in the history of the Londonderry Railway by George Hardy, he describes how 'about 1863 the frame work [of No.1 Loco] with the cylinders and working gear were fixed on the Pittington waggonway and supplied with steam from a stationary boiler to haul coal waggons along the waggonway.'[15] This adaptation of a steam locomotive, or its design, to become a steam stationary engine was not unique, as the diagrams of the stationary engine for the Khojak inclines in north-west India show (see chapter 8).

Incredibly, a new standard gauge main-and-tail haulage was installed in 1876 on the Hetton Railway. The owners decided that the Byer Engine north of Hetton-le-Hole needed to be replaced, and that the haulage operated by the Flat Engine immediately to the north, 775yds at 1 in 91, would be replaced by haulage operated by the new Byer Engine. Under normal conditions with these new installations, a rope from the Byer Engine went out to a return wheel at the Flat to return to the Byer Engine House to haul fulls up to the Flat. It would then return on the back of a set of empties, running downhill by gravity.

2-11. The Portreath Incline on the former Hayle Railway's branch from Carn Brea to Portreath in west Cornwall. This was one of four inclines on the Hayle Railway. Locomotives worked the branch as far as the incline, which took the line down to Portreath harbour. It was 572yds long on a gradient of 1 in 7, and was opened in 1837. It was double track throughout, with sheaves being used for about ⅔ of its length and rollers for the bottom section. The engine house buildings are just visible to the right at the top. The harbour here was one of the most important in Cornwall, sending copper ore – 140,000 tons in 1840 alone – to South Wales for smelting, with coal being brought back. The incline was closed by the Great Western Railway in 1936. Its route can still easily been seen and it is a Listed structure, whilst the engine house is now a private house.

2-12. The West Somerset Mineral Railway was built between 1857 and 1864 to take iron ore from mines on the Brendon Hills to the harbour at Wachet, where it was loaded on to ships and taken across to South Wales for smelting at Ebbw Vale. The Comberow Incline was ¾ mile long at 1 in 4 and was worked by a stationary engine at the summit. The incline was opened to traffic in May 1858. The mines became unprofitable and closed in 1883 but the railway continued to operate. This picture shows the incline, upon which passengers could travel at their own risk (see photo 3-24), and at its foot stands the 10.45am passenger train to Wachet on a summer's day in 1895, hauled by 0-6-0ST PONTYPOOL, built by Sharp Stewart in 1866, works No. 1677.

2.13. The engine at the summit was unusually sited below the tracks, and its rope drum, seen here, was 18ft in diameter. The railway closed on 8th November 1898. However, the Somerset Mineral Syndicate recommenced mining and reopened the incline in 1907, though it was a short-lived venture and closed in March 1910. The remains of the engine house and its incline can still be seen.

2-14. The original self-acting incline on the Middleton Railway at Leeds was illustrated in chapter 1. In 1827 the railway was extended southwards, ending in a self-acting incline, to serve a pit near Middleton Park Road. When this pit closed in the 1890s, it was decided to retain the landsale coal depot here and to convert the self-acting incline into one worked by a stationary engine. How much of the original equipment was re-used is not known, but this picture, taken in 1898 and looking towards the top of the incline, is worth detailed study. Especially note the unusual crown-wheel and pinion gearing and the rope-gripping mechanism on the drum, explained in more detail in the next illustration.

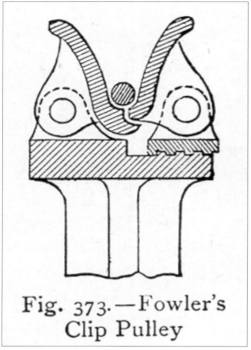

Fig. 373.—Fowler's Clip Pulley

However, in windy conditions the empties would not run properly, and so a tail rope from a separate drum was attached to the back of the fulls, so that at the Flat it could be attached to the front of the empties, allowing them to be hauled down. A more detailed descripton of the engine is included in chapter 6. This provision survived into the 1950s before being abandoned by the National Coal Board.

In his history of the North Eastern Railway, Tomlinson records that by 1841 there were 42½ miles of main line railways in the North East worked by 30 stationary engines. 'These represented a capital outlay of £100,000, the smaller ones (20 to 52 horsepower) costing, on an average, with engine house, ropes, etc., about

2-15. Almost certainly the drum in 2-14 is fitted with a 'Fowler's clip pulley', in which case this is a very rare photograph showing this in use. 'PRACTICAL COAL MINING' Vol.III, edited by W.S.Bolton, London, describes it on p.55 as follows: 'In this clip the throat is made in many segments, each of which is pivoted, as shown [here]. When the rope comes into the open grove of the pulley, it presses the segments down, rotating them about their pivots, in this way narrowing the throat and giving a powerful side grip in the knee-joint thus formed.' The clip thus prevented the rope sliding round the drum.

2-16. Looking up the same incline from just below the bank head in 1950, by which time it was owned by the National Coal Board. The frame supporting the drum wheel can just be seen, with the engine house to the left. The rope is draped across the track. Not long after this the incline was abandoned and became derelict, although some years passed before it was dismantled.

TO BE SOLD BY PRIVATE CONTRACT,

SEVEN STEAM ENGINES, lately in use on Inclines, &c., upon the Stockton and Darlington Railway.

Application to be made to the SECRETARY of the Stockton and Darlington Railway Company, at the Office, Northgate, Darlington; or to Mr WILLIAM BOUCH, Engine Works, Shildon.

"MEETING SLACKS ENGINE," 50 horse-power, nominal; Cylinder, 28¼ inches diameter, Stroke, 5 feet long, Fly Wheel, 18 feet 1½ inch diameter, 3 Rope Rolls, each 6 feet diameter, with Shafting and Spur Gear.

"HOWNS GILL ENGINE," 20 horse-power, nominal; Cylinder, 20 inches diameter, Stroke 5 feet 11¾ inches long, Fly Wheel, 16 feet diameter, 2 Boilers, each 30 feet long by 6 feet diameter, 2 Sets of Rope Rolls, 10 feet diameter, with Shafting and Spur Gear.

"CARR HOUSE ENGINE," 50 horse-power, nominal; Cylinder, 28 inches diameter, Stroke 5 feet ¾ inch long, Fly Wheel, 20 feet diameter, 3 Rope Rolls, one 9 feet 7 inches, and two 6 feet diameter, with Shafting and Spur Gear.

"ETHERLEY OLD INCLINE ENGINE," 40 horse-power, nominal (a pair of Marine Engines); Cylinder, 22 5-9th inches diameter, Stroke 3 feet 2¼ inches long, 1 Fly Wheel, 14 feet diameter, 2 Rope Rolls, one 11 feet and the other 6 feet 2 inches in diameter.

"BRUSSELTON ENGINE," 80 horse-power, nominal; Cylinder, 3 feet diameter, Stroke 5 feet long, Fly Wheel, 21 feet 10 inches diameter, Fly Wheel Shaft, 22 feet 11 inches long by 12 inches diameter, 2 Rope Rolls on ditto, one 13 feet 4 inches diameter, the other 6 feet 2 inches diameter, 4 Boilers, 43 feet long by 5 feet diameter.

"BLACK BOY OLD INCLINE ENGINE," 50 horse-power, nominal; Cylinder, 27 inches diameter, Stroke 6 feet long, Fly Wheel, 18 feet 6 inches diameter, 1 Boiler, 39 feet long by 5 feet 6 inches diameter, 1 Rope Roll, 5 feet diameter, with Shafting and Spur Gear.

"MIDDLESBRO' WATER HOUSE ENGINE," 6 horse-power, nominal; Cylinder, 9 inches diameter, Stroke 2 feet ¼ inch long, Fly Wheel, 8 feet 2 inches diameter, 1 Boiler, 13 feet 9 inches long, by 3 feet 9 inches diameter, 2 Sets of 8-inch Pumps, with the Driving Gear.

Railway Offices, Darlington,
20th July, 1859.

2-17. An advertisement for the sale of seven stationary engines by the Stockton & Darlington Railway, published in the DARLINGTON & STOCKTON TIMES on 23rd July 1859 – a sign of changing times. Note that the boilers of the Carr House Engine were not included; they were re-used for the Stanley Engine near Crook (see chapter 6). On 25th May 1864 the North Eastern Railway advertised all but the Etherley Old Engine again; there was obviously little demand for second-hand railway stationary engines.

2-18. A set of six fulls arriving at Black Fell Bank Head at Eighton Banks on the Bowes Railway in County Durham in April 1965, taken from in front of the engine house. With the set moving at about 20 m.p.h., the set rider is about to pull the pin out of the slip coupling to release the rope, while the bank head man already has his steel hook around the rope to drag it out of the way of the wagon wheels. The engineman has to stop hauling the rope in before it reaches the wooden frame. Once the fulls have run round into the dish and passed the rope end, it will be attached to the rear of the set of empties waiting to descend on the kip.

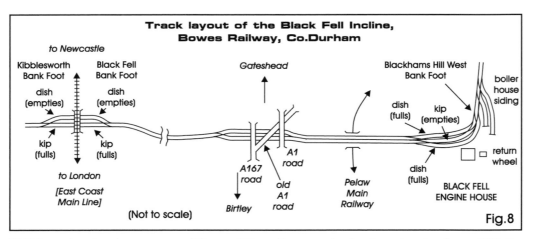

£2,000 each, the larger ones (60 to 120 horsepower) about £4,000. By this system of rope-traction heavy traffic was conveyed generally at a cost of about ½d. per ton per mile.'[16] The cost of working traffic by stationary engines on the Durham & Sunderland Railway and on the busiest section of the Stanhope & Tyne Railway was £485 per mile, or £21,388.50 in 2011 values. There would be many more than 30 stationary engines if those not on main line railways could be added.

However, in the two decades from 1820 the construction of railways which included stationary engines spread well outside North East England, including as far away as Cornwall. The Hayle Railway in western Cornwall linked the engineering works and quays at Hayle with the copper mines of Redruth and Camborne, carrying ore to the port and coal to the mines. The 17-mile line, opened in 1837, incorporated four inclines on its main line, one powered and one self-acting incline (Angarrack and Penponds), together with

2-19. An engine house and its associated buildings in a typical country landscape: the Middleton Engine on the Cromford & High Peak Railway in Derbyhire on 16th August 1958. The engine house itself is behind the 80ft chimney, with the boilers to the left and the engineman's house in the centre of the picture. There was also a loco shed and its water tank here, with a reservoir serving both the shed and the engine.

a second self-acting incline on the Tresavean branch and a second powered incline on the Portreath branch, down into Portreath harbour (see 2-11). Although the first three were subsequently by-passed, the Portreath Incline lasted, under the ownership of the Great Western Railway, into the 1930s.

As the design of steam locomotives developed and they became more powerful, main-and-tail haulage became unnecessary, although in its narrow gauge format it became used widely at collieries, especially underground (see chapter 7). Other inclines became victims of steadily-increasing traffic which they were unable to handle, causing railway companies to build new lines, often quite heavily graded, to avoid them. It was a sign of these changing times that on 23rd July 1859 the Stockton & Darlington Railway placed an advertisement in the *Darlington & Stockton Times* (2-17).

An offer for sale of SEVEN railway stationary engines in one advertisement must be unique. Meeting Slacks, Howns Gill and Carr House were on the former Stanhope & Tyne Railway, while Brusselton and Etherley had been on the original Stockton & Darlington main line (for all of these,

see chapter 5) and Black Boy on one of its branches, with the Middlesbrough Engine from the dock there. Because such details are often difficult to find, their inclusion makes the notice important for research. Yet notice that in the section for the Carr House Engine, the boilers have not been included – because two of them had been re-used in the construction of a <u>new</u> stationary engine on the Stanley branch near Crook (see chapter 6).

Despite this advertisement, the end of stationary engines on surface standard-gauge railways in Britain was over a century away. The Stanley Engine lasted on British Railways until 1951, as did the Crawleyside and Weatherhill Engines on the Stanhope & Tyne, while others lasted much longer. The last powered incline on British Railways was the Sheep Pasture Incline on the Cromford & High Peak Railway in Derbyshire, which worked until 30th April 1967. Those on National Coal Board railways lasted longer still, the Kibblesworth, Black Fell and Blackham's Hill Engines on the Bowes Railway in County Durham not ceasing commercial operation until 4th October 1974. The last powered inclines in Britain continued in use until 1986.

1   This does not necessarily mean that the engine was built by Boulton & Watt at their Soho Works in Birmingham; by the early nineteenth century the term a 'Boulton & Watt engine' was commonly used to describe any single cylinder beam engine using low pressure steam. High pressure engines, developed by Trevithick and others, are often described as simply 'H.P.'[engines].

2   *Ouston Colliery, its Waggonway and Farms* by John Bell, TWA DT.BEL2/287.

3   North of England Institute of Mining & Mechanical Engineers, Newcastle upon Tyne, Buddle-Atkinson Collection, 3410/East/1/142.

4   *The Stockton & Darlington Railway, 1825-1875* by P.J.Holmes, Ayr, 1975, 19.

5   *Railways in England, 1826 and 1827,* by C. von Oeynhausen and H. von Dechen, trans. E.A.Forward, Cambridge, 1971, 22.

6   Thompson describes his system in detail in *The Engineers and Mechanics Encyclopedia,* 1839, 416.

7   Notebook IV of John Rastrick, now held in the Special Collections of the Senate House Library in the University of London, 62 onwards.

8   Northumberland Archives [NA], 725/F/17, 64.

9   At Killingworth the locomotives were hauling sets of only twelve waggons on virtually level track, for a distance of only about two miles each way.

10 Rastrick terms it 'No.3 Engine', with the Winter's Lane Engine 'No.2' and the Staith Engine 'No.1'.

11 *Railways in England, 1826 and 1827,* 38.

12 Report by Charles Robinson, the Hetton Railway's Engineer, to his directors; NA, 725/F/17, 282. Rastrick saw the waggons take ten minutes, though he noted that they 'usually pass this distance in 9 minutes'.

13 Durham County Record Office (DCRO), D/Lo/B/306/22.

14 Beamish, The Living Museum of the North, Regional Resource Centre, Place Collection, 2003-54.7/42.

15 Hardy (1825-1917) worked on the Londonderry Railway from 1855; in 1883 he became Railway Manager, a post which he held until 1902; a copy of his hand-written autobiography is held in the library of the Regional Resource Centre at Beamish. The quotation is from p.230 of this manuscript. No.1 Loco was a 0-4-0 tender engine built by Robert Stephenson & Co at Newcastle upon Tyne in 1849, Works No.753, with 14in by 22in cylinders.

16 Tomlinson, 377. A ½d (a half-penny, pre-decimal money) would be worth about 9p in 2011 values.

Chapter 3 Ropes, chains, illumination, communication and passengers

1. Ropes and chains

When inclines first began to be introduced, the majority used hemp rope. This was used extensively in shipping and a wide range of industries, it was readily available and it could be manufactured or spliced into long lengths. Initially inclines were quite short, but the Whitehill Incline near Gateshead, opened in 1810, was over 1,300yds and the Springwell Colliery Railway's Springwell Incline, descending the same ridge and opened in January 1826, was about 1¼ miles long and so would have needed a hemp rope of more than 2,000yds. To help preserve them some of these early ropes were tarred, which resulted in a smooth, glossy surface and so reduced the wear from friction.

In his history of the Liverpool & Manchester Railway, Thomas[1] states that a 'New Patent India Rubber Rope' was installed in the small tunnel at Liverpool in 1832, while Tomlinson records that, when the inclines on the Stanhope & Tyne Railway were first opened in 1834, the ropes were made of an india rubber solution, but this material was found to swell and become soft in wet weather, and so was unsuitable.[2]

The alternative to hemp was chain. This was used on the inclines of the Lancaster Canal Tramroad in 1803 and on those of the Cromford & High Peak Railway in 1830-31. It would appear that this was preferred when the inclines were very steep and when the choice of haulage was an endless system. Because of the weight involved, it would seem that such inclines rarely exceeded 500-600 yards. It is believed that the chains went round the drum wheels in simple grooves, rather than around sprockets. One can assume that chains lasted longer than hemp, but that their initial cost was considerably higher and that chains about a mile long were difficult to transport and man-handle on site.

An extremely detailed analysis of the first two years' operation of the Hetton Railway, opened in 1822, was written in 1824 by the railway's superintendent, George Dodds.[3] The Hetton Railway at its opening had seven inclines, two worked by stationary engines and five worked by gravity. The seven ropes varied in length between 800 and 1,300 yards (in other words, none exceeded ¾ mile) and there were three different sizes, with circumferences of 4in, 5in and 7¼in. The heaviest (3 tons 2 hundredweights) and most expensive rope (£155), 1,000yds @ 7¼in in girth, was used on the Byer/Byre Engine bank; the lightest, only 15 hundredweights and costing only £37-10s-0d, 800yds @ 4in, was used on the 3rd self-

acting incline. Dodds records the precise life of every rope, and from his tables it is clear that the ropes on the powered inclines had a shorter working life than those on the self-acting inclines, though he does not go on to explain the wide variations, from nearly a year to only 3½ months. Ropes on the self-acting inclines usually lasted about a year, though that on the 4th self-acting incline lasted a year and 8 months, which Dodds pointedly attributed to the other inclines having 'a very strong turn' in them. Because the stationary engines were hauling eight waggons at a time, the ropes had to be thicker, but as the drums were only 7ft in diameter, so 'the rope having to traverse 4 times over itself is greatly injured'.[4] Dodds goes on to say that 'ropes lying on railways are exposed to be cut by malicious or mischievous persons [and] we have had……several accidents by ropes breaking with a train of loaded waggons on the ascending planes which causes great breakage of wheels and rails….'.[5] John Rastrick, visiting the Hetton Railway on 22nd January 1829, actually saw a rope break, and recorded that it took 1½ hours to repair it. Tomlinson gives figures similar to Dodds for the Stanhope & Tyne Railway, the heaviest being 8½in in circumference and weighing 6 tons per mile; the stationary engines worked at speeds between 7 and 11 miles per hour, with loads of 24, 32, 48 and even 96 tons attached to them, and often worked 12 hours a day or more.[6] However, hemp ropes always stretched. Timothy Hackworth told Rastrick on 17th January 1829 that the new rope put on the South Incline at Etherley on the Stockton & Darlington Railway on 1st June 1828 stretched 70 fathoms [420 yards] on its first day of use,[7] while Thomas records that the endless rope in the Lime Street Tunnel at Liverpool, 4,800yds long, 6in in girth, weighing 8½ tons and 'tarred to the point of saturation', stretched nearly 500 yards in its first few weeks of operation.[8]

Such work was far more demanding than anything else done by hemp ropes at the time and so there was an increasing demand for a replacement for both hemp ropes and chains. The breakthrough came with the invention of wire rope by the German mining engineer Wilhelm Ducay between 1831 and 1834, for use in mining in Lower Saxony in Germany. This consisted of six wires twisted around a hemp rope core, and then sets of such strands being added, being twisted in alternating directions for extra stability. Whereas flaws in a chain link, often unseen to the naked eye, could lead to catastrophic failure, flaws in the numerous wires making up a wire cable are less critical as other wires take up the load. Friction between the individual wires, as a consequence of their twist,

3-1. This picture used to hang in the offices of Messrs. Dixon, Corbitt Ltd, Teams Rope Works, Gateshead, Co.Durham. Taken in August 1931, it shows a steel rope 1¼ miles long and 4¼in in circumference, supplied by this firm to the Abdon Clee Stone Quarry Co. Ltd in Shropshire for its Clee Hill Incline in 1909. A note on the picture stated that its average rate of travel was 35 miles per hour and that it had operated continuously for 22 years and appeared good for a similar period. Note that the rails are only flat-bottomed and are simply dogged to the wooden sleepers. Note also that the roller in the foreground has become stuck and been cut through by the rope; this problem was not uncommon.

3-2. Splicing a steel rope at the bank head of one of the Serra Nova inclines on the Sao Paulo Railway in Brazil about 1920. The five inclines here (see chapter 8) used an endless rope system and so the ends of each incline's rope, 5¼in in diameter, had to be spliced together, a labour-intensive job. Note the British influence in the signalling.

further compensates for any flaws. At first the wires were made of wrought iron, to be replaced by steel when inventions in steel manufacture in the second half of the nineteenth century made possible the mass production of cheap steel. The production of wire rope soon spread to Britain, and the first wire ropes on railways in North East England came into use in 1841. Steel wire began to replace iron wire in the late 1860s, and quite quickly became universal.

Railway engineers learned how to use wire ropes to best advantage on haulages. Introducing a length of chain between the end of a rope and the wagon coupling proved to have a number of advantages.

The most vulnerable part of a wire haulage rope proved to be the last few feet at the socket end. It was exposed to damage from the wagon wheels and was constantly man-handled and easily 'kinked' from incorrect handling. With a chain, its flexibility is a great advantage when man-handling the coupling end during its transfer from one set of wagons to another. If a chain should be damaged, the damaged section can be readily replaced. Repairing a damaged rope end requires

the damaged portion to be cut off and the socket on the end to be re-fitted, quite a long job. In addition, when under load and as the length of the rope changes during haulage, it was found that a wire rope needs to rotate to relieve stresses. In the nineteenth century one attempt to overcome this, especially on long inclines, was to introduce a swivel into the rope. In the twentieth century a length of chain was inserted between the socket at the end of the rope and the coupling attached to the wagons, which both helped to reduce the torsion and also damage in this area. The length of the inserted chain varied, as can be seen by comparing photographs 2-5 and 9-50.

It was soon recognised that if failure of haulage ropes, shackles, etc., was to be minimised, regular examination and maintenance was essential. This developed into a statutory obligation whereby periodically the rope end has to be cut off and sent for internal examination. The attachments are thoroughly examined, and depending on the composition of the metal they are made from, they are subject to a heat treatment process. Provided the examination of the cut length shows the rope to be fit for further service, it is re-capped.

3-3. The Bowes Railway's Reel Wagon being used to pay out a new rope for the north drum on the Black Fell Incline on 4th February 1971.

Descriptions of changing a rope are very rare. To replace an old rope on a powered incline was a day's work. The author saw the old rope on the north drum of the Black Fell Engine on the Bowes Railway changed on a Saturday in 1971 (photo 3-3). The new rope, on its wooden drum and carried on what was known as the 'reel wagon', had been worked through to the Engine at the front of the last empties on the Friday evening. First of all the old rope had to be taken off, by the engine paying out the rope slowly and the men outside carrying it round and laying it in a circle, until the end was finally released from the drum. When the drum was empty, the new rope had to be man-handled from the bank head, through the underground gully and round the return wheel at the rear of the engine before being taken into the Engine and attached to the drum. It was then slowly wound on to the drum using the hauler, each new coil being hammered tight against the previous coil. This was done until two widths of the drum were completed; these coils would never come off the drum. Next the men slowly lowered the reel wagon down the incline, paying out the rope and ensuring it followed the correct route. Once at the bottom the chain and the socket would be attached, leaving the reel wagon to be worked back with the next ascending set. On the Bowes Railway a new rope fitted to a powered incline was used for three years and then taken off and used on a self-acting incline for two, perhaps three, more years.

Changing a rope on a self-acting incline was different, not least because there was no stationary engine to help. The following rope change was recorded in the 1950's on No.3 Incline on the Hetton Railway where, as on the Bowes Railway above, it was the men themselves who changed a rope. The men had, through many years' experience, arrived at the best way of doing it with the least amount of effort on their part. The practice on the Hetton Railway was always to fit new ropes. The new rope, usually bought from a manufacturer in Sunderland, was prepared at the National Coal Board's large engineering works at Philadelphia, where it was wound on to a wooden drum and then put on a specially-built small flat wagon with a centrally-mounted horizontal disc, under which were several jacks (photo 3-4). The wagon was then worked through on to the Hetton Railway, to the bank head of No.2 Incline, the incline above No.3, on the back of a full set.

Here the central pin on the rope wagon was removed and the jacks were operated to tilt the disc so that the rope drum slid off. If the men were lucky (and they usually were!), the drum would bounce to stand upright on its two rims; in later days a railway sleeper was used to ensure that this happened. The drum was then rolled down to the oil store there, where it was mounted on snatch blocks kept there for the purpose, while the rope wagon was run down to the bank foot of No.4 Incline before being worked back up the

3-4. The wagon built by the Lambton Railway's Wagon Shops at Philadelphia in Durham for carrying a rope drum out to where a new rope was to be installed on the Hetton Railway (the two railways were linked). Note the jacks to the right of the central spindle, which were used to tilt the wooden disc. It is seen here, disused, on the Lambton Railway at Bank Top Junction, Newbottle, on 16th March 1966.

inclines and on to Philadelphia. Finally, the last full set waiting to go down from No.2 Incline bank head on the Friday afternoon would be increased from five to six wagons.

On the Saturday morning the two men from No.3 Incline bank head went up to No.2 Incline bank head and wound a length of the new rope off the drum. The end was taken up to the front of the last wagon on the full set left waiting there on Friday afternoon and then carried underneath the wagon to be clamped on the downward end of the wagon's front stanchions. The rope was also clamped to the side of the wagon near its rear end, giving 12ft of rope attached to the wagon. The chain and shackle of the normal rope was then attached to the rear end drawbar hook as usual and the set run down to No.3 Incline bank head. The weight of the extra wagon, compared with the five ascending empties, providing the extra weight to compensate for the weight of the new rope, while clamping it to the outside of the wagon meant that the rope would trail down outside the rails and so be kept apart from the normal rope. The set was then run down No.3 Incline in the same way, but on arriving at No.4 Incline it was stopped short of the empties in the dish, the new rope was detached and the fulls then run forward ready to go down No.4 Incline. The 12ft allowed at the outset was the distance required to take the new rope down to the front of the empties

(so only this 12ft had to be carried). The shackle and its chain were then taken off the old rope, the new rope end was capped with molten lead and then the shackle and chain fitted to the new rope. With the new rope now stretched out along the length of the incline, the two men now walked back up the incline, using hooks to lift the old rope out of the four foot and put the new rope into position. Back at the bank head the old rope was taken off the return wheel and the new rope fitted round it (in two 'wraps'), and then the shackle and chain were changed as at the bank foot. The new rope was then ready to work the next set of fulls.

The whole job could be done 'in a morning'. Only three men were needed, the two rope men and the brakesman, and physical exertion was reduced to a minimum. The final job was the removal of the old rope, now lying alongside the track. This would be clamped to the back of a full set and worked down to the bottom of No.4 Incline, where a locomotive would draw it off. Even then a use might still be found for it; fencing comprising concrete posts and incline rope could still be seen alongside the trackbed of the Hetton Railway in Sunderland fifty years after the line closed.

Details of ropes and chains on specific haulages may be found throughout the book.

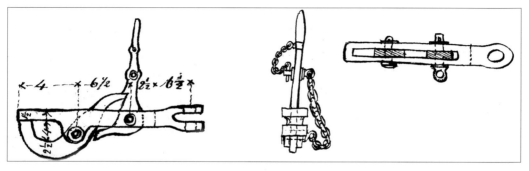

3-5. *The rope coupling used on the Stockton & Darlington Railway's inclines, drawn by John Rastrick in his notebook during his visit of 17th January 1829.*

2. Attaching and detaching the rope

For most surface haulages the end of a rope had to be attached to the vehicles, but with an endless system the vehicles have to be attached to the moving rope. The devices used in narrow gauge endless systems are discussed in Chapter 7.

There would appear to be no surviving detailed written descriptions of attaching a hemp rope. Perhaps it is simplistic to suggest that the end of the rope was formed into a loop and this was put over a hook on the waggon's headstock; if this did happen, it was probably not done for long, because of wear and tear, strain and breakages. The few surviving pictures from the first half of the nineteenth century do not show sufficient detail to understand what was done. The most interesting is probably Strickland's water colour of a train on the self-acting incline on the Middleton Railway in Leeds, done in 1825, which appears to show the rope attached to a chain, which in turn is connected to the top of the waggon's headstock. We also have Rastrick's drawings of the rope couplings he saw used on the Stockton & Darlington and Hetton Railways in 1829, of which the former is illustrated here (3-5).

Slightly more information is available describing how vehicles were attached to endless ropes. The chief example is the system used on the Sheep Pasture and Middleton Inclines of the Cromford & High Peak Railway. Because it was publicly-owned, its accidents were investigated by the Railway Inspectorate and recorded and the Middleton Incline itself survived until 1963. Whilst what is known from the second half of the twentieth century may not necessarily be accurate for earlier years, there is a strong possibility that little had changed for many years.

The first stage involved fitting a 'tackling chain' to the leading wagon to descend. On inclines which were straight, one end of this chain was linked on to the coupling at the rear end of the wagon and then fed under the rear axle and over the front axle for the other end to be hooked on to the front

drawbar hook. To the other end of the tackling chain were attached two smaller-link chains, which were then plaited around the rope in opposite directions. These chains were made of progressively smaller links, which gave them a tapering effect and so they tightened when put under pressure. At their ends were two leather thongs, which were also plaited around the rope. When chains and thongs were in good condition and put on correctly, as happened for the majority of the time, everything worked well. But it was obviously cumbersome and time-consuming to fit, which in turn was only possible because the traffic was light by comparison with elsewhere. A similar system, with tapering chains and leather thongs, was also used in later years on the Chapel Incline of the Peak Forest Tramway, and this method might well go back to the opening of the incline in 1796.

On some early inclines with curves, a 'donkey' had to be fitted, to keep the incline rope low enough that it would stay in the sheaves on the incline. This was an iron bar, forked at each end, hung from the coupling hook at the upper end of a wagon by a pin and cotter and attached by its lower fork to the tackling chain by another pin and cotter. To prevent the donkey from swinging sideways on the coupling and to ensure the rope stayed in position, additional chains, known as 'guide chains', were fastened from the bottom of the donkey around the wagon buffers. On inclines with curves built later in the nineteenth century the donkey and its system were abandoned in favour of erecting large vertical rollers on the inside of the curve but outside the rails and attaching the rope to the set by means of a slip coupling, so that on a curve the rope went outside the four foot and went round the rollers.

A similar system to the tackling chain was used in the Liverpool tunnels. Here all trains were allowed to descend by gravity, with a tunnel-breaksman in addition to the guard for every five additional coaches to a maximum of fifteen coaches. Trains were limited to ten miles per hour. The rope

3-6. Two wagons, photographed in 1897, at the bottom of the Sheep Pasture Incline on the Cromford & High Peak Railway, showing the chain from the front drawbar hook, the donkey on the rear drawbar hook, the chains looped over the buffers and the tapering chains plaited around the rope, tied off with the leather thongs.

haulage was only used for uphill traffic. A contemporary diagram (see Fig.26, chapter 5) shows a 'messenger rope', attached to the vehicles looped once around a plain hook, with the end of the rope divided, though the 'tails' were probably longer than shown. The messenger rope was held taut by the train guard if the train had fewer than five coaches, though additional tunnel-breaksmen were used as for descending trains. The messenger rope was released when the train reached the top of the tunnel.

As the nineteenth century progressed, engineers soon appreciated that inclines, whether self-acting or powered, could be operated more quickly if the rope was directly 'hung on the wagons'. But it was one thing to attach it when the wagons were stationary; it used time if they had to be brought to a halt before it could be released. One solution was never to release it, by attaching it permanently to a small wagon, sometimes called a 'runner'. All that was then required was to use a shunting pole to attach and detach the runner's 3-link coupling

3-7. The 'hanger-on' (wearing his cap with its British Railways London Midland Region badge) plaiting the leather straps around the rope at Middleton Top on the Cromford & High Peak Railway in September 1961.

3-8. An example of a 'runner wagon': Clee Hill No.3, used on the Clee Hill Incline in Shropshire, taken on 26th June 1955. Note again the 'donkey' (see text) and that the wagon is braked by a hand-wheel mounted inside and operated by the brakeman travelling in it.

3-9. Another runner wagon, this time at Arthur & Edward Colliery (also known as Waterloo Colliery) near Miery Stock in the Forest of Dean in Gloucestershire, in August 1948. Note that the rope is attached to a simple 3-link coupling, itself attached to the wagon in the normal way. The colliery was closed in December 1959.

3-10. This ungainly fitting was used on the self-acting Stargate Incline near Ryton in Co.Durham, seen here in 1960. Why a British Railways 21-ton coal hopper was being used as a 'runner' on a NCB incline is not known.

to the wagon on the uphill end of a set, a simple, quick operation. A few inclines using runners survived past the Second World War, with three very different examples illustrated here. Once again, a 'donkey' was needed so that the rope would not rise out of the sheaves on the incline.

As engineers demanded that ropes be made increasingly longer, quite commonly longer than a mile long and sometimes very much more (and one wonders what problems this caused the manufacturers) a new and unforeseen problem began to appear, that of the rope twisting. The worst example before 1850 emerged in the ropes used on the London & Blackwall Railway (see chapter 5). Ropes attached directly to the set could be damaged when they were released and could snake along the ground until they stopped. More seriously, as a rope is wound on to a drum a small amount of twisting occurs, and this led to the rope 'unwinding' when it was released. It appeared that the longer the rope the worse this torsion became. Engineers of the period, from Robert Stephenson downwards, were puzzled as to the cause and tried various solutions, none of them with any great success. Eventually the solution proved to be inserting a length of chain between the rope and the coupling to be attached to the wagons. When this because common practice is unknown, but it seems to have been well known by the 1930s.

The end of the rope was fed into a steel socket, where it was encased in lead or white metal. The chain was then attached to the other side of the socket and to the coupling by shackles. When the tension on the chain was released, the links became slack, cancelling out any torsion and minimising any damage. Quite commonly, but not universally, a swivel unit was also incorporated, usually at the socket end, to release the torsion.

On the LNER inclines in Durham, and perhaps elsewhere too, a design of coupling was adopted which incorporated a hinged arm pointing forwards. The end of this arm passed through a circular ring, known to the men as a 'quoit',[9] which maintained the assembly of the coupling when it was under tension. When the set reached the top/bottom of the incline and the rope went slack, the set-rider struck the quoit with his foot ('kicked the quoit'), releasing the arm and allowing the coupling to dis-assemble and fall off the set. The rope continued to move, allowing a second man alongside the track to capture it with a long hook and pull it out of the way of the front wagon's wheels.

This still required the set-riders to ride every set, a wretched, cold job in bad weather, and the National Coal Board in Durham was determined to get the set-riders off the wagons. So the coupling was

3-11. A rope coupling on a set at Stanley Bank Head on the LNER Pontop & South Shields branch about 1933. The second link of the coupling chain used two circular steel rings. One was linked to the steel bar of the coupling, which was held in place against the previous link by the second ring, known from its shape as the 'quoit', which in turn was held in place by a split pin connected to a small chain. At the right point, when the hauling chain/rope went slack, the set rider pulled out the pin and then 'kicked the quoit' off the bar, allowing the coupling to dis-assemble and fall off the wagon. Note the flat tops on the buffer guides for the set rider to stand on.

3-12. The final Bowes Railway coupling was developed in the 1960s. This reversed the LNER design, replaced the quoit with a hinged arm and considerably lengthened the chain on the split pit, so that it could be hooked on to a handrail of the wagon. When the set arrived at the bank head one of the bank head men took the hook off the handrail and when the chain/rope went slack, he pulled out the pin, allowing the coupling to dis-assemble and fall off, if necessary striking the hinged arm with his brake stick. This enabled the set-riders to come off the wagons and become bank head men.

3-13. Heworth Bank Foot on the Pelaw Main Railway about 1904, showing one of the railway's lighting 'gibbets' and its firebasket lying upside down nearby, while on the right is the gas light which superceded it.

3-14. Firelamps awaiting darkness at Kibblesworth Bank Head on the Bowes Railway on 8th May 1969. Some second-hand rollers, one with a hole cut in it by a rope, also lie around.

re-designed by simply reversing it by 180 degrees, so that the arm now pointed backwards and was held in position by a re-designed hinged 'quoit', held in position by a split pin to which was attached a length of chain, the other end of which was hooked over the wagon's handrail. Two men were still needed, but the set-rider no longer had to ride the sets; instead when a set arrived at the bank head one man unhooked the chain from the handrail and when the rope went slack, he was able to pull the pin from the coupling, which allowed the quoit to fall and the whole coupling to fall off the wagon, allowing the second man to hook the rope and pull it out of the way of the wagons. The first man then began pinning down the wagon brakes to bring the set to a stand. To prevent the men from tripping on the sleepers, the working area was boarded over.

For this to be successful, skills and timing were critical, as there were only a few seconds when it was possible. The haulerman had to reduce power in order for the full tension to come off the rope, but continue to haul; the first man had to pull the pin almost immediately and the second man had to hook the rope and pull it out of the way. If the first man failed to pull the pin out, the set would continue moving with the rope still attached to the set. At worst, the set could be pulled into the front of the engine house – as the brickwork at the front of the Starrs Engine on the Pelaw Main Railway in Gateshead testified (see 9-39).

All of the early railways suffered from the problem of the rope breaking, and various devices were invented to minimise the results. On the Stockton & Darlington Railway a 'cow' was used – a pronged

3-15. The 'bell gallows', shown on William Strickland's water colour painting of the Middleton Railway at Leeds, dated 30th April 1825.

3-17. One of the white discs used at the bank heads on the Hetton Railway which when raised indicated that the rope was attached at the bank foot and the men there were ready. Note the auxiliary bell apparatus to give an audible warning to the men here as it was raised.

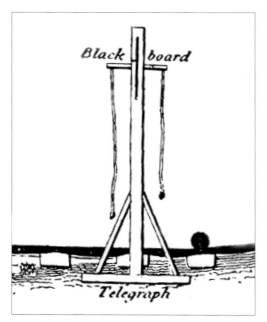

3-16. The telegraph which replaced the bell gallows on the reproduction of Strickland's painting in Tomlinson's THE HISTORY OF THE NORTH EASTERN RAILWAY, published in 1914.

implement attached to the drawbar hook on the rear waggon of an ascending set. While the rope remained attached to the waggons, the 'cow' trailed over the ground; but as soon as the waggons broke loose, it dug into the ground and either stopped them or threw them off the line. Later a large hinged wooden bar was fitted to the ascending side of a kip. Its end, hollowed out, was knocked down by the axles of the wagons as they passed over it, but if the wagons ran back for any reason, the nearest axle to the bar went back into it and the set was held in position. Perhaps with the memory of the 'cow', this bar was called a 'bull', though it also seems to have been called a 'monkey' in some places. Another safety device which became commonly installed on the fulls roads at a bank head was a 'chock'. The earliest of these comprised a single large block of oak which was positioned across one rail to prevent the set leaving the bank head until it was withdrawn. In later years some bank heads had a chock across each rail, shaped to accommodate the wheel of the nearest wagon and with its top surface covered with a steel plate to strengthen it. The two chocks were retracted inwards simultaneously by a large lever alongside the track when the set was to be run.

3. Illumination

Because of the congestion of traffic at certain points, or on colliery railways because of the demands of coal shipments, inclines often had to work during the night, with the increased risk of danger to life and property. The earliest-known lighting was what

Tomlinson calls 'low ropes'[10] – circular iron baskets, filled with a coal fire, suspended from poles like gibbets. Photographs included in *The Railway Magazine* in December 1898 show that they were used on the North Eastern Railway. In 2002 a series of sixteen superb photographs of the Ouston section of the Pelaw Main Railway in County Durham was discovered, taken about 1904, and many of these also show these gibbets and their baskets.[11] The men also carried torches made from short lengths of old tarred incline ropes. This lighting had to suffice until gas lighting began to spread towards the end of the nineteenth century, subsequently superceded by electricity. It was also important at night time for the men to see where the sets were on the incline. For this 'firelamps' were used – again an iron basket of fire, this time cylindrical and easily made by a blacksmith, on to which was hooked a handle, with a second hook used to hook the firelamp on to a handrail on a wagon. As the sets moved at 20 m.p.h. or more, the wind roused the fire, creating flames and sparks, making them easily visible. After the Second World War alternatives were tried: oil lamps – but these blew out – or battery lamps, like those used around road works at night – but these did not give a sufficiently powerful light when viewed from three-quarters of a mile away. The Kibblesworth Incline used firelamps right up to its closure in October 1974.

3-18. *The elaborate elevated 'rapper' at Whitehill Bank Head on the Pelaw Main Railway about 1904. Note the heavy counterweight hanging between the frame posts.*

4. Communication

It is axiomatic in the operation of inclines that it is essential for those at the bottom of an incline to communicate with the top – or to re-phrase, those at the top must not begin operations until they know that the vehicles at the bottom have been attached safely to the rope. From the early days both audible and visual signals were used. The two earliest-known illustrations show bells, on the Ouston Waggonway survey mentioned above (1820) and on William Strickland's water-colour paintings of the Middleton Railway (1825), where he calls it a 'bell gallows' (3-15). It shows a bell, beneath which Strickland has written 'The bell is rung when the empty wagons are attached to the rope.' Curiously, when Tomlinson reproduced the paintings ninety

3-19. *The rapper at Black Fell Bank Head on the Bowes Railway, again with a counterweight. Note the device for increasing the tension on the wire.*

3-20. The rapper at Kibblesworth Bank Head on the Bowes Railway, this time with a 'ball-and-chain' counterweight to give an additional sound signal, 12th September 1971. However, note the railway chairs put on top of the hammer to make it inoperative.

years later the bell gallows was replaced by a 'telegraph'. This appears to show a bar, perhaps painted white with the 'black board' behind it so that those at the top could see it, which could be tilted by pulling on one of the ropes; perhaps horizontal meant 'stop' and angled meant 'go'.

It was soon evident that having the signal at the bottom of the incline and relying on those at the top to hear or see it was not satisfactory or safe. In addition to fog, there was also darkness, quite apart from inclines that were curved; instead, the men at the bottom had to operate visible or audible signals which worked at the top. On the Hetton Railway (1822) the men at the bottom operated a large lever, pulling a wire which raised a large white disc up a post at the top to indicate the set was ready to run; these survived until the railway closed in 1959, although latterly they were not used. The Stockton & Darlington Railway (1825) used a similar system, turning a white disc on top of a pole 20ft high in the direction of the engine. These methods might be expected to work reasonably safely when the inclines were only 300-400 yards long, but difficulties arose as inclines became longer. At least one of the enginemen in the Stockton & Darlington stationary engines was provided with a telescope mounted beside his seat to help him to see the white disc better when weather conditions were difficult. When the 1,400-yard incline on the Saltom waggonway near Whitehaven in

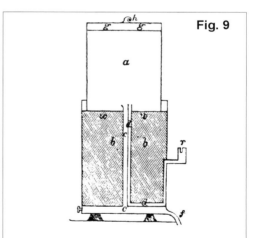

'Gasometer' for operating pneumatic signals in Lime Street and Wapping Tunnels. The air-chamber a is suspended by a rope from a beam, attached to hook h. When released, the air-chamber, weighted at g with lead, gradually sinks into the water vessel b, forcing the air through the tube c and the tunnel pipe f into a whistle or organ-pipe in the distant engine house, to produce a sustained note. On being hoisted by the rope, the air-chamber is refilled through the valve r and the tube d.

Fig.9 The 'gasometer', introduced in 1836 on the Lime Street Tunnel Incline at Liverpool on the Liverpool & Manchester Railway. There was a delay of only four seconds between its operation and the organ pipe sounding in the engine house ¾ mile away.

3-21. The telegraph at the bottom of the Middleton Incline on the Cromford & High Peak Railway, with 'B' for 'Stand by', 'G' for 'Go' and 'S' for 'Stop'.

Cumberland was opened in 1828, the haulerman was also provided with a telescope to see the signals from the men at the bank foot....but when fog drifted in from the nearby Irish Sea the telescope had to be replaced by a messenger running between the two points![12]

On the Stanhope & Tyne Railway (1834) the signal consisted of two poles, one at the top and the other at the bottom; to indicate 'go' the latter was pulled over until it lay nearly flat on the ground, raising the pole at the top of the incline.

Some railways in County Durham used what were called 'rappers'. These comprised an 'anvil', usually the end of a wagon buffer. Above it was a rectangular block of iron, from which ran a wire down to the foot of the incline. When the wire was pulled, the iron block 'rapped' on the anvil, giving the signal that the bank foot was ready. In later years, when the system was no longer required for its original use, it gained a new purpose. If something happened to a set on an incline, or if, for example, a trespasser was sighted, the set-rider was required to jump off and pull the wire (no mean feat at 20 m.p.h or more), warning the bank head men that there was an emergency, so that they could tell the haulerman to stop the set. However, the system had become disused before the set-riders were taken off the sets, after which the sets were allowed to 'run safe'.

In the tunnels at Liverpool on the Liverpool & Manchester Railway the signal to start the ropes was by bell; but the wire running along the side of the tunnel often broke, causing serious delays to traffic. So when the Lime Street Tunnel was opened in 1836 a pneumatic signal was installed for communicating between Lime Street Station and the engine house. It consisted of a ½in. gas pipe with a 'gasometer' at each end, supplied and laid by the local gas company. The gasometer is illustrated in Fig.9. The air-chamber *a* was suspended by a rope from a beam, attached to the hook *h*. When released, the air-chamber, weighted at *g* with lead, gradually sank into the water vessel *b*, forcing the air through the tube *c* and into the tunnel pipe *j*, which sounded a whistle or organ-pipe in the distant engine house, producing a sustained note. On being hoisted by the rope, the air-chamber was refilled through the valve *r* and the tube *d*, ready for its next application. Soon afterwards the bell in the original tunnel of 1830 was replaced by a similar gasometer. In 1838 Robert Stephenson installed this system on the incline between Euston and Camden on the London & Birmingham Railway; it was reported that the compressed air took less than four seconds to reach Camden.

For many years the inclines on the Cromford & High Peak Railway used a different form of telegraph system, though whether this went back to the opening of the railway in 1830 is not known.

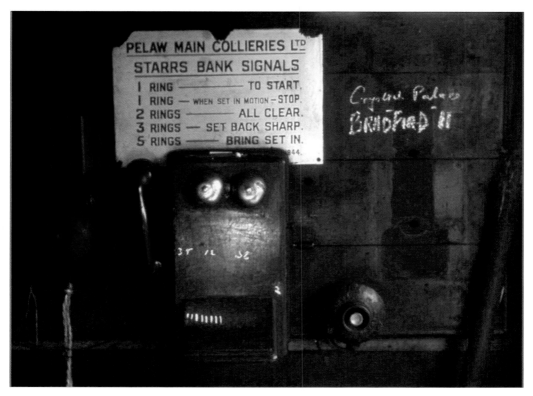

3-22. The bell codes in the bank foot cabin for the Starrs Incline on the Pelaw Main Railway at Gateshead, with the bell push to the right of the magneto 'omnibus' telephone, 24th October 1969.

At the bottom of an incline there was a large circular disc, fitted with a pointer. This could be set to one of three positions, S for Stop, G for Go and B for Stand By. The pointer was linked by a wire to a similarly-marked telegraph at the top of an incline, so that when the pointer was moved, it also showed the same instruction at the bank top. The engine house was also provided with the same apparatus, so that the engineman also knew the position, without a man from the bank head having to come in to tell him.

The C&HPR system shows two new features. The first was need to involve the engineman in the signals as well as those at the bank top and bottom; indeed, there was clearly a case for also involving others directly involved in the operation of an incline, such as those in charge of level crossings. Secondly, there was an increasing realisation of the need for more signals than just Go, or Stop and Go – the need for a system which provided a means of giving other information or instructions. Both of these depended on the application of new technology.

One such development came with the invention of the Electric Magnetic Telegraph by William Cooke (1806-1869) and Professor Charles Wheatstone (1802-1875), which they patented in 1837. In the following year the Great Western Railway signed an agreement for its installation between Paddington and West Drayton, a distance of thirteen miles. Using five wires, the 'dial' comprised a central row of five magnetic needles, with ten letters of the alphabet above and a further ten below this row. A letter was indicated by the convergence of two of the needles. This was tapped out at each end by an operator, whose attention was attracted by a warning bell. It was installed on the GWR between 1838 and 1839. At the same time the London & Blackwall 'Commercial' Railway was under construction, engineered by Robert Stephenson (1803-1859) and George Bidder (1806-1878). A more extensive description of this line will be found in Chapter 5, but its 3¾ miles were to be operated by a continuous rope system, with a 15-minute passenger service in busy periods. Following the electric telegraph's success on the Great Western Railway, Stephenson and Bidder recommended its adoption on the London & Blackwall Railway, which thus became the first railway to rely solely on the electric telegraph for its operations when it opened in July 1840 (see 5-47).

BROOMSIDE COLLIERY, PITTINGTON, DURHAM.

Published by W. Fordyce Newcastle

3-23. The lithograph of Thomas Hair's watercolour of Broomside Colliery, near Durham City, showing a mixed train of coal waggons and passenger carriages travelling west of the Pittington Engine on the Durham & Sunderland Railway. The original painting bears the date of 1839.

Later in the nineteenth century the Leclanche battery cells were invented. Although these had to be thrown away when they were exhausted, they produced a low voltage and lasted well, making it possible to introduce a bell system on inclines. The keys to real improvement and safer operation were the telephone and electricity, and by the First World War it would seem that most remaining inclines had both. The former used the magneto system, where a current was created by turning a handle and then using a code to speak to whichever location was required. This was slow and of little use in an emergency, and the electric bell system came into almost universal use. This could bring all locations on an incline into the same circuit, making operations safer. To give an instruction a bell was rung, either by pressing a plunger or by using the whole hand to pull a small bar at the bottom of an instrument forwards. Different bell codes, known as 'raps', could then be given quickly for a range of instructions and information, the list of raps usually being put on an enamel plate near the haulerman's chair. Bell domes of different sizes could be used to avoid confusion where a stationary engine operated two inclines. A standard number of basic raps became established, and for narrow gauge haulage, both on the surface and underground, these were set into law, so that they were common everywhere in the country. Internal telephones were also introduced, the 'bus' (omnibus) phone, where each

location on the circuit had a ring code and where everyone on the system could hear everyone else. This was not used for operating the inclines, but it did allow for other messages to be passed along the line, from the amount of coal still needed to complete the loading of a ship, the time when the inclines might finish for the day, to 'your wage packet is on the last wagon of the next set' and 'young Arthur is coming up for his haircut on the next set'.

5. Carrying passengers on inclines
It was normal practice for public railways in the 1830s to carry passengers on rope-worked inclines. Neither the operators nor the passengers seem to have thought very much about the risks of this; it was a different age. Indeed, as has been noted above, where endless rope haulage was being used, carriages were sometimes lowered down inclines simply on their brakes. What little is known comes mainly from newspaper accounts of opening days, from operating regulations drawn up by railway companies and from a small number of illustrations. The oil painting of the opening of the Canterbury & Whitstable Railway in 1830 by Thomas Baynes (1794-1854) and some of the aquatints of the Liverpool & Manchester Railway in 1830-31 by Thomas Bury (1811-1877) can be seen in chapter 5. Note that in the former the carriages are shown completely open, whereas in the latter they have roofs. So too do

3-24. The vehicle which passengers used on the Comberow Incline in Somerset, in the 1890s. Note the three chains, all fixed permanently to the wagon, and that one of the passengers is a woman.

3-25. The author's pass to travel over the National Coal Board's Bowes Railway, including its inclines, issued in January 1966 by its Railway Manager, Mr. J.W. ('Bill') Storey.

the carriages on the Durham & Sunderland Railway shown in the water colour paintings by Thomas Hair, a series now held by the Hatton Gallery in the University of Newcastle. These were subsequently reproduced as lithographs, although curiously with minor differences, and as they are easier to reproduce, they are included here.

The Cromford & High Peak Railway also allowed passenger services, but let the rights out to George Wheatcroft & Sons of Cromford. German Wheatcroft (1773-1841) was involved in various entrepreneurial enterprises, and began the service, from Cromford over the inclines and through to Whaley Bridge, in May 1833. For the benefit of passengers, he also ran a stagecoach service from Whaley Bridge to Manchester. When these Wheatcroft services ceased is not known. In later years the company provided a 'fly' coach for those who wished to travel. Officially passengers had to get out and trudge up the remaining inclines, but one account[13] tells of a journey in August 1877 when passengers stayed in the 'fly'. The London & North Western Railway stopped the service soon afterwards when one of the passengers was killed.

Even at the time thinkers about the operation of railways recognised that the passengers had a different experience travelling up one incline, such as the Camden Incline out of Euston, to that when travelling along a series of inclines such as those on the Durham & Sunderland Railway, with their delays and jolts from changing from one rope to another to longer delays if a rope broke. Yet the London & Blackwall Railway was designed by Robert Stephenson for high speed, high volume, rope-hauled passenger traffic, including the serving of intermediate stations, and unbelievably was carrying 2½ million passengers a year by 1844.

Elsewhere the Hayle Railway in Cornwall included four inclines, Angarrack (powered) and Penponds (self-acting) on the main line and Trevasean (self-acting) and Portreath (powered) on its branches, and opened in 1838. The casual carrying of passengers had begun by 1841, to be replaced by organised passenger services in 1843, but this only lasted nine years before being diverted over the new routes that avoided all of the inclines except the last. How they were operated, and what facilities were provided for passengers, remains unknown.

A passenger service was also provided on the Comberow Incline of the West Somerset Mineral Railway. As noted in the previous chapter, this incline was opened in 1858, and a public passenger service from Wachet to Comberow was begun on 4th September 1865. For those wishing to travel up the incline and on to Gupworthy, an open truck was provided, free but at one's own risk. Some, especially women and children, must have found this a daunting prospect – nearly ¾ mile at a gradient of 1 in 4. However, proper stations were provided, at the top, called Brendon Hill, and at Gupworthy. The service ceased on 8th November 1898, when the railway was owned by the Ebbw Vale Steel, Iron & Coal Co. Ltd.

The passenger services over inclines which had begun in the 1830s had mostly ceased by 1860. Several were replaced by locomotive haulage when locomotive development made it possible for steeper gradients to be climbed. Where this was not possible avoiding lines were built, as on the NER Pontop & South Shields branch. Other inclines simply closed, ending the service. So by the beginning of the twentieth century the transport of passengers on inclines had effectively come to an end. This was not the case elsewhere in the world, as examples in chapter 8 show. Nor was it quite the end in Britain. In 1966 the National Coal Board issued to the author an official permit allowing him to travel on the Bowes Railway in County Durham, including on the inclines then still operating. This meant standing on the buffer guide of a wagon and holding the handrails. To travel six miles solely on wagons on six continuous rope inclines was a unique experience – not least wondering whether the uphill empty set, reduced to hardly any movement, was going to make it over the top of the kip on the Springwell Incline!

1   R.H.G.Thomas, *The Liverpool & Manchester Railway*, London, 1980, 114.

2   W.W.Tomlinson, *The North Eastern Railway – Its Rise & Development,* Newcastle upon Tyne, 1914, 377-8.

3   *Observations on Railways with the most Eligible Motive Power for Carriages travelling thereon humbly addressed to the Committee for enquiring as to a better communication between Newcastle and Carlisle by their most obediently Humble Servant George Dodds. [Dated] Hetton Colliery, Decr 1824.* The original volume is in private ownership.

4   Dodds, 3.

5   Dodds, 9.

6   Tomlinson, 377.

7   John Rastrick, Notebook IV, 30.

8   Thomas, 113.

9   The game of quoits, once common in North East England and still played in a few places, uses a smaller steel quoit than elsewhere in the country, almost identical to that shown here.

10   Tomlinson, 379.

11   They were published in *Archive*, Issue 68, December 2010.

12   H.Quayle, *Whitehaven : The Railways and Waggonways of a Unique Cumberland Port*, Pinner, 2007.

13   A.Rimmer, *The Cromford & High Peak Railway*, Oxford, 1956, 85.

Chapter 4 The first tramways and waggonways incorporating inclines

The development of inclines brought about a gradual change in thinking about tramways and waggonways, more particularly after about 1790. The routes of most seventeenth and eighteenth century waggonways were almost certainly decided by two main factors. The first was the geography of the area; the route had to be within the capacity of one horse with its one waggon. The horse would pull the waggon uphill and if the waggon went downhill by gravity, the horse would be tethered at the back to act as a brake. The second factor was the ability of the coal owner to obtain a 'wayleave agreement' with the owner of the land he wished his waggonway to cross. Acts of Parliament were rarely obtained – the Middleton Railroad's Act in 1758 was very much the exception – but obtaining a wayleave could be fraught with disadvantages. The agreement usually provided for a payment of so much a ton of each mineral that the line carried. These rates could be high if the landowner was otherwise able to block a desired route, and were usually contracted for longer periods than the economic cycles involving the rise and fall of mineral prices. It was therefore not surprising that not infrequently they caused disputes between their signatories.

Assuming that the full load was to travel downhill, incorporating a self-acting incline into a route meant that a waggonway could be taken down steeper gradients than hitherto. The first important tramway where this was done was the **Peak Forest Tramway** in Derbyshire. This served the Peak Forest Canal, which obtained its Act in 1794, varied a year later. The purpose of the canal was to bring limestone down from the Peak District to Manchester and further afield, burnt lime being increasingly used in improving agriculture. The engineer was Benjamin Outram (1764-1805), one of the leading civil and mechanical engineers of the period, who had set up an engineering and ironworks at Butterley in Derbyshire in 1790. The Peak Forest was a narrow canal, running from the Ashton Canal at Dukinfield, with two pounds, each nearly seven miles long, divided by a flight of 16 locks at Marple. The 1795 variation allowed the western end of the canal to finish at Bugsworth (now Buxworth), although subsequently a branch was built to Whaley Bridge.

Originally the tramway was to run from Chapel Milton to Dove Holes, a distance of about four miles. Following the 1795 variation, the tramway

started instead at the Bugsworth basin and ran for six miles, via Chinley and Chapel-en-le-Frith, to Lodes Knowle Quarry. It was a plateway, using L-shaped cast iron rails 3ft long and 4$\frac{5}{16}$ wide, mounted on stone blocks. The gauge was 4ft 2ins, measured inside the rail flanges. The waggons and the rails were supplied by Outram's works at Butterley. The former weighed between 0.8 tons and one ton empty and carried between two and 2.5 tons of limestone. The tramway, with its section of the canal, was opened on 31st August 1796. Initially it incorporated two inclines, the smaller one taking limestone down from Lodes Knowle Quarry. This was only 33yds long, was double track and was operated by a horse gin; presumably this was needed because although the limestone travelled downhill, the incline also handled full waggons travelling uphill. The incline was short-lived, because the demand for limestone soon exceeded the capacity of the quarry and it was replaced by a short extension to far greater deposits at Dove Holes.

The other incline was needed south of Chapel-en-le-Frith where there was a steep hillside, and its impact on the neighbourhood saw it called the 'Great Inclined Plane'. It was 512yds long and rose 209ft, but not on an even gradient; the resident engineer, Thomas Brown, designed it so that the gradient at the top was 1 in 6$\frac{1}{4}$ which declined to 1 in 8$\frac{1}{4}$ at the bottom. This reduced the action of gravity as the waggons approached the top and bottom respectively and also offset the changing weight of the incline chain/rope. The incline was double track throughout its length, and a maximum of eight loaded waggons was permitted to descend. When this maximum was used, a gross weight of between 22$\frac{1}{2}$ and 28 tons at the top was hauling up a net weight of between 6$\frac{1}{2}$ and 8 tons at the bottom. Three 'catches' were provided near the top of the plane to stop runaway waggons but it is not known how effective they were; perhaps they became disused, for in later years runaways are recorded as damaging the overbridge near the foot of the incline. Initially a hemp rope was used, but this did not last long, almost certainly because it stretched badly. It was replaced by a wrought-iron chain, but this proved to be not strong enough, and in 1809 it too was replaced, by a chain manufactured in Birmingham at a cost of £500 (rather more than £17,000 in 2011). The rope/chain was supported on the incline by wooden blocks placed between the rails every ten yards.

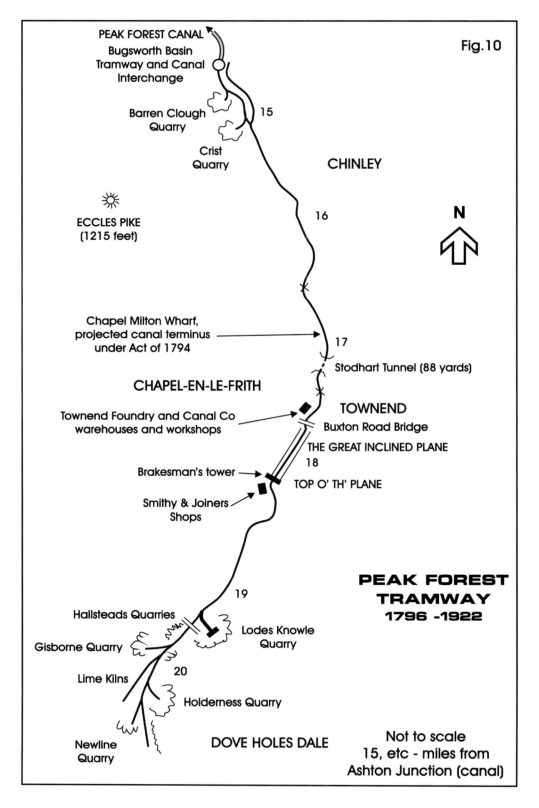

Fig.10

PEAK FOREST CANAL
Bugsworth Basin
Tramway and Canal
Interchange

Barren Clough
Quarry

15

Crist
Quarry

CHINLEY

☀
ECCLES PIKE
(1215 feet)

16

Chapel Milton Wharf,
projected canal terminus
under Act of 1794

17

Stodhart Tunnel (88 yards)

CHAPEL-EN-LE-FRITH

Townend Foundry and Canal Co
warehouses and workshops

TOWNEND
Buxton Road Bridge

THE GREAT INCLINED PLANE

18

Brakesman's tower

TOP O' TH' PLANE

Smithy & Joiners
Shops

PEAK FOREST
TRAMWAY
1796 -1922

19

Hallsteads Quarries

Lodes Knowle
Quarry

Gisborne Quarry

20

Lime Kilns

Holderness Quarry

Newline
Quarry

DOVE HOLES DALE

Not to scale
15, etc - miles from
Ashton Junction (canal)

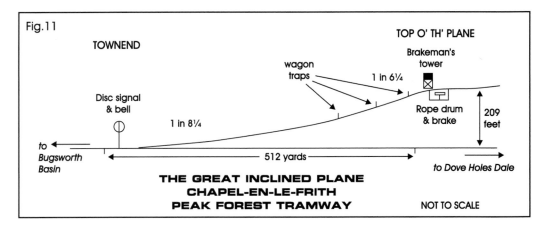

Fig.11

TOWNEND

TOP O' TH' PLANE

Brakeman's tower

wagon traps

1 in 6¼

Disc signal & bell

1 in 8¼

Rope drum & brake

209 feet

to Bugsworth Basin

512 yards

to Dove Holes Dale

THE GREAT INCLINED PLANE CHAPEL-EN-LE-FRITH PEAK FOREST TRAMWAY

NOT TO SCALE

At the top of the incline the rope/chain passed underground into a pit, where it was wound for one and a half turns around a horizontal drum measuring 14ft in diameter; almost certainly what is called a drum would more accurately be termed a drum wheel. This is described as having a groove lined with wooden blocks with the grain facing outwards to increase the friction. Above the groove was an integral brake wheel about 5in wide. A wrought iron (later steel) band brake encircled this, making almost a 360° arc of contact with the brake wheel. The band too was lined with wooden blocks to increase the friction, this time with the grain facing inwards. The band brake was anchored to the back wall of the pit and at the front one end was cranked upwards and the other end cranked downwards. The upward crank was attached above the fulcrum of the brake lever and the downward crank was attached below the fulcrum. The brake lever itself was about 15ft long and it extended into the hut at the top of the brakesman's tower. Despite the considerable mechanical advantage provided by the brake lever, the brakeman was unable to apply the brake unaided, and so to increase the mechanical advantage further, a pulley block was attached to the lever, the brakesman using this to apply the brake.

4-1. Looking up from the bottom of the Chapel Incline on the Peak Forest Tramway, possibly about 1900. The plate rails are clearly visible – the gauge was 4ft 2ins - as is the 'signal' used to communicate with the brakesman at the top of the incline 512 yards away.

At both the top and bottom of the incline a man called a 'hanger-on' was employed to attach the waggons to the rope, by connecting two special chains to the waggon on the uphill end and plaiting them round the rope/chain. At the end of these chains were leather thongs, which were fastened off by also being plaited round the chain. When the waggons were set in motion the plaiting of the chains had the effect of tightening their grip on the main chain. This would appear to be a very similar system to that used later on the nearby Cromford & High Peak Railway's inclines (see chapter 5).

At the foot of the incline, between the tracks, there was an iron post which supported a disc and a bell. When everything was ready at the bottom the man there used the disc to signal to the brakeman, probably by turning it parallel with the rails. At night time or in mist or fog the bell was used. The brakeman had a commanding view of the incline from his elevated hut. When he was satisfied that everything at the top was ready too, he released the brake and the descending wagons were pushed on to the incline. The variation in gradient slowed both sets of waggons as they neared the ends of the journeys, and when he was satisfied that the sets had completed their runs, he made a full application of the brake.

Running up to eight waggons at a time on the incline meant that the horses on the sections above and below it had to pull far more than a single waggon. The tramway's byelaws stated that the maximum in a train was twelve waggons, but on occasions up to forty were run, often running downhill by gravity without a horse. The traffic grew so much that in 1803 the whole tramway was rebuilt with double track, apart from the bridge near the bottom of the incline and the 88-yard Stodhart Tunnel, now regarded as the first railway tunnel in the world. After this there was little alteration to the basic design of the tramway. The incline chain was replaced again in 1817 and again in 1831, being now recorded as 1,075yds long and weighing about 7 tons. Probably during the 1860s the chain was replaced by a steel rope, 2ins in diameter and weighing about 5 tons.

In 1848 the Peak Forest Canal and the tramway were purchased by the Manchester, Sheffield & Lincolnshire Railway, which in 1897 changed its name to the Great Central Railway. In 1922 this was absorbed into the new London & North Eastern Railway. In that same year the last commercial train ran on the tramway, still a plateway and with the incline still operating in the same way that it had for 130 years. The tramway was officially abandoned in July 1925.

The next significant step forward, a tramway incorporating several self-acting inclines, was a very different line. The Peak Forest Tramway was a plateway constructed at a gauge wider than four feet to act as a feeder to a canal for

4-2. The brakesman's tower at the top of the incline. Here the brakesman pulled on a 15ft long lever to apply the band brake on the return wheel in the wheel pit.

4-3. Loaded waggons also came up the incline, and this shows what appears to be timber arriving at the bank head. The wire rope(s) can clearly be seen.

carrying limestone. The **Penrhyn Tramway** in North Wales was, unusually, a narrow gauge line, using edge rails built to carry slate to the sea for shipment. Although it was again a local businessman taking the initiative, he was a very different kind of man. Richard Pennant (1737-1808) owned 8,000 acres of sugar plantations in

Jamaica, with 600 slaves and was twice M.P. for Liverpool; he was created Baron Penrhyn in 1783. After inheriting the Penrhyn estate he devoted much of the huge profits from sugar in developing the estate and its slate quarries. He opened the Penrhyn Quarry at Bethesda in 1785 and began building roads in the area, together with developing Port Penrhyn, just east of Bangor at the mouth of the River Cegin. With the quarry output still small, it could be handled by horse and cart, but this began to restrict output, and in 1800 he ordered his Land Agent, Benjamin Wyatt, to construct for him a railway between the quarry and the port.

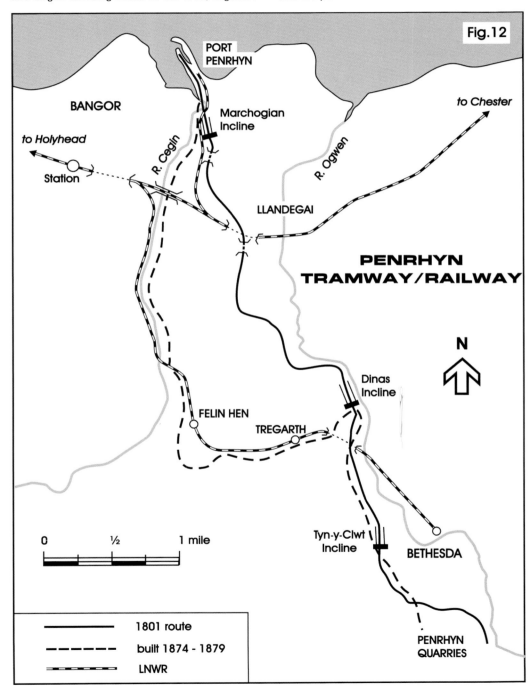

Fig.12

PENRHYN TRAMWAY/RAILWAY

Legend:
- ——— 1801 route
- – – – built 1874 - 1879
- ┼┼┼ LNWR

Initially Wyatt would seem to have been undecided between building a canal or a tramway. However, two years earlier a tramway had been opened to Port Penrhyn from a mill at Llandegai, a hamlet about a mile to the south. Chert[1] was quarried here and its crushed chips were mixed with clay to make flat cakes called 'blongs'. These were then taken down to the port to be shipped to Liverpool where they were made into dishes. The tramway was a narrow gauge line and despite its short length it included two self-acting inclines, one close to the mill and one near the port. Wyatt decided to commission canal engineer Thomas Dadford (1730-1809) and his son, also called Thomas (c1761-1801) to undertake a survey and make recommendations. Their report, dated 5th June 1800, is now in Gwynedd Archives.[2] They firmly rejected a canal in favour of a tramway. From Coed y Parc at the quarry, later the quarry's engineering and maintenance centre. The first two miles and 5 furlongs would have a slight declining gradient of 8in to the chain (22yds) - one source gives all the gradients between the inclines as on a downhill gradient of 1 in 100 - presumably to help the horses pull the full waggons. Then would come the first incline, 143yds at 1 in 6.79, falling 63ft. Three-quarters of a mile at 8in to the chain would be followed by the second incline, 220yds at 1 in 11.6, falling 58ft. Then followed a section of 7 furlongs, again at 8in to the chain, to the third incline, incorporated from the Llandegai Tramway, 330yds at 1 in 9.7, falling 102ft, leaving a short distance to Port Penrhyn and giving a total length of 6 miles and six furlongs, or 6¾ miles. The gauge was presumably to be the same as the Llandegai Tramway and has caused confusion in the past, as it measured 2ft 0in between the rail centres and 1ft 10¾in inside the rails. The wagons used double-flanged wheels measuring 14in in diameter. Wyatt claimed to have invented edge rails, with a flange on the wheels of the waggons, but this is disputed.

Dadford describes the inclines as being double track, with one road for fulls and the other for empties. They would be worked using an endless chain, rotating around wheels at the top and the bottom. He anticipates that a 'tolerable horse' would pull six full waggons containing up to two tons of slate each, this number being divided into two sets of three to travel on the inclines. He estimated that the line would handle between 100 and 200 tons of slate per day. The cost of construction was estimated at £8,328-5s-0d (about £275,000 at 2011 values). Construction began on 2nd September 1800 and the first train of slate ran on 25th June 1801.

Whilst the second incline, near Tregarth, is always called the Dinas Incline, the one nearest the port is recorded as the Maesgirchen Incline, although Marchogion is more common, while the third incline, near Tanysfagell, is sometimes called the

Cilgeraint Incline, although it is more commonly recorded as Tyn-y-Clwt. In fact, by the end of 1801 the system had five inclines; in addition to the three on the 'main line', the mill at Llandegai retained its link to the tramway with its incline, while an incline down from the quarry to the main line was completed in the late summer. These two also are believed to have been worked by drums/drum wheels. The incline at Llandegai village was removed on 10th May 1831, together with the rail connection to the mill.

Despite Dadford reporting that the operation of the inclines would be by continuous chain, revolving around wheels at the top and bottom of the inclines, historians of the line have usually held that 'vertical drums' were used and that the inclines were 'balanced'; a hemp rope was used, with the 'long end' at the bottom and the 'short end' at the top, with the three full descending waggons being balanced by three ascending empties. No illustrations of vertical drums[3] being used anywhere appear to have survived, and it is thus unclear what the arrangements at the top of an incline would be with a vertical drum. In addition, there is evidence that the tramway was used to bring in household goods and coal for the growing number of inhabitants at Bethesda, while the quarry itself would create a demand for materials that would need to be brought to it. This traffic seems to have been handled primarily on a Saturday. To accommodate it the 'drums' were capable of being operated as a gin, with a horse or an oxen connected to a bar and then walking round in a circle in order to haul full waggons up the inclines. Again, how this was done using a vertical drum is unknown. Subsequently the development of the local road system, stimulated both by Telford's toll road to Holyhead and the Penrhyn estate's own investment, reduced the need to use the tramway for such traffic, and it seems to have ceased altogether by about 1830.

Meanwhile the demand for roofing slates had grown enormously. The development of the slate industry around Blaenau Ffestiniog was well under way and in 1836 the Festiniog Railway had been opened down to Portmadoc to give them access to shipment. At Dinorwic Quarry at Llanberis the 1824 2ft 0in gauge tramway across Fachwen to Port Dinorwic was already suffering from its limited capacity, to be replaced in 1843 by a 4ft 0in gauge line. The demand for Penrhyn slates was already more than the quarry could meet. So the Chief Agent for the Penrhyn Estate, James Wyatt, and the quarry manager, William Francis, began examining every aspect of their operations to see if any improvements could be made.

Noting that the trains averaged about thirty-six waggons pulled by three horses, they saw that when they reached an incline the detached horses at the top and the bottom stood around for over an hour while the waggons were worked on the incline. This was limiting the number of trains that could use the inclines to four per day, even in the summer. As a result, it was taking about 1½ days for slate to travel the 6¾ miles between the quarry and the port, and yet in this time the horses had been standing around unproductively for many hours.

The first known operational change was in the arrangements for the horses. Instead of standing around, they were attached to a train when about half of the empty wagons had ascended each incline and took them to the bottom of the next incline. This reduced the standing time for the horses to about half-an-hour, but of course left half of a train standing at the bank head. It was then a simple change to attach this to the next 'half-train', and again the horses were only standing for half-an-hour between arriving with the laden Down train before they returned with an empty Up train. This not only reduced the lost production time for the horses but allowed the number of daily trains to be increased to six, with the result that the time of slate in transit was reduced to about 1¼ days. This method of working was implemented in May 1838 and was called 'Train Working by Pieces'.

Then it was realised that if the operation of the inclines themselves was changed, further improvements would be achieved. The 'balance working' then in use meant that the Up and Down trains used alternate tracks at the top and bottom of each incline, and much time was spent uncoupling the horses and shunting the wagons. So it was decided to re-fit the inclines with a continuous rope system using pulleys mounted in the track, attaching the Up and Down waggons to the rope three at a time. As was noted in chapter 2, the hemp ropes continually stretched and for a continuous rope to remain in tension some form of tensioning apparatus was necessary, as of course was a means of braking, but it is not clear how these issues were resolved here. A continuous rope meant that one side could be permanently designated the Down side and the other the Up side, and this in turn resulted in changes at the top and bottom of the inclines, levelling the ground, simplifying the trackwork and increasing the storage space for waggons. These changes seem to have been done gradually between 1838 and 1840, as the foundry was able to produce the parts needed. Only at the foot of the Marchogion Incline was no change made, presumably because of its close proximity to the harbour. Collectively these changes made it possible for eight trains to run the full length of the main line in a long day, and this was sufficient for the quarry to meet the demands of the market.

The next important change occurred on 20th September 1849, when the hemp ropes were replaced by wire ropes. This meant that the limit on a set of waggons could be raised from three to four,

and in fact the incline men found that they could actually run five, albeit against the rules. This made the completion of eight trains a day more certain. The final major change was the replacement of the Welsh 'cobs' by the newly-bred heavy horses, Shires and Clydesdales, which in turn meant the train lengths could be raised from a maximum of thirty-six waggons to fifty waggons. This was first noted on 14th July 1851, but may have occurred slightly before this. The number of waggons passed daily down to the port varied that week between 338 and 353. In April 1852, when the new 12-hour day 'Summer Timetable' was introduced, the number varied between 385 and 390 a day. This enabled the quarry to meet the demand created by the opening of the London & North Western Railway's branch through Port Penrhyn, opened on 7th January 1852.[4]

The reserves of slate at Bethesda were so vast that the Penrhyn Quarries were destined to become the biggest slate quarries in the world, in an industry that reached its peak in the second half of the nineteenth century. However, by the 1870s the tramway with its three inclines was increasingly decrepit and completely unable to cope. So in 1874 the decision was taken to replace the whole line with a new route capable of being worked throughout by steam locomotives. The gauge was now officially 1ft 10¾in. The work was begun in 1876 and was done in stages. From the quarry as far as the top of the Dinas Incline the new route closely followed the old, and in fact incorporated a short section of about ½ mile; but thereafter, under the direction of Charles Spooner (1818-1889), the Engineer of the Festiniog Railway, the route swung westwards to reach the valley of the River Cegin, which it then followed down to the port. The southern section, south of Dinas, was completed in 1876 and the remainder by 1879. The Penrhyn Railway, as it now became, was closed on 24th July 1962, but the quarries continue in production.

The Peak Forest and Penrhyn Tramways, although very different in detail, both incorporated self-acting inclines in order to create a direct route between a source of production and a shipping point. They depended on the full load travelling downhill; but the development of the steam stationary engine to haul loads uphill meant that entrepreneurs could build their waggonways anywhere they wanted, subject only to the cost and to obtaining permission for the route to cross the land involved.

The first to recognise this opportunity were the coal owners of the North East. This area had the biggest concentration of waggonways in the country by 1800, perhaps 150 miles, but they had wooden rails and almost no inclines at that date. As noted in chapter 2, the first stationary engine to be installed in the North East was at Black Fell near Birtley, about two miles south of Gateshead.

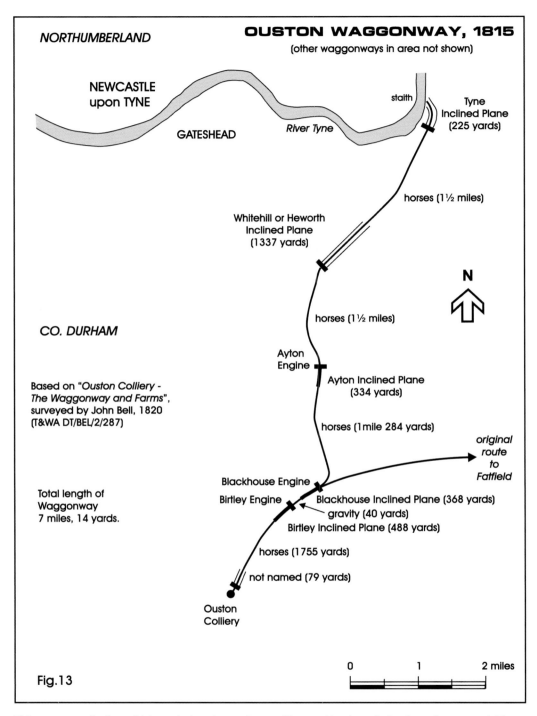

NORTHUMBERLAND

OUSTON WAGGONWAY, 1815

(other waggonways in area not shown)

NEWCASTLE
upon TYNE

GATESHEAD

staith

Tyne
Inclined Plane
(225 yards)

River Tyne

horses (1½ miles)

Whitehill or Heworth
Inclined Plane
(1337 yards)

horses (1½ miles)

N

CO. DURHAM

Ayton
Engine

Ayton Inclined Plane
(334 yards)

Based on "Ouston Colliery -
The Waggonway and Farms",
surveyed by John Bell, 1820
(T&WA DT/BEL/2/287)

horses (1 mile 284 yards)

original
route
to
Fatfield

Blackhouse Engine

Birtley Engine

Blackhouse Inclined Plane (368 yards)

Total length of
Waggonway
7 miles, 14 yards.

gravity (40 yards)

Birtley Inclined Plane (488 yards)

horses (1755 yards)

not named (79 yards)

Ouston
Colliery

0   1   2 miles

Fig.13

This was part of a line which carried coal over the northern ridge of the Team valley down to the River Wear at Fatfield, part of the latter section being a self-acting incline. Soon afterwards, probably about 1807-1808, the line passed to Messrs. Harrison & Cooke, who were sinking a colliery near Urpeth, about 2½ miles north-west of Chester-le-Street. They realised that using stationary engines meant a waggonway could be routed anywhere, and so they decided to build a new line to Bill Quay, about four miles from the mouth of the River Tyne; siting staiths here would mean they could be rid of the transhipment costs and inconvenience of using the keels. The new route was opened on 17th May 1809, with two more stationary engines, one to divide the Black Fell incline into two sections and the other near Ayton Cottage [today called Eighton Banks] to take the line on the level to the point where the descent to the Tyne began. According to the description of the opening in the *Newcastle Courant,* the inclines were said to have replaced 203 horses and men and to have worked waggons at 9 m.p.h. Although there is no definitive evidence, almost certainly hemp ropes were used, rather than chain.

It would seem that horses were used temporarily for the 3¾ miles to the Tyne while the Whitehill, or Heworth, Incline was being completed. It was opened on 15th March 1810, at 1,337yds perhaps the longest self-acting incline to that date. However, Messrs. Harrison and Cooke were bankrupted shortly afterwards when one of their supporting banks failed, and Benjamin Thompson (1779-1867) was brought from the iron industry at Sheffield in 1811 to rescue the business. He closed the original collieries, sank a new one at Ouston, about a mile from Urpeth, and rebuilt the

southern end of the waggonway. This line, now called **the Ouston Waggonway**, opened on 17th November 1815.

The waggonway is described in *Des Chemins de Fer en Angleterre, Nottament a Newcastle*, compiled by Louis de Gallois (1777-1825), the Engineer in Chief to the Royal Mines in France and published in the *Annales des Mines* in 1818. When de Gallois visited the line in 1817 the section to the River Wear was still in use, and he says that it was four miles long and having two descending inclined planes. The next detailed description of the line is found in a large-scale book of plans entitled *Ouston Colliery – The Waggonway and Farms*, surveyed by John Bell between 1820 and 1824, which is now held by Tyne & Wear Archives & Museums in Newcastle upon Tyne (TWA DT BEL2/287). Despite being written only a few years apart, these two primary sources do not agree in places; indeed, Bell's plans even contradict themselves, illustrating the problems of working with what one might hope would be straightforward sources.

Bell's plans make no mention of the line to the River Wear, so presumably it had been closed by this time. They start at Ouston Colliery, from which there was a self-acting incline of only 79yds down

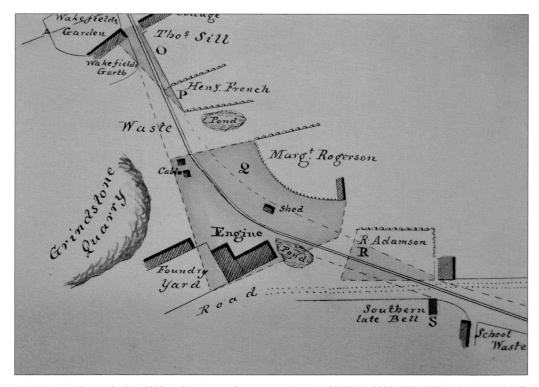

4-4. The Ayton Engine, built in 1809, and its surrounding area, as shown in OUSTON COLLIERY, THE WAGGONWAY AND FARMS, surveyed by John Bell between 1820 and 1824. The engine was hauling uphill from the top of the plan.

to the floor of the valley. Then comes what was obviously a horse-worked section of 1,755yds to the foot of the next incline. The text on the plans gives the Turnpike Inclined Plane and the Birtley Inclined Plane coming next, with a short distance dividing the two; but the drawing seems clearly to show that these were one incline, about 470yds long, worked by the Birtley Engine. This worked two sets simultaneously that passed just above the Durham Turnpike Road. The waggons travelled the next forty yards by gravity. Then came the Blackhouse Inclined Plane, 368yds up to the Blackhouse Engine, the engine of 1805 and 25 h.p., working sets alternately (see 2-4). Here a 'stable' is marked, presumably for the horses which worked the next mile and 284yds to the foot of the Ayton Inclined Plane, near which the route of the original Urpeth Waggonway is shown. The Ayton Engine (later Eighton) also worked two sets at once on its short bank of 334yds. The existence of the three engines is also confirmed by de Gallois, who gives the total rise as 406ft and adds that 'the combined force of the three engines equals 69 horses'.

In describing the section between the top of the Ayton Incline and the River Tyne, the sources disagree. De Gallois states that this included three descending self-acting planes, with one nearly a mile long, presumably the Heworth Incline at 1,337yds; but Bell's plans appear to show that the 1 mile 906 yards to the top of the Heworth Incline was worked by horses, as was the 1 mile 887 yards between Heworth bank foot and the staiths, where a final self-acting incline, the Tyne Inclined Plane, 225yds, took the waggons down to the loading points. Bell gives the distance between the colliery and the Tyne as 7 miles, 14 yards. The gauge of the Waggonway is not known.

Benjamin Thompson, the owner of the waggonway, was a leading advocate of rope haulage in the 1820s. As noted in chapter 2, he led the way in the introduction of main-and-tail haulage to replace horses on the flatter sections of waggonways, and in 1821 he implemented this between the top of the Blackhouse Incline and the top of the Ayton Incline.[5] One has to assume that he similarly converted the section between the top of the Ayton Incline and the top of the Heworth Incline, but no evidence has been found to confirm this or to indicate how it was done. Over the final horse-worked section, between Heworth bank foot and the top of the staiths' incline, there was a gradient in favour of the load, but it was insufficient for a self-acting incline. So Thompson retained the single line and installed a stationary engine at the bank foot; the fulls travelled to the river by gravity, dragging the rope, and the empties being hauled back by the engine. The first two sections were subsequently converted to locomotive haulage, but the section to the staiths continued, and indeed became more complicated when Heworth Colliery, under different owners, built its own self-acting incline to Heworth bank foot, so that the stationary engine there had to handle Heworth fulls and empties too.

In 1882 the Ouston waggonway merged with the Team Waggonway and the combined system became known as the Pelaw Main Railway. This railway, still using various types of incline, lasted well into the twentieth century and is described in chapter 9.

At the same time as the Ouston waggonway was being developed to by-pass the use of keels on the Tyne, the first waggonway to achieve the same on the River Wear was also being built. This was the Nesham or **Newbottle Waggonway**. The Nesham family had owned collieries in the Newbottle area of mid-Durham, north east of Houghton-le-Spring, since 1734. These were served by a waggonway which ran to the eastern bank of the River Wear at Fatfield. About 1810 John Douthwaite Nesham of Houghton-le-Spring decided to sink a new pit, the Dorothea, to join the two others currently in production and collectively known as Newbottle Colliery, and to build a new waggonway 5½ miles long directly to Sunderland, both to handle the increased output and to eliminate the need for keels. As it was to be almost entirely horse-worked, it had to make a large detour eastwards to avoid the hilly ground between Rainton and Sunderland, rising to over 400ft in places, which blocked a more direct route. The biggest problem was at Sunderland itself. The unoccupied ground closest to the mouth of the River Wear lay upstream of the Iron Bridge (built in 1779), but access to it was barred by a deep ravine called Galley's Gill. The only way of reaching the river was by constructing a self-acting incline; but to accommodate this, a steeply-inclined wooden viaduct had to be built down to the ravine, followed by a short tunnel to reach the riverbank. The line was engineered by Edward Steel. It was laid with cast iron rails and the gauge was 4ft 2ins.

The sinking of the Dorothea Pit began in July 1811, and from the dating of the wayleave agreements, the opening of the waggonway probably took place on 22nd August 1812, with the old waggonway to Fatfield being disposed of.

However, in March 1815 a large body of keelmen, seeing their livelihood threatened by the new waggonway, pulled down the wooden viaduct at Sunderland and set fire to neighbouring buildings, causing one death, numerous injuries and £6,000 of damage, while in July that year an experimental steam locomotive[6] there exploded, causing more deaths. Nesham soon faced other difficulties: the sinking of the Dorothea Pit was

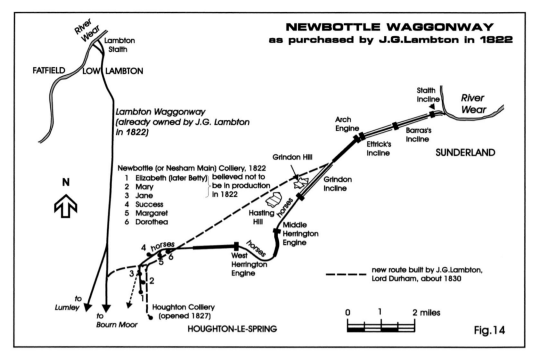

NEWBOTTLE WAGGONWAY
as purchased by J.G.Lambton in 1822

Fig.14

completed in March 1816, and within eighteen months its output was equalling the other pits combined, putting the capacity of the waggonway under severe strain. The result was a report from George Hill of Gateshead dated 26th May 1818[7] proposing the installation of rope haulage on certain sections. This had been partially completed by April 1819, bringing about a significant reduction in operating costs.

However, at this point coal politics intervened; Nesham was to find that he owned a waggonway of strategic importance to three of his neighbours, all of whose enterprises were to make them the leading colliery owners in the county. In April 1819 Charles Stewart (1778-1854), to become the 3rd Marquess of Londonderry in 1822, married Frances Vane Tempest and so gained control of her considerable colliery estate. He immediately replaced her Agent, Arthur Mowbray, with the leading colliery engineer and agent of the time, John Buddle (1779-1843). In turn Mowbray became managing partner of the newly-formed Hetton Coal Company, looking to sink the first colliery through the magnesian limestone covering east Durham, and needing an outlet to Sunderland; while to the west were the extensive collieries of John George Lambton (1792-1840), who was elevated through the peerage to become the 1st Earl of Durham in 1833. Nesham sank into financial difficulties and his affairs were put into the hands of trustees, who, unusually in the history of the coal industry in Durham, decided to

offer everything, collieries, farms and waggonway, as one lot for auction in Sunderland on 2nd July 1822. Stewart and Buddle disliked Mowbray intensely, and to prevent Mowbray acquiring the waggonway for the Hetton company, they proposed a division of the area under which Lambton got Newbottle and Stewart got the Seaham area.[8] This was more or less what happened, with Lambton being the only bidder at the auction. The auction papers and map survive, and give a detailed description of the waggonway.

The waggonway as described in 1822 differs considerably from Hill's proposals of 1818, but it is possible that the first three miles were the same. The first 1,232yds, serving the Success, Margaret and Dorothea Pits, were horse-worked, the calculations at that time being that a horse would work for 12 hours a day at 2 m.p.h. This brought the wagons to the West Herrington Incline, 1,308yds at 1 in 72, where sets of twelve were hauled up by the 30 h.p. West Herrington Engine. Hill's proposals continue '......a horse must be employed to assist the return of the empty waggons, the descent of the Plane not being enough to enable them to descend with the rope attached to them.' If this did in fact happen, it would be the first recorded example of an incline where a stationary engine hauled uphill and a horse pulled the empties and the rope back down. The next 1,181yds were horse-worked, skirting between Herrington Hill and Hasting Hill to reach the hamlet of Middle Herrington, where the line next curved 180 degrees to climb the southern side of Hasting Hill. This incline was 557yds at 1 in 54, worked by the 16 h.p. Middle Herrington Engine. Then followed another horse-worked section, 920yds long, to bring the waggons to Grindon Bank Head on the south-west side of Grindon Hill. Here Hill had proposed a short self-acting incline followed by more horse-working, but by 1822 this section was the Grindon self-acting incline, about 1,610yds long at 1 in 36 to 1 in 48, taking the waggons down to the foot of the Arch Bank. This was 620yds long at 1 in 48, worked by the Arch Engine (16 h.p.). Then came three more self-acting inclines. The first was Ettrick's Incline (about 980yds), followed by Barrass' Incline (about 1,740yds). At the foot of this, at Hylton Road in Sunderland, the line was crossed by the Hetton Railway (see chapter 5). This brought the line to the original Staiths Incline, about 150yds, down to staiths at the river. The whole line was estimated at 10,192 yards, or 5.79 miles.

Yet in little more than ten years Lambton had abandoned two-thirds of this route, replacing it with a completely new line, and had radically rebuilt the remainder – a very rare example of one largely rope-worked railway being replaced by another rope-worked line. His reasons are not known, but they may have included a desire to rid himself of extortionate way-leave payments and a need to increase the capacity of the line, very often a major reason for rebuilding a line, as already noted above. Detailed records of this work seem not to have survived. However, in 1835 Buddle was commissioned to produce a comprehensive report on the Earl's collieries and railways and their working expenses,[9] which contains much interesting information (although not the length of each incline). Buddle gives a figure of 49,141 chaldrons as shipped in the half-year ending 30th June 1835, which assuming that these were chaldrons of 53 hundredweight capacity, gives a total of 130,222 tons, or an annual figure of 260,444 tons, a not inconsiderable figure for 1835.

The Newbottle Railway became part of the very extensive system known by 1850 as the Lambton Railway. In 1865 the Earl of Durham obtained running powers to Sunderland over the North Eastern Railway's Pensher Branch and the inclines to Sunderland were abandoned soon afterwards. The Lambton Railway became by far the largest of Co.Durham's private railways, with the final section not closing until 1986.[10]

So in twenty five years inclines had come to the forefront of tramway and waggonway development. From being a simple haulage in a short link between production point and shipping point, inclines were being incorporated into increasingly sophisticated waggonway systems. This process was greatly aided by the development of powered inclines. Inclines were also becoming longer, as these examples above show, from being a few hundred yards to now over a mile. Endless chain haulage was being used, but so also was direct haulage using hemp rope. With the development of steam locomotives and of iron rails, the railway age is about to dawn, but with both self-acting and powered inclines an integral part.

---

1   Chert is a form of microcrystallite quartz, a hard rock that can be broken to form very sharp edges, like flint.

2   Gwynedd Archives, Caernarfon, XM 7004/5.

3   The exact definition of a 'vertical drum' is uncertain. On the one hand it could be a drum positioned vertically; on the other it could be a drum mounted horizontally with vertical supports at each end.

4   For the information and detail included in the last six paragraphs I am much indebted to Mr.Eric Foulkes.

5   see chapter 2, 30.

6   This locomotive was driven by steam-powered legs. It was designed by William Brunton (1771-1851), built by the Butterley Company in Derbyshire and assembled at Newbottle in 1814. In July 1815 it was fitted with a new boiler, which exploded the first time it was put into steam.

7   Buddle-Atkinson collection, 3410/East/1/142, housed at the North of England Institute of Mining & Mechanical Engineers, Newcastle upon Tyne.

8   Durham County Record Office, D/Lo/C/142/4.

9   Buddle-Atkinson collection, 3410/Bud/28, housed at the North of England Institute of Mining & Mechanical Engineers, Newcastle upon Tyne.

10 For a detailed history of the Lambton Railway, see *The Private Railways of County Durham*, by Colin E.Mountford, Melton Mowbray, 2004, 145-218.

Chapter 5 Railways, inclines and haulages, 1822-1840

Alongside the development since 1796 of tramways and waggonways incorporating inclines, at first self-acting and then also powered, so too there had been quite wide-ranging experiments with steam locomotives, both developments aimed at replacing horses and speeding up the transport of goods. The only major difference between these two developments before 1822 was that all of the locomotives had been tried out on existing lines, usually after they had been relaid with iron rails. It was thus inevitable that eventually there would be a new 'railway' which was designed to use locomotives on parts of its route. This distinction was achieved by the **Hetton Railway** in Co.Durham, opened on 18th November 1822.

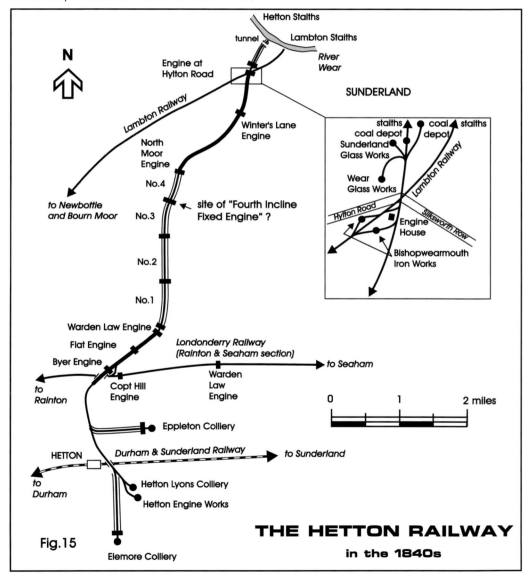

Hetton Staiths
Lambton Staiths
tunnel
River Wear
Engine at Hylton Road
N
SUNDERLAND
Lambton Railway
Winter's Lane Engine
North Moor Engine
staiths · coal · staiths
coal depot · depot
Sunderland Glass Works
Wear Glass Works
Lambton Railway
No.4
to Newbottle and Bourn Moor
No.3
site of "Fourth Incline Fixed Engine" ?
Hylton Road
Silksworth Row
Engine House
Bishopwearmouth Iron Works
No.2
No.1
Warden Law Engine
Flat Engine
Byer Engine
Londonderry Railway (Rainton & Seaham section)
to Seaham
to Rainton
Copt Hill Engine
Warden Law Engine
0   1   2 miles
Eppleton Colliery
HETTON
Durham & Sunderland Railway
to Sunderland
to Durham
Hetton Lyons Colliery
Hetton Engine Works
Fig.15
Elemore Colliery
THE HETTON RAILWAY in the 1840s

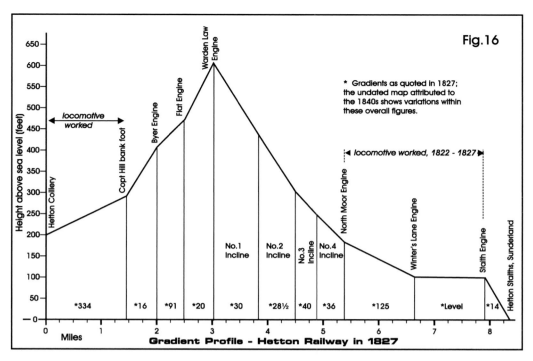

Fig.16 Gradient profile of the Hetton Railway in 1827.

As noted in the last chapter, Arthur Mowbray, dismissed as Agent to Charles Stewart, formed The Hetton Coal Company early in 1820 to sink a colliery at Hetton-le-Hole, south-east of Houghton-le-Spring, through the thick stratum of magnesian limestone, under which, it was popularly believed, there was no coal. Like the owner of the Newbottle Waggonway before him, he wanted to be free of any reliance upon keels and to have a railway direct to the mouth of the River Wear, so that coal could be loaded straight into ships bound for London, where the best prices were to be had. It soon became obvious to Mowbray that to achieve this he would have to build a line of his own, and the evidence suggests that in the summer of 1820 he issued an invitation to local engineers to submit their proposals for routes and costs. Tradition has it that George Stephenson (1781-1848), well-known locally for his improvements to the steam locomotive, obtained leave from his employers, the coal owners known as the 'Grand Allies', to undertake the work, and it was his scheme which was adopted. The construction of the line began in April 1821, but in the following month Stephenson was appointed Engineer of the much larger scheme, the Stockton & Darlington Railway, and so it was his younger brother, Robert, who supervised the work at Hetton.[1]

The direct route between Hetton and Sunderland was not the most ideal from an engineering point of view, as in between them the land rose to 636ft

at Warden Law. The line as built was 13,793½ yards long, or a little over 7¾ miles, with an ascent of 296ft to Warden Law and a descent of 557ft 4in from Warden Law to the staith on the River Wear. Historians are extremely fortunate that in 2004 a extensive report entitled *Observations on Railways.......* came to light written by George Dodds, describing and listing in detail the whole of the line and its operation between its opening in November 1822 and December 1824, during which he was the Railway's Superintendent. Although this is in private hands, it has been made readily available for research. In addition, within months of their opening the railway and its staith were giving the company's directors cause for serious concern, and between 1823 and 1830 they commissioned a series of reports, now held by the North of England Institute of Mining and Mechanical Engineers in Newcastle upon Tyne. The railway was also visited by the Prussian engineers von Oeynhausen and von Dechen about July 1827 and by John Rastrick in January 1829. Consequently, the line's early years are exceptionally well-documented.

The original railway was changed radically in the first five years of its operation and so it is very helpful to have Dodds' description of it at the beginning. The 1½ miles between the colliery and the foot of Copt Hill bank was worked by Stephenson's locomotive(s). This section had been

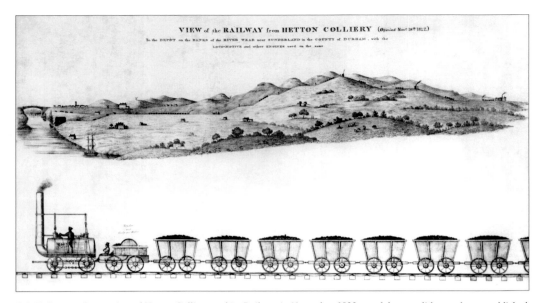

5-1. Following the opening of Hetton Colliery and its Railway in November 1822, a celebratory lithograph was published, subsequently reprinted variously modified. This, the second version, with all the compliments in the middle section removed, shows the colliery on the far right, and the two engine houses raising the line to the summit at Warden Law before the four self-acting inclines bring the line down towards Sunderland. The fifth self-acting incline close to the river is also shown.

built with a gently declining gradient, but by 1824 it had been raised by four feet, using 6,000 chaldrons of coal, to 'equalise the way for the Locomotive Engines'.[2] It was believed for many years that five of Stephenson's locomotives were employed from the beginning, but it is clear from Dodds' document that, until December 1823, there were only three, with perhaps one on this southern end and two on the northern end. From the end of this section the Byer/Byre Engine worked fulls and empties simultaneously up the 882-yard [Byer] Engine bank, also known as the Copt Hill Incline. The next incline, operated by what Dodds calls the Mill Engine but which is universally known as the Warden Law Engine, comprised two equal sections of 775yds and used a form of direct rope haulage almost certainly unique. The first section had a gradient averaging 1 in 90 and the second a gradient of 1 in 22, the two sections being linked by a meetings. As the engine hauled a set of eight fulls up from the meetings, a tail rope attached to the rear of the waggons hauled up a second set of eight from the Byer Engine 775yds behind them.[3] This completed, both ropes were transferred to sets of empties, which were then lowered, a procedure which must have required great operational care. Both of the haulers were 60 h.p. condensing engines, but their builders are unknown.

From Warden Law four consecutive self-acting inclines took the waggons down to the outskirts of Sunderland. These respectively were 1,302, 1,224, 716 and 902 yards, and again four in succession is believed to be unique.[4] The brake wheel around

which the rope went at the top of each incline lay beneath the rails.[5] Then followed 2½ miles worked by locomotives, which brought the waggons almost to the river, where a fifth self-acting incline of 325yds took them down to the staith.

It is perhaps not surprising that the section between the Byer and Warden Law Engines was the first to receive attention. In February 1826 Mowbray advertised for two high pressure steam engines, of one 30 h.p. and one of 12 h.p. Almost certainly the first was to be installed at the meetings, known as 'the Flat', between the two 775 yard sections, so that each was provided with its own engine, with fulls and empties being run alternately. However, because the gradient was only 1 in 90 on the Flat Engine's incline, it ran sets of sixteen, double the number on the other inclines.

But a much more serious problem was looming. The evidence strongly suggests that Stephenson's design was based on an annual 'vend' (sale) of 60,000 chaldrons, or 159,000 tons. This might have been managed had the line served only one colliery, but in the first half of 1825 the sinking of two more collieries, Elemore and Eppleton, to the South and North of Hetton, began. As early as April 1823 the directors were seeking the implications of the railway's tonnage being raised to 100,000 chaldrons a year; by 1829 they were asking their engineer to report on an increase to 180,000 chaldrons a year (477,000 tons), three times Stephenson's original estimate.

5-2. *Copt Hill bank foot at Rough Dene, Hetton, on the Hetton Railway in August 1959. The rope end, with its short connecting chain, lies between the rails, where the last set of empties was knocked off. The rising gradient was approximately 1 in 16. To the right can be seen the long iron lever, which when pulled down raised the wooden white disc at the bank head to indicate to the men there that the set at the bottom was ready to run (see photo 3-17).*

5-3. *Looking down the Copt Hill Incline on its three-rail section from above the level crossing on the B1404 road from Houghton-le-Spring to Seaham in August 1959. The four-lever signal box was installed by The Westinghouse Brake & Signal Co Ltd of Chippenham in 1923, but the crossing gates which it controlled appear to be missing, presumably away for repair. Note the siding to the former landsale depot, and the two sets of catch points between the photographer and the crossing.*

5-4. *Looking down the Warden Law Incline towards Hetton on 20th June 1956. In the middle distance, at the end of the Incline's two-rail section, lies the Flatt Pumping Engine, the site of a winding engine until 1876. In the distance can be seen the chimney of the Byer Engine at the top of the Engine Bank. Also visible is the large Rainton pit heap, the central stone disposal point for the Lambton Railway's collieries at this time.*

5-5. *The drum house of the Warden Law Engine of 1836, open to the weather at the front as many of the drum houses in Durham were at this time. Note too the narrow drum, only 2ft 6in wide; the other drum is hidden by the right-hand wall. Only one of the four gear wheels is visible. For a full description of the Engine, see chapter 6.*

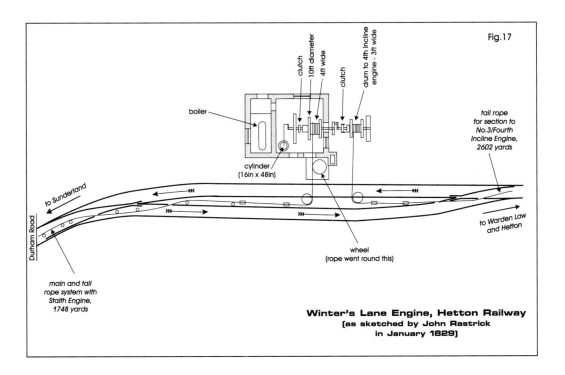

Fig.17

clutch

10ft diameter
4ft wide

clutch

drum to 4th Incline
engine - 3ft wide

boiler

cylinder
(16in x 48in)

tail rope
for section to
No.3/Fourth
Incline Engine,
2602 yards

to Sunderland

Durham Road

to Warden Law
and Hetton

wheel
(rope went round this)

main and tail
rope system with
Staith Engine,
1748 yards

Winter's Lane Engine, Hetton Railway
(as sketched by John Rastrick
in January 1829)

5-6. *The bank head of No.2 self-acting incline on the Hetton Railway in the summer of 1959. On the left the rope is being attached for the fulls to descend No.3 Incline, while the empties in the dish await their rope being attached. To the right of the empties can be seen a hand-operated winch, used to pull the fulls back when they had run through the catch points at the bank head. There was a similar winch on the left-hand side just beyond the cabin. Note the white disc, the raising of which by the men at the bottom of No.3 Incline indicated that they had completed their work; latterly these discs were replaced by bell signals.*

5-7. The meetings on No.3 Incline on the Hetton Railway; this was recorded in the autumn of 1959, after closure and the removal of the rope. Note all the apparatus needed to accommodate the rope around the curve, with the vertical rollers mounted on wooden platforms and the thin steel plates for the rope to slide up to the roller. Note too that the inside rail of the outer track is a flat-bottomed rail only pinned to the sleepers! Presumably this was a short term job decided by the imminent closure of the Railway on 9th September 1959.

The main problem was now the locomotive-worked section near Sunderland. A report of July 1823 to the directors by the engineer William Chapman (1749-1832)[6] described how locomotives hauling trains of sixteen waggons normally travelled at 5 m.p.h., but that their speed on the final 1,533yds up to the foot of No.4 self-acting incline fell to 2½-3 mph, due to the curves and gradients (between 1 in 109 and 1 in 139). The locomotives were expected to make ten round trips totalling fifty miles in fourteen hours. Chapman continued by saying that while the situation could be managed given the existing vend, if the traffic increased it would be essential to acquire an extra locomotive or to re-model the track.

In the event the directors took neither course. With Elemore Colliery commencing production in 1827, they decided to replace the locomotives altogether with three more stationary engines. The first, situated at the foot of No.4 Incline and thus known as the Fourth Incline Engine, worked the first 2,602yds by direct haulage, lowering sixteen fulls down and then hauling sixteen empties back. The next two, the Winter's Lane Engine and the Staith Engine, worked the remaining 1,748yds by main-and-tail haulage. The new rope haulage commenced work at the end of May 1827.[7] The increased capacity of the new system was dramatic; von Oeynhausen and von Dechen, visiting only a few weeks after it

started, recorded the Fourth Engine working sets of sixteen, the same as the locomotive, but at 10 mph, while on the main-and-tail section sets of twenty-four were run, and sometimes twenty-eight or thirty, again at 10 mph, and of course both sections were now working simultaneously.[8] Rastrick includes a sketch of what he called the No. 2 (Winter's Lane) Engine, visited in January 1829, which shows the engine with two drums (Fig.17), from which it would appear that there was also a tail rope to assist the Fourth Incline (No.3) Engine when it was necessary, perhaps not surprisingly given that it was direct haulage on a very shallow gradient. This was presumably added after the Prussians' visit, and was perhaps retained until this haulage was abandoned in the 1850s.

In 1836 the directors replaced the Warden Law Engine with a new single-cylinder 97½ h.p. condensing engine built by Thomas Murray of Chester-le-Street (see Chapter 6), but there were no further changes until the mid-1850s, when the three engines of 1827 on the northern section were replaced by locomotives. The Byer and Flat Engines appear to have survived until 1876, when a new Byer Engine was installed (again, see Chapter 6). Several sections of the line in Sunderland were re-routed before the First World War, but otherwise the Railway remained largely unchanged well into the twentieth century.

The next railway to be designed by George Stephenson was the **Stockton & Darlington Railway**, famous throughout the world as the first-ever public railway, designed to carry passengers using steam locomotives. Its Act in April 1821 authorised a railway 26 miles long, and the opening day, on 27th September 1825, with *Locomotion* driven by George Stephenson himself, is supposedly known by every British schoolboy. But only the section between Shildon and Stockton employed Stephenson's locomotives, under the supervision of Timothy Hackworth (1786-1850). The railway was conceived initially to carry coal and began at Witton Park, and the section from Shildon westwards to Witton Park, just over 3¼ miles long, was operated almost entirely by rope haulage. Disappointingly for such a well-known railway, the published information about this is often poor and inaccurate, despite the inclines being described by Oeynhausen and Dechen when they visited in the summer of 1827 and also by James Walker and John Rastrick in January 1829.

The Phoenix Pit of Old Etherley Colliery at Witton Park lay about 450ft above sea level, and the most direct route to Shildon involved crossing two hilly ridges divided by the River Gaunless. George Stephenson decided that the first incline, 1,109yds[9] on a gradient of 1 in 33, up to the summit at Etherley, would be worked by a stationary engine, with the descent to the Gaunless at West Auckland, 2,185yds at 1 in 30¾, being a self-acting incline. This was one of the longest inclines built so far. After a short section worked by horses, the incline up to the summit at Brusselton was 1,851yds at 1 in 33½, followed by a much shorter incline, 825yds also at 1 in 33½, down to Shildon; but here the stationary engine worked both inclines, almost certainly the first time this had been done. The Etherley South bank was presumably a standard self-acting incline; the other three were single track, with fulls and empties being run alternately.

Both stationary engines were ordered in November 1823 from Robert Stephenson & Company of Newcastle upon Tyne, the first substantial order the firm had received since it had been set up five months earlier. Robert Stephenson completed both designs just before he left for Columbia, and interestingly both followed the marine engine layout, with twin cylinders and the beams mounted near the floor.

The Etherley Engine was a condensing engine with two cylinders measuring 21in by 38in,[10] producing a nominal 30 h.p. Originally this just hauled and lowered on the Etherley North incline, but Timothy Hackworth had soon modified it so that the self-acting incline was done away with and both inclines were operated simultaneously, in an unusual and perhaps unique arrangement. Rastrick describes this in his notes, very fortunately adding a diagram (5-8), which includes the dimensions of the gearing. Now, with fulls and empties both at the summit, the rope

from the small barrel/drum was attached to the front of eight full waggons at the North Incline bank foot, while at the bank head the rope from the large barrel was attached to the rear of eight full waggons waiting to descend the South Incline. With the drums disengaged from the engine, the fulls descending the South Incline then hauled up the fulls on the North side (remembering that the south side was steeper). The waggons on the south side would need some careful controlling when the north side set had arrived at the summit. The ropes were then changed to the empties at the South bank foot and at the summit waiting to descend the North bank, and with the engine and drums in gear the engine would haul the south side empties up to the summit, assisted by the descending empties on the north side. This system would speed up the handling of traffic, while both hauling and braking requirements would be greatly improved because of the counterbalancing introduced.

The sale notice for the engine, in July 1859 (see 2-17), still describes it as 'a pair of Marine Engines', but now at 40 h.p. nominal, with cylinders 22⅝in by 38½in, larger 'rolls'/drums at 6ft 2in and 11ft 0in and a 14ft diameter flywheel. These are all slightly larger than the engine described by Rastrick in 1829, so perhaps it was rebuilt or replaced at some point.

The Brusselton Engine comprised two cylinders 30in in diameter with a 60in stroke, producing a nominal 30 h.p. each. It too was a condensing engine, taking steam from two boilers 20ft long by 8ft in diameter. Its cost had been estimated at £3,482-15s-0d, although the makers' records suggest the actual cost was about £2,750, about 4½ times the cost of a new steam locomotive at this time. Oeynhausen & Dechen give a detailed description of the engines, and add that the two boilers were 15ft long and 7½ft in diameter, with 'flues which run round the sides'. On the Railway's opening day thousands of spectators gathered to watch the first ascent of a set up the West Incline, twelve waggons of coal plus a waggon carrying sacks of flour as well as a number of unauthorised passengers, the journey taking about nine minutes.

When new the cylinders reportedly drove a vertical drum, although this is not confirmed. It would also seem to have been unsatisfactory, because in 1826 Hackworth replaced it with a horizontal shaft and a two-part drum, the diameter of the two sections being in proportion to the lengths of the two inclines. This would seem to suggest that this new system required two ropes, one for each side, perhaps used in some kind of counterbalancing system as at Etherley. If so, it again did not last long, for when Rastrick saw the system in 1829, he recorded that a set of eight full waggons was hauled up the West Incline (1,851yds) in 7 minutes, and that once at the summit, the same rope was attached to the rear of the set to descend the East Incline (825yds). This it did in 3½ minutes, 'with the Engine stoker applying

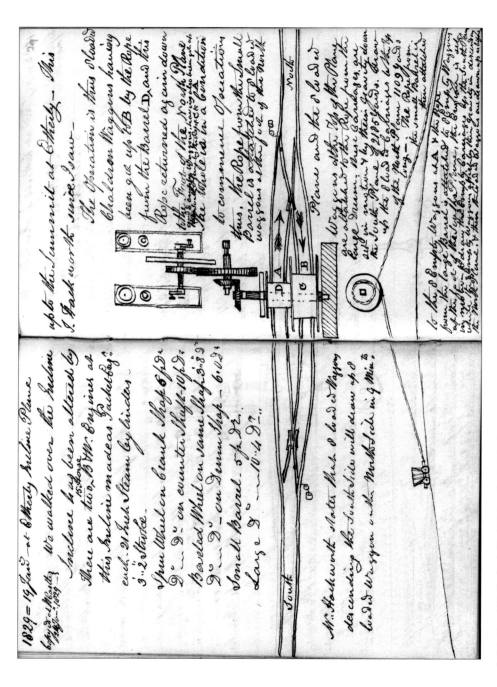

5-8. The pages in John Rastrick's Notebook IV which describe the Etherley Engine and the operation of its inclines on 19th January 1829. The left hand page lists the main dimensions, while the right hand page describes how the inclines were operated following the modifications made by Timothy Hackworth. It can be read and gives an eye-witness account by a nationally-known engineer of how this incline was operated at this time.

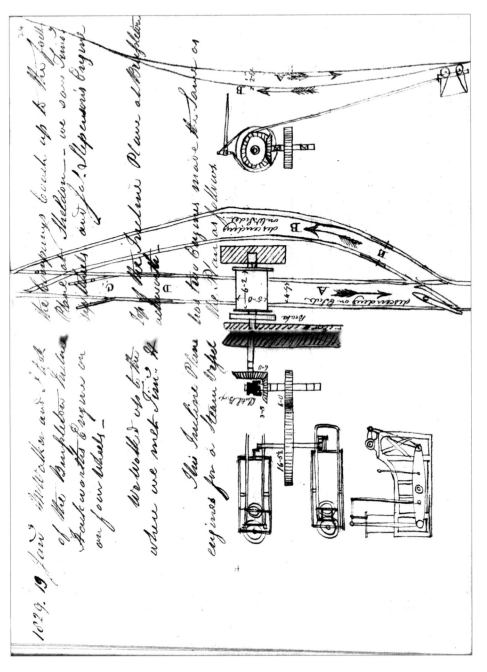

5-9. The pages in Rastrick's Notebook IV which record that on 19th January 1829 he and James Walker took the Stockton & Darlington coach to the foot of the Brusselton [East] Incline, walking to the summit, where they met Timothy Hackworth. Then he sketched the Brusselton Engine and the bank head - again, the only-known evidence of how this was laid out. Note in the bottom left corner Rastrick's sketch showing the packet (marine-type) engine, designed by Robert Stephenson.

the brake to the drum occasionally'. Once at the bottom, the rope was attached to eight empties, which the Engine hauled to the summit in 2¾ minutes, and then after the Engine and the drum had been 'thrown out of gear', the set descended the West incline in 4½ minutes.

Oeynhausen and Dechen noted that in order to indicate to the engineman at these considerable distances when the train was ready, a tall signal post was used, at the top of which a disc was turned in an appointed direction; but it was difficult to see these signals at so great a distance, so a telescope, continually pointed towards the post, was placed beside the engineman's seat for him to look through when necessary. When he could not see them at all (as, for example, in fog), long pulling wires had to be used, but the Prussians do not explain what these wires operated.

Rastrick records problems with the ropes here. The first rope, made of hemp, put on the West Incline was made by John Grimshaw of Bishop Wearmouth, near Sunderland (see chapter 3). This was 1,864yds, weighed rather more than 3½ tons and cost £185-9s-2d. It had soon stretched 40 fathoms, and by the time it was worn out it had stretched 100 fathoms, or 600ft, an incredible amount.

Yet again these arrangements at Brusselton were short-lived, for in 1831 the engine was replaced altogether, by a new 80 h.p. engine built by R. & W. Hawthorn of Newcastle upon Tyne, works No. 137.

This is said to have had a 10ft diameter drum, so perhaps again it hauled up one side and lowered down the other, using the same rope. If so, it was subsequently rebuilt, for the advertisement for its sale in 1859 (see 2-17) shows that by then it had two 'Rope Rolls', one 13ft 4in in diameter and the other 6ft 2in, presumably for working both inclines simultaneously. The drive shaft was 22ft 11in long and the flywheel was 21ft 10ins. It had a single cylinder, 3ft in diameter with a 5ft stroke, presumably mounted vertically and driving a single beam. For this engine a completely new engine house was built on the opposite side of the track to the original one.

Initially the Stockton & Darlington directors were uncertain as to the best way to manage the operation of their railway. At first they paid all of the operating expenses, but from 17th February 1826 the Brusselton engineman, William Mowtrey, was contracted to undertake everything, with his income covering the wages of his fireman and assistants, as well as the work and cost of materials for greasing the bearings of the waggon wheels, together with supplies of coal, tallow, oil, hemp, etc, for all of which he was paid 1½d per ton handled. Six months later this was changed to a payment of 22 shillings a week; but after only six more weeks this reverted to 1¼d per ton handled, only for it to be changed again to a shilling per set, with a guarantee of eighteen sets a day. He must have done very well on some days, for up to 6th September 1839 the daily record at Brusselton was 67 sets of 12 waggons, or 904 waggons carrying 2,120 tons of coal.

5-10. The ruins of the Brusselton Engine about 1880, looking from the west. On the left is the 1831 engine house and its chimney, with the remains of the drum house straddling the track bed. The original engine house of 1825 is the cross-building on the right, showing three windows and a door. The building with its front in shadow was the engineman's house.

Between Etherley South bank and Brusselton West bank lay the settlement of St.Helens Auckland, and from here the four-mile long Haggerleazes branch along the valley of the Gaunless was opened on 1st October 1830. This brought more traffic on to the Brusselton inclines. On 1st December 1833 a passenger service was started between St.Helens and Shildon, presumably with the carriage simply being attached to coal waggons.

In 1827 the Railway had opened the Black Boy branch from Shildon northwards to collieries south of Bishop Auckland. This too incorporated two inclines worked by a stationary engine. In 1842 the Shildon Tunnel was opened, thus avoiding these inclines, and on 8th November 1843 the Bishop Auckland & Weardale Railway, a subsidiary of the Stockton & Darlington Railway, opened its line from Bishop Auckland to Crook via Witton Park, thus making the Etherley inclines redundant, although some traffic may have continued to take the old route.

The increasing traffic from the Haggerleazes branch led to the Stockton & Darlington building what was called the 'Tunnel Branch', a new line from St.Helens Auckland to the northern end of Shildon Tunnel. This was opened on 13th September 1856, making the Brusselton inclines redundant. In fact the passenger service over the inclines continued to operate, and not until 13th October 1858 were both the Brusselton and Etherley Inclines officially closed. The boilers and chimney at Brusselton were eventually replaced by a row of houses, whilst the remains of both of the 1825 engine houses were also converted into houses. Even then it was not the end: the track on the Brusselton East bank remained in place for many years afterwards to allow a condemned waggon to be propelled to the summit for the residents to dismantle as a source of firewood, whilst even later the track became a source of fish-bellied rail for museums!

Four months after the opening of the Stockton & Darlington Railway the first section of the **Springwell Colliery Railway**, some 25 miles to the north, was also opened. This was owned by the most powerful partnership in the north-east coal industry, known locally as the 'Grand Allies', originally formed in 1726 by members of the Wortley, Ord, Liddell and Bowes families, and renewed a century later.

On 8th May 1821 the 'Allies' began the sinking of Springwell Colliery, about four miles south-east of Gateshead. Not far away lay Mount Moor Colliery, which had been won nearly a century earlier and whose coal was carried by a waggonway 2¼ miles long to staiths on the River Wear near Washington; but this involved

transhipping the coal in keels down to colliers at Sunderland. The 'Allies' had seen the advantages of the Newbottle and Ouston Waggonways and were determined to end this system. So they commissioned John Buddle to develop a proposal for a waggonway between their Stanley Colliery in north-west Durham via Mount Moor and Springwell Collieries to the River Tyne at Jarrow. Buddle drew up plans for a line 11½ miles long, with six rope inclines and two locomotive-worked sections.[11] However, the 'Allies' first decided not to go ahead with the section west of Mount Moor and then commissioned George Stephenson, who had been their employee at Killingworth Colliery in Northumberland, to re-design the remainder. In the event, Stephenson was heavily involved with the construction of the Stockton & Darlington Railway, and it seems likely that the design was the work of the young Joseph Locke (1805-1860), who was then an employee of Robert Stephenson & Co at Newcastle upon Tyne. Coal from Mount Moor Colliery would be hauled up a 750-yard incline on a gradient of 1 in 15 to the Blackham's Hill Engine (later spelling), which would then lower the waggons down to Springwell Colliery, a distance of 1,170yds at 1 in 70. From Springwell a self-acting incline 1¼ miles long on an average gradient of 1 in 24, one of the longest self-acting inclines yet built, would lower the waggons down to the Leam Lane, whence locomotives would take over for the final 4¾ miles to Jarrow. With the exception of the Springwell Incline, the whole line was single track, presumably with passing places between Springwell Bank Foot and Jarrow.

Orders for two locomotives and subsequently for two stationary engines were placed with Robert Stephenson & Co in 1824; these were order nos. 11, 12, 21 and 22, according to Dr. Michael Bailey's reconstruction of the company's orders list.[12] At the beginning of 1826 nothing had been delivered, but with the line from Springwell to Jarrow complete, it was opened, using horses, on 17th January. The two locomotives were delivered in April 1826. Both of the stationary engines are described as colliery engines, a 20 h.p. example being condensing and the other a 30 h.p. high pressure engine. As the former was delivered in the summer of 1826 and the second not until March 1827, and as the extension to Mount Moor is said to have been opened in June 1826, presumably it was the 20 h.p. condensing engine which was installed at Blackham's Hill.

Little is known about the engine. Oral tradition recorded in the 1930s said that it had a drum over the track and it worked the two inclines alternately. It was replaced in 1854-55. The Railway lasted well into the twentieth century as part of what became a much larger system.

The next major railway to be opened was the **Bolton & Leigh Railway**, the first public railway in Lancashire. It obtained its Act in March 1825, and was promoted to carry coal and goods between the Manchester, Bolton & Bury Canal and the Leeds & Liverpool Canal. It was surveyed by George Stephenson but engineered by Robert Daglish (c1777-1865), a Northumbrian who had moved to Lancashire, where he had built several locomotives for the Orrell tramway and had developed a significant engineering business. The first 7½ miles from Bolton was opened on 1st August 1828. Subsequently an extension 2½ miles long was built to link the line to the Liverpool & Manchester Railway at Kenyon Junction near Warrington, the whole line being completed in March 1830. Originally the line carried only freight, but a passenger service was begun on 13th June 1831. As elsewhere, the line was basically single track.

Once again the railway used a mix of locomotives and inclines, and also horses, according to Francis Whishaw (1804-1856).[13] From Kenyon Junction a locomotive worked for nearly five miles to the foot of the Chequer Bent Incline. This rose for 1 mile 434 yards, mostly at 1 in 30. It was worked by a 50 h.p. condensing engine taking steam at about 7 p.s.i. Its builders are not known. Whishaw notes that the rope was manufactured by Webster of Sunderland, was 6in in diameter and weighed about 5 tons, running over sheaves that were either 14 or 18in diameter, spaced eight yards apart. The locomotive was drawn up on the rope with its train, Whishaw recording that on his journey in November 1839, the haul took 8 minutes at 9¼ m.p.h. The train then proceeded to the foot of the Daubhill Incline, where it would seem that the locomotive came off and ran around its train. Whishaw states that the engine here was 20 h.p., but the original engine here was built by Robert Stephenson & Co, whose records describe it as 10 h.p. This was a 'high pressure' engine, with a vertical-cylinder whose dimensions are given as 18in by 36in (possibly 38in). It was completed in November 1827 at a cost of £500. Perhaps Whishaw was misinformed, or perhaps the original engine had been replaced. When the train was attached to the rope, the signal to the engineman was given by pulling back the carriages slightly, causing a spanner placed on the rope to fall off! Once at the summit, the train descended the other side, a distance of about a mile, by gravity, the gradient varying between 1 in 33 and 1 in 55. It would seem that the same rope was attached to the rear of the train, with the engine acting as a brake. The rope was then in position to haul the next train up. According to Whishaw, horses then drew the trains to Bolton. He also noted that when the Chequer Bent rope was worn, it was transferred to Daubhill for further use, one of the earliest-known examples of such a transfer being undertaken. The route involving the inclines was eventually by-passed by a new route, which opened in 1885.

The next important railway was the **Canterbury & Whitstable Railway** in Kent, the first major public railway in the south of England and the first to run a regular passenger service hauled by a steam locomotive. Canterbury was an important city and religious centre, but depended for the transport of goods brought by sea, notably coal, on the meandering and badly-silted River Stour. In the 1820s William James (1771-1837) surveyed possible routes and in 1825 the railway obtained its first Act. The directors then persuaded George Stephenson to become their engineer, but in the event Stephenson was too busy with the Liverpool & Manchester Railway and was only able to visit Canterbury twice. Construction work was begun under John Dixon (1796-1865), from the Stockton & Darlington Railway, and continued under Robert Stephenson after his return from South America in 1827.

The railway was six miles long on more or less a direct route, but the land rose to over 200ft between the two ends. So the initial plan provided for three stationary engines and horses. From Canterbury a huge incline 3,300yds long and dead straight on gradients between 1 in 41 and 1 in 56 would take the line up Tyler Hill, passing through a tunnel of 828yds, the first on a public railway. The tunnel had a very narrow bore, which presented little problem to rope-hauled trains but meant specially cut-down locomotives were needed latterly. The illustrative evidence would suggest that the incline was single line, although there was a passing place just below the downhill end of the tunnel. The Tyler Hill Engine was 230ft above sea level. The next 1,980yds had a ruling gradient of only 1 in 750, taking the line up to the Clowes Wood Engine at 237ft, after which the line descended for about a mile at gradients between 1 in 28 and 1 in 31. It would appear that the Engine worked both of these sections, though the method used on the long flatter section is not known. Again it would seem that both of these sections were single line.

Then followed 2,200yds on the level, followed by 880yds falling at 1 in 53 and finally 440yds on the level to the harbour at Whitstable. It would seem that the original intention was for the Whitstable Engine to work the 1 in 53 section, with horses working the sections on either side. Robert Stephenson & Co began work began on three 25 h.p. 'high pressure' engines in March 1827, but a month later all work was stopped. The directors, already finding that the cost of construction was much higher than they had anticipated, clearly felt that a locomotive could be used at the Whitstable end, perhaps from the bottom of the 1 in 31 descent, although horses were to be used at the harbour. Eventually this was agreed, and work was resumed on the first two engines in May 1828.

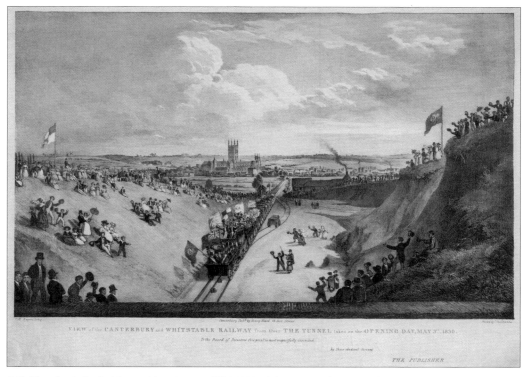

5-11. The oil painting by Thomas Mann Baynes (1794-1854) of the opening of the Canterbury & Whitstable Railway on 3rd May 1830. With Canterbury Cathedral in the background, a passenger train of ten waggons is shown being hauled up the Tyler Hill Incline. Note that the second vehicle is of a stage-coach design.

Although the engines were finished in the autumn that year, it was November 1829 before they were shipped, while it would seem that the locomotive, called *Invicta*, was not delivered until April 1830. The line was opened, with huge ceremony, on 3rd May 1830. Whitstable harbour was rebuilt in 1832 under the direction of Thomas Telford (1757-1834).

Invicta soon proved to be inadequate, probably because she had to haul imported coal up the half mile gradient of 1 in 53, and in 1836 a 15 h.p. stationary engine was installed near South Street in Whitstable. The power of the other stationary engines was increased at the same time, apparently by fitting Cornish boilers. The line did not realise its promotors' ambitions and was virtually bankrupt when the South Eastern Railway agreed to take it over in 1844. The inclines were removed two years later. Amazingly, *Invicta* was retained, as were some parts from the Tyler Hill Engine.

Four months after the opening of the Canterbury & Whitstable Railway, the **Liverpool & Manchester Railway** was opened, on 15th September 1830. As is well known, this 31-mile line was a significant milestone in the history of railways. Its purpose was to achieve cheap transport of raw materials and

finished goods between the port of Liverpool and its hinterland, including the rapidly-growing city of Manchester - the first-ever inter-city line. It also carried passengers on fully-timetabled trains, incredibly nearly half a million of them in 1831. It is equally well-known that the railway was a tipping point in the struggle between haulage by stationary engines and locomotives. The detail is too long to give fully here, the best account being in *The Liverpool & Manchester Railway* by R.H.G. Thomas, published in 1980, but the outline can be given.

With their first Acts obtained in 1826 and George Stephenson re-instated as their Engineer, the directors of the railway were divided between whether it should be operated by ropes, with stationary engines now being seen as a reliable form of haulage, or by locomotives, which still seemed to many to be primitive and unreliable. Those in favour of the latter had the important support of George Stephenson. The first step by the Company to resolve the matter came in October 1828, when three directors were asked to visit the Stockton & Darlington Railway to observe and report on the locomotives, horses and stationary engines used. Their report seems to have been inconclusive, and it was referred to

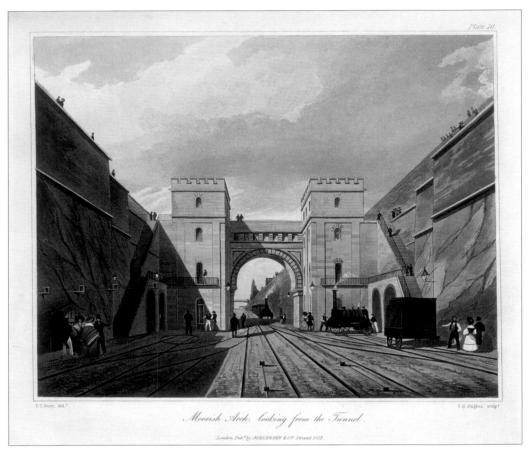

5-12. One of the famous series of paintings of the Liverpool & Manchester Railway by Thomas Bury (1811-1877), produced as aquatints by the London publisher Rudolf Ackermann (1764-1834). This shows the 'Moorish Arch' looking from the Wapping Tunnel at Edgehill in Liverpool. The two castellated buildings were the original engine houses here, and the ropes for the tunnels can be seen emerging from underground.

Stephenson, who in turn reported on it on 5th November in a long document presenting all the points in favour of the locomotive and all the disadvantages of fixed engines.[14]

Based on an estimate of 2,400 tons per day to be moved, Stephenson states that 54 stationary engines of 19 h.p. each would be needed, each costing £1,200, a total of £64,800, with those used across Chat Moss costing more. There would be additional capital costs of £7,128 for sheaves, £1,740 for 'extra power', £6,500 for ropes and £832 for contingencies, giving a total outlay of £81,000. An engine working 12 hours a day could be expected to break down once a year, and even if it took only three hours to repair, the 54 engines could account for a complete stoppage of traffic of about a fortnight a year, since the failure of one engine would immobilise the whole line. Twelve minutes would be required for travelling between each engine, including the time taken in changing

ropes and signalling to the next engine. By contrast, he states that the same work could be done by 48 locomotive engines at £600 each, with a total expense of only £13,080, and there would be none of these disadvantages. Given that the line was 31 miles long, one wonders at his estimate of 54 stationary engines, or one approximately every 1,000yds, or which manufacturers were going to supply either 54 stationary engines or 48 locomotives, and indeed whether the whole report was totally impartial.

Despite Stephenson's report, the directors were not convinced about the merits of locomotive engines, and in mid-November they invited two eminent engineers, James Walker (1781-1862) of London and John Rastrick (1780-1856) of Stourbridge, to visit all the major railways in the north of England and to report their opinions on the comparative merits of Fixed and Locomotive Engines. This they did, but their report in March

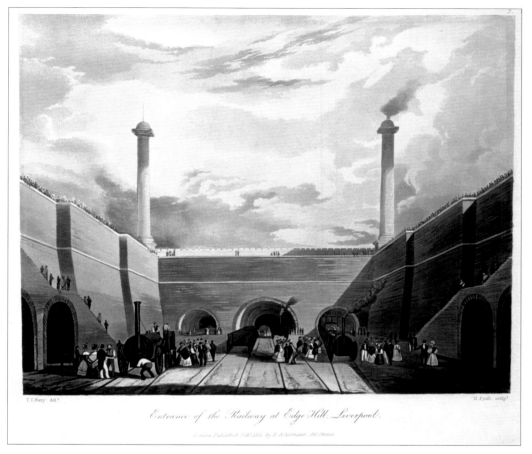

5-13. The same position at Edgehill, but looking towards the tunnels. The middle tunnel led to the Wapping Wharf, the right hand tunnel to the original Liverpool station at Crown Street. The left hand 'entrance' was originally blind, and created purely for the symmetrical effect, but it was subsequently developed into another tunnel, worked by locomotives, to serve the Crown Street coal yard. Note the ornate chimneys for the boiler houses, created from one course of spiral brickwork and over 100ft high.

1829 was broadly in favour of fixed engines. Robert Stephenson and Joseph Locke quickly produced a reply refuting Walker and Rastrick's arguments, but it was a suggestion at the end of Walker's report which found favour with the L & M Board - to offer a 'premium' of £500 for a 'Locomotive Engine which shall be a decided improvement on those now in use'. Rules were drawn up, a venue chosen – at Rainhill – and the opening day for the Trials set for 6th October 1829.

Much has been written about the Rainhill Trials, which Robert Stephenson's *Rocket*, with its multi-tubular boiler, won convincingly. The opening of the Railway on 15th September 1830 can justifiably be said to mark the beginning of the modern railway age. Locomotives hauled trains over most of the route and passenger traffic quickly exceeded all expectations. Yet alongside this a myth also developed – that the victory of *Rocket* and the success of the Railway marked the end of rope and

chain-worked inclines on railways and all trains were now to be hauled by locomotives, a myth that was quite untrue. It was not even true on the Liverpool & Manchester Railway itself.

At the Liverpool end of the line locomotive-hauled passenger trains terminated at Edgehill, but that was not the Liverpool terminus. About thirty yards west of Edgehill Station there were three tunnel portals, although the left-hand portal was initially provided only for symmetry and was blind. The first passenger terminus, together with a coal depot, was sited at Crown Street and was served by the right-hand or northern tunnel rising from Edgehill, 290yds long, 16ft 9ins wide and 12ft high. This section was worked by rope haulage. At the end of the rope was fitted a small, four-wheeled carriage known as a 'pilot' and from this the rope went round a horizontal drum, 3ft wide by 3ft 4in in diameter, and then down to the engine at Edgehill. The pilot was attached to the train for it to be hauled up, and once it had been run past and put in the station, the drum was put out of gear and a horse pulled the pilot back to the bottom ready for the next train. Although it is not stated, presumably trains leaving Crown Street were attached to the pilot and lowered down, rather than descending by gravity under the control of a brakesman. The tunnel was whitewashed and gas lit. From the end of the tunnel to Edgehill Station was about thirty yards. Goods traffic for Liverpool was handled at the Wapping Depot, served by the central portal at Edgehill. This tunnel had a gentle curve on the level for 270 yards, followed by a descent of 1,980 yards at 1 in 48, giving a total length of 2,250 yards (Whishaw gives 2,216 yards) and was 22ft wide and 16ft high. It too was whitewashed and gas lit. The incline was served by an endless rope system running down the centre of one track and back along the other. The main pulley, driven by spur gears from the main drive shaft, was 10ft in diameter and positioned horizontally below rail level. In line with it were two 5ft pulleys, also set horizontally 11ft apart. The rope passed twice round both the large pulley and the centre one and once round the third, the last being mounted on a small carriage running on a small

track and to which was attached by a chain a counterweight of 2½ tons suspended in a well 100yds deep. This enabled the rope to be kept under tension, taking up the slack when the rope stretched. These two tunnels were the first in the world to be driven under a metropolis.

Initially both inclines were worked by one stationary engine, supplied by Robert Stephenson & Co in September 1829 at a cost of £1,600. Unfortunately, the ship on which it was being conveyed to Liverpool was wrecked off Aberdeen and a new engine had to be constructed, possibly using parts salvaged from the original. About three weeks after the opening of the Railway in September 1830 it was apparent that one engine was inadequate and a second engine was ordered from Stephensons at a cost of £1,800. The two 50 h.p. 'high pressure' engines were of similar design, with single cylinders of 24in diameter and 6ft stroke; the beams were 13ft 4in long and the flywheels 20ft in diameter. They were housed in two engine houses flanking the famous 'Moorish Arch'. Steam was supplied from two return-flue boilers on each side, set in excavations in the sides of the Edgehill cutting near the engines.

5-14. A view inside the Wapping Tunnel at Edgehill; Ackermann published several versions of this. The public were allowed to inspect the tunnel, for a charge, before it was opened for traffic.

Railway Office, Liverpool.

London, Pub.d by R. ACKERMANN, 96 Strand, 1831.

5-15. This view was officially entitled 'Railway Office, Liverpool', but in fact shows the Crown Street Station. It is a fascinating study of passenger activity at a major station in the 1830s, albeit with the trains handled by rope haulage. The station was too far from the centre of Liverpool - hence the stagecoach shown – and was replaced by a new station, served by a new tunnel and still worked by rope haulage, at Lime Street in August 1836.

The two boiler house chimneys were over 100ft high. Unusually they were built of one course of brickwork ascending spirally, and were finished to resemble Doric columns with pediments and capitals of stone. In 1832 the operation of the two engines was made more flexible by installing underground a steam pipe between the boilers, so that either set could be used for either engine, together with an underground passage both for men to pass between the engines and to accommodate a shaft to allow the 'South Engine to work the Little Tunnel rope without putting in motion the Big Spur Wheel.'

The first ropes for the two inclines were made in Sunderland and cost £60 per ton. They were 4,000yds long and 5½ins in circumference, and lasted just over a year. In September 1832 a 'new Patent India Rubber Rope' was installed in the Crown Street tunnel to handle the ten-wagon coal trains going up to the Crown Street coal depot.

As early as 1831 it became clear that the Crown Street station was inadequate and also inconveniently distant from the centre of Liverpool, with the company having to provide horse-drawn buses to carry passengers. So in 1832 an Act was obtained for the construction of a much larger station at Lime Street, linked by a new tunnel to Edgehill, where another new station would be built. The tunnel was to be 2,230yds long on a gradient of 1 in 88 and measured 17ft high and 22ft wide; a further 140yds was in the open. At first the directors were minded to heat the tunnel with hot water pipes, but this idea was subsequently abandoned, although it was to be gas lit, like the others. Following strong recommendations that two stationary engines should be installed to allow one to be in reserve in the case of the failure of the other, two engines were ordered from Messrs. Mather, Dixon & Co of the Bath Street Foundry in Liverpool in April 1834 at a cost, with the rope gearing, of £2,880. Designed by John Grantham

(1809-1874), later to join the manufacturers as a partner, they were two-cylinder non-condensing engines of the marine type. The cylinders were 25in in diameter with a 6ft stroke and they worked the connecting rods downwards to the 18ft beam, situated in a vault cut out of the sandstone rock; the beam pedestals were fixed to the rock floor of the pit. Two new engine houses, looking not unlike Georgian town houses of the period, were provided for them at the eastern end of the new Edgehill Station. They were connected by a series of underground chambers in which the winding equipment was located. Both engines could rotate the main shaft, which ran beneath the line and on which the 21ft diameter drum wheel was mounted, this effectively acting as a flywheel.

The endless hemp rope was 4,800yds long, 6in in circumference and weighed 8½ tons. Heavily tarred, it stretched nearly 500yds in the first few weeks of operation. It ran in a 10in groove around the circumference of the drum, guided on by a series of six horizontal and vertical sheaves 5ft in diameter; one of these sheaves was mounted on a travelling carriage to maintain the tension. After running in a covered channel past the station buildings, it passed over 474 sheaves set at 8ft intervals down to Lime Street, passing round a 5ft horizontal pulley at the bottom to return up the other track.

Two new boilers were needed for the new engines, but they could not be accommodated nearby and so were sited near the old boilers (making eight in all there), some 450yds away. Unlike the earlier boilers, these were multi-tubular, with 3in diameter tubes. The steam was fed to the engines through 10in diameter pipes laid in a small bore tunnel excavated through the rock.

Despite not being finished, Lime Street Station was opened on 15th August 1836. The engine could haul a 55-ton train up the 2,370 yard incline in six minutes. When trains arrived at Edgehill for Lime Street, the locomotive was detached and lighted oil lamps were hung outside the sliding window of each carriage door. The train was then pushed by hand to the mouth of the tunnel, which it descended by gravity under the control of the brakesman.

Three weeks after the opening, on the afternoon of 8th September, the chain of the balance weight broke, the rope stopped and the train returned to Lime Street. Two locomotives were sent to haul it out and they continued to haul the trains up to Edgehill until the following morning. By 1839 the tensioning chain had been replaced by a rope. Nor was the main rope free from trouble, being maliciously cut several times in the first ten years of operation. Meanwhile, the closure of the Crown Street Station allowed its conversion into

workshops, including a large smithy, a foundry and a wagon building and repair shop, as well as an expansion of the coal depot. Whishaw records that in 1839 Crown Street received between twelve to eighteen trains per day of about twelve loaded wagons each.

The signal to start the ropes in the original tunnels was to pull a wire rope to operate a bell. Breakages of the wire rope caused delays to traffic, and when the Lime Street tunnel was opened a pneumatic signal was installed. This consisted of a ½in gas pipe with a 'gasometer' at each end, supplied by the local gas company. When air was forced along the pipe it sounded a whistle at the engine. Soon afterwards a similar system was installed in the Wapping Tunnel.

Changes, modifications and further investment came steadily through the 1830s. In September 1835 an additional small compact engine with a 13¼in cylinder was installed with the dual purpose of pumping water to the new boilers and handling the Crown Street traffic, leaving the two Stephenson engines to handle the Wapping traffic. After the flue of one of the boilers burst, in December 1836 the directors ordered that steam whistles be fitted to the boilers arranged to sound automatically when the water level fell below three inches. Five months later the first of several hot-air, smoke-consuming apparatus was installed. These appear not to have worked, for in 1839 the six boilers in use were producing 'a volume of smoke objectionable to the neighbourhood', and in 1840 a set of coke-fired tubular boilers were installed, producing greater efficiency on half the fuel consumption – 15 tons of coke per week.

In 1845 the company obtained Parliamentary powers for two more tunnels from Edgehill. The first utilised the blind left hand portal to drive a new tunnel to the Crown Street coal depot. This was initially single line, but was doubled in 1864, and was loco-worked. It would seem that with the opening of this new tunnel, the 1829 tunnel eventually fell into disuse. The second route was to serve the North Docks near Waterloo Road and comprised two tunnels, separated by a short open cutting. From Edgehill the first tunnel was the Victoria Tunnel, 1 mile 947 yards long and laid with double track. This was worked by ropes down as far as a cutting near Byrom Street, where the two tracks became four to allow the interchange of rope and locomotive-hauled traffic. Then came the Waterloo Tunnel, 850yds on a much shallower gradient down to the dock and the Waterloo Goods Depot and worked by locomotives. At the Edgehill end of the Victoria Tunnel new engine houses were provided, together with a boiler plant comprising six boilers, which also served the new stationary engines installed for working the Wapping Tunnel. Unfortunately, the published sources do not give specific details about these engines. Although there were two tunnels on the new route, it was usually known throughout as the Victoria Tunnel, and it was opened for goods traffic on 1st August 1849.

Rope haulage in the Lime Street Tunnel was replaced by locomotives in 1870, but the resultant smoke caused such a nuisance that in 1881 the tunnel was opened out, save for short sections supporting streets overhead; it was further widened four years later. Today only one such section, 50yds long, survives. On 16th February 1895 the rope in the Victoria Tunnel broke and locomotive haulage replaced it. Plans were already in hand for a new station near the bottom of the Waterloo Tunnel, to be called Liverpool Riverside and built by the Mersey Docks & Harbour Board for Atlantic passenger traffic. This opened on 12th June 1895, with passenger trains now running through from Edgehill. On 11th May 1896 rope haulage through the Wapping Tunnel was also replaced by locomotive haulage. All the tunnels ceased to be used in 1972. The Crown Street coal depot closed on 1st May, and is now a landscaped park; the Wapping Tunnel followed on 15th May and the Victoria and Waterloo tunnels closed on 19th November.

It was once considered that the single vertical-cylinder beam engine now in the Manchester Museum of Science & Industry and known as the Haydock Engine might have come originally from Edgehill, but this has now been discounted.

Some nine months after the opening of the Liverpool & Manchester Railway the first section of the **Edinburgh & Dalkeith Railway** was opened, on 4th July 1831. It was not the first railway in Scotland - the Monkland & Kirkintilloch Railway had opened in 1826 - but it was the first railway in Edinburgh, Scotland's capital. It was promoted chiefly by the 5th Duke of Buccleugh (1806-1884), and its engineer was Robert Stevenson (1772-1850), the Scottish engineer famous for his lighthouses. It ran for 8½ miles from collieries south east of the city at South Eske to a station at St. Leonards, was double track throughout and was built to the so-called 'Scotch' gauge of 4ft 6in. A further section was opened in October 1831, and a passenger service was begun in July 1832. It was horse-worked apart from a powered incline up to St. Leonards. It was a rare example of a public passanger service worked partly by horses and by a rope incline; from the absence of steam locomotives it was known as the 'Innocent Railway'.

The Edinburgh Incline was 1,160yds long on a gradient of 1 in 30, straight on the upper half but considerably curved below this. Unusually, it passed through a 572-yard tunnel, which for the benefit of the passengers was lit by 25 gas lamps.

The stationary engine was built by Messrs. Carmichael of Dundee and cost £2,000, including the boilers. It had twin cylinders 28in in diameter with a 78in stroke, and was a low pressure, condensing design, taking steam at 5 p.s.i. The flywheel was 12ft in diameter and weighed 3½ tons. There was only one rope roll, or drum, 11ft in diameter and 3ft wide, but two ropes, which must mean that both were on the same drum, with one paying out as the other was wound in. The engine took about five minutes to haul up a set of eight waggons, each carrying 2½ tons, handling about twenty sets per day, together with eight passenger trains, each comprising three coaches. Signals from the bottom of the incline were given using an airtube about ¾in in diameter, which operated a bell in the engine house.

In October 1845 the railway was purchased by the North British Railway, who quickly rebuilt it to standard gauge and in 1846 diverted the passenger service to what became Edinburgh Waverley Station, closing the St.Leonards Station, which was instead developed into a major coal depot. When the stationary engine was dispensed with is uncertain.

5-16. The company seal of the Dundee & Newtyle Railway, a very rare example of a seal with a picture of a stationary engine hauling (?) a loaded train. The Latin inscription reads, rather enigmatically, 'Private Danger, Public Usefulness'.[15]

On 16th December 1831 the first section of the **Dundee & Newtyle Railway** was opened. This was the first railway in the northern part of Scotland, 10½ miles long and linking Newtyle and the Vale of Strathmore to the port of Dundee. Built to the gauge of 4ft 6½in, it was also Scotland's first passenger railway, beginning some seven months before the service on the Edinbugh & Dalkeith Railway. It was also another fairly rare example of a line which combined the use of horses, fixed haulage and steam locomotives.

The first section took the line from Newtyle to the top of the Hatton Incline, the first of three on the railway, all of them straight throughout. This incline was 1,000yds long with a gradient of 1 in 13. It was worked by a single vertical-cylindered, low pressure condensing engine, its cylinder being 26¾in diameter with a 54in stroke and taking steam at 4½ p.s.i. Its makers, like the two other engines on the line, are not recorded in published material. The rope drum/roll was 12ft in diameter. The incline was single line, with fulls and empties being worked alternately.

The completed line was opened in April 1832, and included two more inclines. From the top of the Hatton Incline the summit level ran for 4¾ miles to the top of the Balbeuchly Incline. This was approximately 1,700yds on a gradient of 1 in 25, and was worked by a very similar engine to the Hatton Engine. The incline was again a single line and the engine could haul 16 tons in six minutes. From here a further level of 4¾ miles took the line to the top of the Law Incline, which the railway descended to the outskirts of Dundee. It was 1,060yds long on a gradient of 1 in 10, but was very different from the other two. It had three rails at the top, four in the middle for trains to pass and two for the bottom section. It was worked by a 40 h.p., high-pressure engine, with a single vertical-cylinder 21in diameter and a 60in stroke, and had a single drum 12ft in diameter. The engine was said to have cost £2,750. Probably because of the severity of the gradient and the passenger service, the method of working was unusual. Accompanying every ascending train was a 'ballast waggon' weighing four tons, which was fitted with a brake and 'clutches' to stop the train in the event of the rope breaking. The rope was 7½in in circumference. The load varied between 20 and 24 tons, and an ascent could be completed in about six minutes.

Two types of passenger carriage were used, first class and mixed. The former had three compartments, each holding eight people; the latter had a central compartment, the 'extra' first class, holding four people, flanked by two open compartments, similar to stage coaches, which held eight people each. Locomotives were introduced in 1833 and eventually took over the work on the two levels and at the ends.

The inclines were eventually replaced by deviation routes, longer but quicker. The Balbeuchly deviation was opened in November 1860, followed by the Law deviation in April 1861. The Hatton Incline was eventually by-passed in August 1868, three years after the railway had been acquired by the Caledonian Railway.

The Dundee & Newtyle Railway illustrated railway engineers' willingness to take their lines over increasingly severe gradients, steeper than would

ever be operated by conventional steam locomotives. Nowhere was this better illustrated by the longest railway opened in England in the same year, 1831, the **Cromford & High Peak Railway**. A great deal has been published about this railway and about the records of the Butterley Company at Ripley, which supplied much of the original equipment and largely funded it.

This line owed nothing to George Stephenson or to the tradition of inclines in North East England. Its origins lay in a suggestion for a link between the Peak Forest and Cromford Canals; but a junction canal across the mountainous ground of the Peak District was clearly impractical, so it was decided to build a railway instead. The company obtained its Act in 1825. Its engineer was Josias Jessop (1781-1826), the second son of the noted engineer William Jessop (1745-1814). However, the younger Jessop died before construction began, and he was replaced by Thomas Woodhouse (1793-1855). The line was to link Cromford on the Cromford Canal with Whaley Bridge on the Peak Forest Canal, then in Cheshire but now also in Derbyshire. In concept the line replicated a canal, with inclines equivalent to flights of locks, separated by level sections, equivalent to pounds, worked by horses, although the company's unusual perceptiveness provided for locomotive traction in the Act. As it was anticipated that goods would pass in both directions, all of the inclines were to be worked by stationary engines except that at Whaley Bridge.

The first section, between Cromford and Hurdlow, a distance of 15½ miles, was opened on 29th May 1830 and took the line up nearly 1,000ft to 1,254ft. Leaving Cromford, the Cromford Lower Incline rose 205ft at 1 in 9 and the Cromford Upper Incline a further 260ft at 1 in 8, a total of 1,320yds. A level section 1½ miles long then took the line to the bottom of the Middleton Incline, 708yds at 1 in 8½, and before reaching Hurdlow there were two more inclines, Hopton, 457yds at 1 in 14, and Hurdlow itself, 850yds at 1 in 16. The remainder of the line, nearly 18 miles, was opened on 6th July 1831, giving an overall length of almost 34 miles. The summit section, which rose to 1,266ft at Ladmanlow, became famous for its curves, with 21 of 110yds radius or less, three of them of 66yds radius and the Gotham Curve only 55yds radius, turning the line through 80 degrees. Then came the two Bunsall (originally called Buxton) Inclines, the Upper Incline 660yds at 1 in 7½ and the Lower 455yds at 1 in 7. Another level section was followed by the Shallcross Incline, 817yds at 1 in 10¼, with finally the Whaley Bridge Incline, 180yds at 1 in 13½, down to the wharf on the Peak Forest Canal. Initially these inclines were numbered sequentially from 1, but from the late 1850s/early 1860s the numbers fell into disuse and were replaced by names.

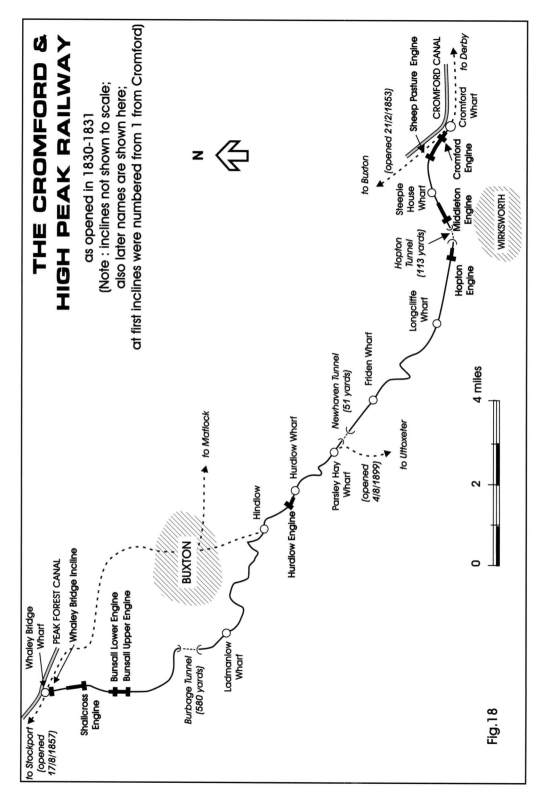

Fig.18

5-17. *Cromford Goods Yard on the Cromford & High Peak Railway about 1949. The bottom section and bank foot of Sheep Pasture Incline can be seen. Wagons were attached to the endless rope just this side of the road bridge. On the right are the railway's Cromford Workshops. The white post standing against the end wall was a very tall semaphore signal.*

5-18. *A 'hanger on' inspecting the tackling chains at Sheep Pasture Bottom. Note the extra protection around his legs. The leather thongs for tying these chains around the rope can be seen. The wagon buffer guides are unusual.*

These were some of the most fearsome grades ever constructed on a standard gauge railway in Britain. Leaving aside the Whaley Bridge Incline briefly, it was no doubt because of their severity that it was decided to operate all of them by endless chain, like the inclines of 1803 on the Lancaster Canal tramway. It should be noted that they were all less than half a mile long, doubtless linked to the need to keep down the lengths and weights of the chains.

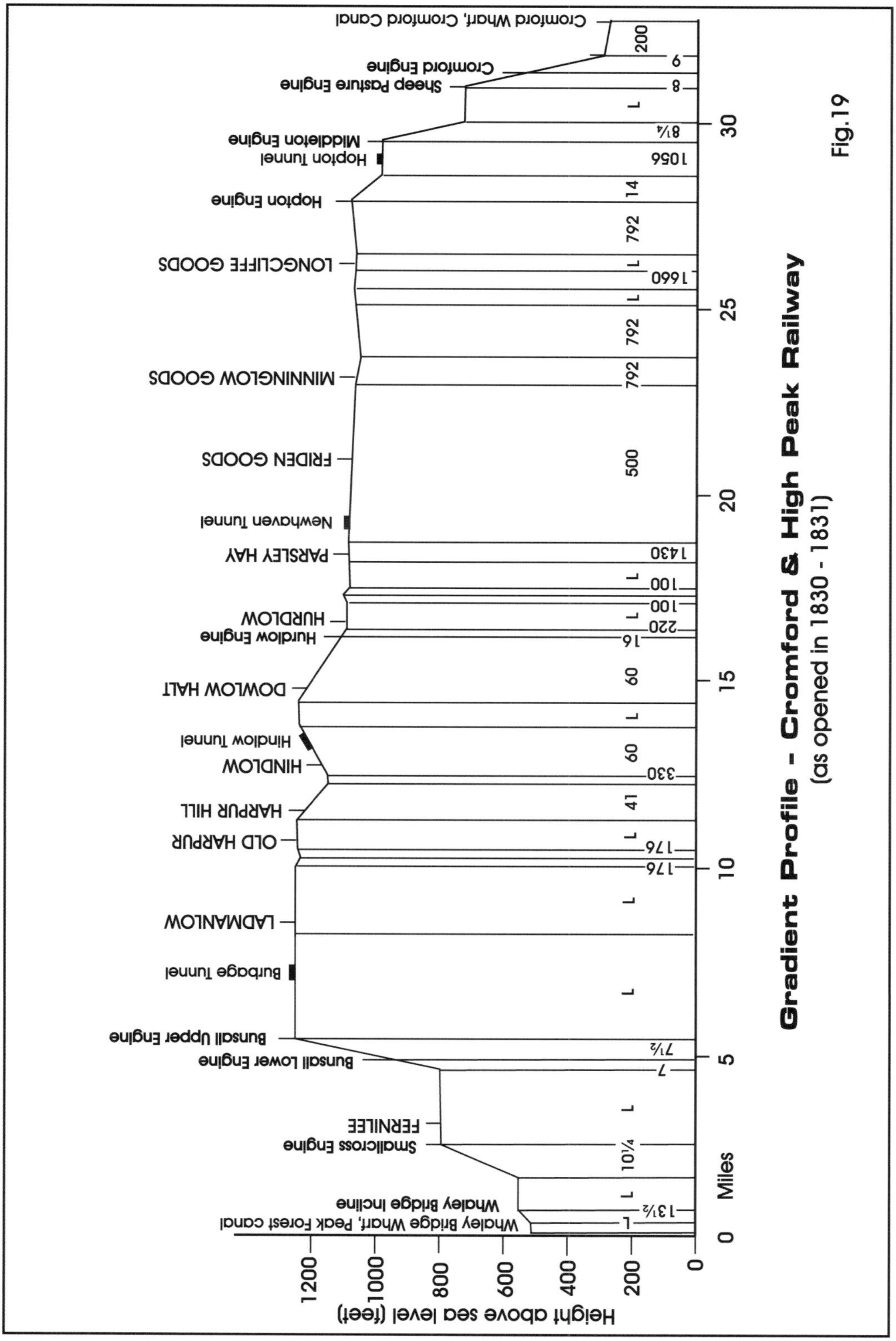

Gradient Profile – Cromford & High Peak Railway
(as opened in 1830 - 1831)

Fig.19

Unusually in haulage history, all of the stationary engines, the chains, sheaves and other equipment and also all the rails for the Railway, were supplied by one company, the Butterley Company. This created a high level of standardisation rarely seen elsewhere. The company's foundry records survive and these contain details of weights, costs and deliveries. The Butterley company was itself served by the Cromford Canal, and probably transport to the railway under construction was partly by canal and then by road. The two engine houses that survive were built from local gritstone and their shape, with the front having three angled facets, each fitted with a large Georgian window, reflects the common turnpike toll house design of the period. Archaeological excavations of the Cromford Lower Engine in 2008-09 showed that this was the same design, while the Ordnance Survey maps show that all of the engine houses were the same shape, although the position of the boiler house varied, as did the position of the winding engines in relation to the line.

The engine houses at Cromford Lower and Upper, Middleton, Buxton Upper and Lower and Shallcross were all fitted with two vertical-cylindered condensing beam engines driving a common crankshaft and delivering 20 h.p. each, 40 h.p. in total. Each cylinder had a 25in bore and a 60in stroke. The engine house was an integral part of the engine; a detailed description of the Middleton Engine can be found in chapter 6. Each of these larger engines cost £2,000 for the pair. This price did not include the floor bearers, floor plates, chain wheel, brake gear, the patterns for the machinery or miscellaneous other equipment. The total cost of the Cromford Engine was £2,521-19s-7d, not including its building. The engines at Hopton and Hurdlow were of the same design but delivered 10 h.p., 20 h.p. in total. Only some dimensional details survive for these engines and these do not include the size of the cylinders. The overall cost of the Hopton Engine was £1,547-2s-10½ d. The Whaley Bridge Incline was unusual from the beginning. Initially this was worked by horses, but in June 1833 a stationary engine was installed. This had two engines of 5 h.p. each and cost £667-18s-6d.

Little seems to be known about how these continuous chain inclines were operated when they were built, for example, whether they included a tensioning carriage, or how the waggons were attached to the chain. When ropes were introduced, this was done by wrapping tackling chains round the rope, so this may have been done with the chains too (this system was also used on the earlier 'Great Inclined Plane' near Chapel-en-le-Frith on the Peak Forest Tramway, also in Derbyshire, described in chapter 4). Marshall[16] gives some of the weights and all of the costs of the original chains made by the Butterley Company, which (excluding the short Whaley Bridge Incline) varied between £843-10s-5d

for the Upper Buxton/Bunsall Incline and £176-4s-2d for the Hopton Incline. Later 'best chain iron' was supplied by the Coalbrookdale Company in Staffordshire.

The C&HPR initially had no powers as a common carrier and users of the line had to supply their own waggons and horses. Limestone, travelling both north and south, soon became the main traffic. In May 1833 a passenger service was begun on the Railway, operated by German Wheatcroft & Sons. German Wheatcroft (1773-1841) was appointed the first wharfinger at Bugsworth Wharf on the Peak Forest Canal in 1794, and he was subsequently in charge of the 'Great Inclined Plane' on the Peak Forest Tramway. After being dismissed in 1809 he set up his own family carrying business, conducting trade on road, canal and rail. His passenger service ran the whole length of the C&HPR, including over the inclines, probably taking about two days, and a stagecoach service was also provided between Whaley Bridge and Manchester. His Fly service between Derby and Manchester, by canal and the C&HPR, was certainly running in 1842. It is not known how long his service over the C&HPR lasted.

When the Railway opened, there seem to have been few rules for the operation of the inclines, not least with regard to the maximum number of wagons to be attached to the chain. The Middleton Incline soon became notorious. As early as 14th December 1830 nine wagons broke away while descending it. In 1831 there were five breakaways here in one week. Another breakaway was reported in the local press on 3rd October 1833. Six wagons arrived at Middleton Top in the early evening; one was carrying a load, another was carrying six passengers and four were empty. The engineman ordered the passengers to disembark and walk down, but when he went back into the engine house to set the chain in motion, they all got back in the wagon again. The train had not gone far when a link of the chain broke. At the downhill end of the train there was a 'preventer'. It is not clear exactly what this was or how it was operated, but it seems to have been a bar to dig into the ballast when a break happened. This worked, but only partially; four passengers jumped out, but two were still in the wagon when the preventer failed and doubled under the wagon. Speed increased and the front wagon was derailed, the two remaining passengers being killed when the other wagons piled on top of them. It would seem that it was after this that the number of wagons on an incline was restricted to two, up or down.

A proposed connection with the Liverpool & Manchester Railway never materialised, and the C&HPR remained in splendid isolation until 1853, when a link was laid to the Manchester, Buxton, Matlock & Midland Junction Railway (later part of the Midland Railway) near High Peak Wharf.

5-19. Looking up the Sheep Pasture Incline. Note that all the sheaves are set at an angle to keep the rope from rising above that level and note too their wooden frames, no doubt with a metal strip on top, to allow the rope to slide across smoothly into the sheaves.

5-20. Sheep Pasture Top, with on the right a couple of wagons being run forward to be attached to the rope. The chain, tackling chains and leather thongs can be seen between the rails, as can the rope itself emerging from its gully from the engine house. The unusual three-sided front of the engine houses on this Railway can be clearly seen. Stephenson Clarke & Associated Cos Ltd were a major industrial combine; besides owning quarries in the Peak District, they were major shippers of coal, with a large fleet. The firm only ceased trading in 2012.

Four years later an extension of ¼ mile was laid from Whaley Bridge to the Stockport, Disley and Whaley Bridge Railway (later part of the London & North Western Railway). In between, in 1855, the C&HPR itself obtained a new Act and set out upon a period of change under its recently-appointed engineer, Captain William Moorsom (1804-1863). In 1856 work began to convert the two Cromford and the two Bunsall inclines to single line, so that both could be worked by a single stationary engine. The new Bunsall Incline (for a while still known as 6/7) began work on 6th June 1857 and the combined Cromford inclines, which soon became known as the Sheep Pasture Incline, on 16th October. Both were now worked with wire ropes, and it would seem that many of the inclines had their chains replaced with wire ropes during this period, although not on the Hopton Incline. At the same time as this work was being done, the Middleton Incline was also modified. This was done to accommodate a small quarry which was opened in November 1856 about half way down and the line converted to single track. The engine was rebuilt to work with a winding drum and the continuous chain was replaced with a rope 800yds long, presumably working full and empty sets, known as 'runs' on the C&HPR, up and down alternately. The quarry had closed by 1865, but the single line working continued for another thirty years.

The Act of 1855 gave the company powers to run its own traffic, whereupon it took over the passenger service then operating. From 1856 this ran between Cromford and Ladmanlow, on the summit level, from where there was a coach to Buxton. It comprised a single coach with seats both inside and outside. It was horse-drawn on the level sections, but the Rule Book of 1858 forbade passengers being carried on the inclines, compelling them to wait until the descending train was in motion before they could set off to walk down, although they could climb up to the top of an incline before the train was drawn up. It may well be that the passenger service did not operate all the year round and was a seasonal activity for tourists. The service often ran the whole length of the Railway and in 1874 the time from High Peak Wharf to Whaley Bridge was 5 hours 25 minutes. It was also certainly hauled by a steam locomotive on the level sections by 1872.

In 1862 the LNWR obtained an Act under which it leased the C&HPR from 25th March 1861, a change which brought much better management to the impoverished railway; amalgamation of the two railways occurred in 1887. In his book on the Railway mentioned earlier, Marshall quotes various dates soon after the LNWR take-over when wire ropes replaced hemp ropes on some of the inclines. However, these depend on the interpretation of information in one of the railway manager's handbooks in the latter half of the nineteenth century,

and so have been omitted here. Even whether the Railway actually used any hemp ropes is uncertain.

The Whaley Bridge Incline received early attention from the LNWR. A report of July 1862 noted that the Whaley Bridge Engine was out of use because coal mining subsidence had affected its foundations, and the incline was being worked by a horse. In April 1863 it was decided not to undertake repairs but instead to install a horizontal wheel fitted with a 'break' - a horse gin. This had hardly been approved when on 3rd September 1863 the LNWR gave permission for John Barraclough Fell (1815-1902) to experiment on the incline with a centre-rail locomotive to establish the feasibility of this system for the projected railway over the Mont Cenis Pass between France and Italy. In the Fell system, designed to tackle the problem of trains ascending steep gradients, a third rail was laid between the two rails of the train tracks which was gripped on its sides by additional drive wheels on a specially-designed locomotive as well as the brake shoes of a special brake van. Experiments took place between September 1863 and February 1864, mostly on the Whaley Bridge Incline, 180yds at 1 in 13½, but also latterly on a nearby location at 1 in 12 which included some reverse curves. The locomotive was built by Thomas Brassey (1805-1870), the famous contractor, at his Canada Works at Birkenhead. It had outside cylinders 11¾in by 18in driving the four-coupled driving wheels and two inside cylinders 11in by 10in driving the four horizontal wheels which drove against the centre rail. A more detailed description of the locomotive and the trials can be found in Marshall.[17] The trials were a success and attracted the interest of several governments, and the Fell System went on to be adopted in various countries world-wide.

Meanwhile, the horse gin was brought into use on the Whaley Bridge Incline, utilising a new chain, on 6th July 1864. The horse was harnessed to a horizontal pole about 8ft long that was in turn attached to the top of a vertical shaft that arose from the wheel pit, the pit itself being covered by boards. At the bottom of the shaft was a pinion which meshed with a larger gear wheel. A pulley was fastened to the same shaft as the larger gear wheel, around which passed the endless chain from the incline. At the bottom of the incline there was another pit and covered wheel to return the chain up the incline. Horses continued to work the traffic both at the bottom of the incline and between the top of the incline and the sidings at Shallcross Yard.

The next incline to receive attention was the Hurdlow Incline, 850yds at 1 in 16. As early as 1863 a report to the LNWR recommended a deviation to avoid this incline, pointing out that it was located between two levels of twelve miles each, necessitating the use of three locomotives as well as the stationary engine. A deviation would remove the stationary engine and

5-21. *Photographs at Whaley Bridge, at the northern end of the line nearly 34 miles from Cromford, are rare. This shows the whole incline, 180yds at 1 in 13½.*

5-22. *An even rarer picture of the bar for the horse gin at the top of the Whaley Bridge Incline, unfortunately without the horse. Note that the areas between the rails are cobbled, to provide grip for the horses that shunted wagons between here and Shallcross Yard.*

5-23. *A tender full of water ascending the Middleton Incline, with an empty tender descending in the distance, in June 1961. These were needed to supply the engine houses, locomotive sheds and cottages along the line in the absence of any local supply. They were filled from a large tank supplied by a spring at Sheep Pasture Bottom.*

5-24. *Middleton Top, with ascended wagons on the left and wagons waiting to descend on the right, together with the semaphore signal and the cabin for the planemen. Note that the catch points are correctly set to derail in the event of a runaway. Behind is the Middleton Engine house and its 80ft chimney. Out of sight are the boilers, loco shed and engineman's cottage.*

one locomotive and create a 24-mile section between the summits of the Hopton and Bunsall Inclines. It took some time to bring this scheme to fruition, but the last traffic passed over the Hurdlow Incline on 1st January 1869. Its chain was re-used on the Hopton Incline, where it was replaced by a new chain in 1871.

On 7th August 1869 the Middleton Engine was stopped for major repairs, including new cylinders, valve gear and probably boilers. To replace it temporarily, a locomotive was used, presumably adapted to work as a winding engine. The engine resumed work on 7th February 1870. It is not known whether a locomotive was used in this way when similar repairs were needed to the other engines, but it would seem likely.

In a report on a collision between two goods trains in December 1875, Captain Henry Tyler (1827-1908) of the Railway Inspectorate commented that the railway had never been inspected for the carriage of passengers to enable a certificate to be issued under the C&HPR Act of 1855 and that this should be done. The LNWR clearly did not think this was justified, given the number of passengers, and the service was discontinued at the end of April 1876. This did not bring about the end of unofficial passengers, as a description of a journey between Shallcross and Cromford in July 1880, included in Marshall,[18] shows; the traveller rode down the Middleton and Sheep Pasture Inclines on the wagon buffer guides.

The winding engine and its boilers at Hopton were becoming worn out, and this may be the reason behind another experiment with locomotive power being held there in 1876, where it will be remembered that the incline was 457yds

long on a gradient of 1 in 14. The LNWR approved a trial proposed by the Handyside Steep Gradient Co Ltd of Bristol using a 0-6-0 saddle tank fitted with a steam winch, effectively a mobile winding engine. The locomotive had been built by Fox, Walker & Co of Bristol, almost certainly works no. 316 of 1876. It was a standard design of its makers, with 13in by 20in outside cylinders and 3ft 6in wheels. A winding drum was fitted at the rear of the engine, worked by two vertical-cylinders 10in by 9in, on which was wound a steel wire 300yds long. In addition to its normal brakes, the locomotive was fitted with braking struts between the first and second wheels, which were applied to the rails by a fifth cylinder 10in in diameter with a 10in stroke.

The locomotive was on trial on the C&HPR for three months beginning in August 1876, if not before, working traffic between Middleton Top and Hopton Top. When collecting a train at Middleton, it shunted there if necessary and also at some quarry sidings en route to Hopton Bottom. Here the locomotive was detached and its rope attached to the train before it ascended about half way up the incline, paying out the rope. All the brakes were then applied and the train was then hauled up to where the locomotive had stopped. The engine then proceeded to the top of the incline, where everything happened again. A load of 20 tons, one loaded wagon of coal and two empties, took about 7½ minutes to travel between the bottom and the top. The additional braking power was successfully demonstrated with a train of 75 tons descending the incline. Handyside himself claimed that weights of up to 70 tons uphill and 164 tons downhill could be managed.[19]

5-25. The Handyside patent standard gauge 0-6-0 saddletank used on the Hopton Incline in 1876, as illustrated in ENGINEERING on 13th October 1876, built by Fox, Walker & Co of Bristol and believed to be Works No. 316 of 1876. Note the winding drum at the rear end and the additional brakes between the first and second driving wheels.

5-26. One of the LNWR 2-4-0 locos used on the Hopton Incline after 1877 when the chain was taken off. They were originally tender engines, rebuilt with side tanks to give extra adhesion for the work here. This one is No.3049, photographed on the 1 in 14 incline between June 1889, when it received this number, and June 1894, when it was scrapped.

5-27. The only-known photograph of the frame, cylinders and motion of the 0-6-0 Ramsbottom DX 0-6-0 tender engine installed in the Sheep Pasture Engine House in 1884 to replace the original engine. The location of the rope wheel and how it was driven are uncertain. The steam exhaust can be seen to the left of the live steam inlet pipe, while the hand wheel to the right of the motion has probably been installed to reverse the engine on the rare occasions when this would be necessary.

5-28. The catch pit installed near the bottom of the Sheep Pasture Incline in 1888-89 following a major runaway on 1st March 1888. The original pit had no roof, but one was later added, probably in 1903. Note the angled sheaves with their wooden slides to accommodate the rope curving around the pit.

5-29. A more general view of the Sheep Pasture catch pit, with the catchpitman's cabin and its gong for the man on duty to assess whether the speed of the wagons was acceptable. The points are set, correctly, for the pit, awaiting the decision of the catchpitman.

If Handyside hoped the LNWR would adopt his system at Hopton, he was disappointed. The LNWR found that Crewe 2-4-0 goods tender engines rebuilt with side tanks were able to climb the incline with two or three wagons and could thus replace the chain haulage, as well as end horse haulage between Middleton Top and Hopton Bottom. So on 16th April 1877 the Hopton stationary engine went out of use, although it remained in situ for many years afterwards, as did the two tracks on the incline, although only one was used. Much of the gradient was eased in 1903, leaving only 200yds of 1 in 14 near the top, although this still left it the steepest standard gauge gradient worked by adhesion in Britain.

Locomotive power was also brought in at Sheep Pasture, albeit in a different way. By 1883 the original winding engine here was beyond economic repair too, and in its place a two-cylinder horizontal engine was installed, converted from a Ramsbottom DX Class 0-6-0 goods engine. The cylinders were 17in by 24in and it took steam at 80 p.s.i. from an old DX Class boiler. This began work on 10th February 1884.

Inevitably, accidents continued on the inclines, for a wide variety of reasons. The most spectacular runaway occurred on 1st March 1888 on the Sheep Pasture Incline. At about 7.00pm, after dark, a wagon loaded with lime and a brake van carrying gunpowder in boxes cased in iron were just beginning their descent when the connecting chain broke. The men on board jumped for their lives. At the bottom, where the speed was calculated at 120 m.p.h (the *Derbyshire Times* quoted 400 m.p.h on 10th March!), they came off the track, cleared the Cromford Canal, although damaging its banks, and bounced over a stone wall. One of the canisters of gunpowder then exploded, and the remains of the vehicles then crossed the Midland Railway line, damaging the track on both the Up and Down lines. A Midland train was expected but was stopped by telegraph, thus avoiding a potentially-serious accident.

As a result of this, a 'catch pit' was installed on the incline just above the road bridge, approximately a third of the distance from the bottom. The running lines were diverted round the pit while catch points were set for the pit; on the ascending line they were weighted, on the descending line they were controlled by a 'catchpitman'[20] in an adjacent cabin. To enable him to decide whether to take action, the wheels of the wagons actuated a series of treadles higher up the incline, in turn sounding a gong; if from the sound he thought the speed was excessive, he left the points as they were and rapidly retreated to a safe distance. A local paper described the construction of the pit in October 1889. The rails dipped into the pit on a gradient of 1 in 3 and at the far end was a barrier 'specially

prepared for the contingency', comprising a bed of heather pressed between sleepers with a solid bed of masonry behind. To 'prevent missiles flying', the pit was to be covered with iron girders and sleepers. The pit was reported as finished on 15th January 1890, but it was apparently without its planned roof, as it would seem that not until after another runaway in 1903 was a roof fitted. A catchpit was also thought to have been constructed near the bottom of the Bunsall Incline, probably about the same time, as there is a reference to it in the LNWR 'Rules and Regulations applying to the Cromford & High Peak Section', dated April 1891.[21]

The C&HPR had continued to be linked to other lines, and in 1887 the LNWR obtained an Act to construct a line between Buxton and Hurdlow and abandon most of its northern section. The new line opened on 27th July 1892, the Shallcross and Bunsall Inclines closing on the same day. The Shallcross, Bunsall and Hopton Engines were dismantled, together with the track between Shallcross and Ladmanlow, with everything having gone by October 1894. The LNWR also had plans to by-pass the Hopton and Middleton Inclines, but these met strong local opposition and did not proceed. Instead, the Middleton Incline was restored to double-track endless rope operation. The engine was again modified accordingly, receiving a new drum wheel, an idler wheel and an endless rope 1,800yds long. The incline was brought back into use in this new form on 2nd April 1894. The final section of new line planned, a branch from Parsley Hay to Ashbourne on the North Staffordshire Railway, was opened on 4th August 1899.

The original C&HPR was now continuous from High Peak Junction to Ladmanlow, with the stub of Shallcross Yard to Whaley Bridge connected to the LNWR at the northern end. At Whaley Bridge the horse gin continued to be used, but only two of the other eight original stationary engine houses survived, and one of those housed an engine adapted from a steam locomotive. Only at Middleton did the original engine, albeit rebuilt, survive in its engine house, working its incline much as it had done from 1830, albeit now with a wire rope rather than a chain.

The next significant development is found on the **Leicester & Swannington Railway,** put forward by its promoters to bring coal from collieries in west Leicestershire into Leicester. It was to be a pivotal moment in the transport history of the East Midlands, which for a considerable time had been dominated by the rivalry between the coalowners of Nottinghamshire and Leicestershire. The former, with access to the Erewash Canal and the River Soar Navigation, which in 1794 was extended to Leicester. With the coming of railways, the Leicestershire owners saw their opportunity to retaliate.

5-30. A view of the Swannington Engine from the cylinder end, one of a series of photographs taken here in November 1923. The piston valve can clearly be seen, mounted on top of the cylinder. The drive from the crankshaft to the drum was located below the floor, going through the wall to the drum outside the building.

5-31. The drum of the Swannington Engine in November 1923, located unusually between the rails. Note the very basic end of the rope to couple to the wagons, just a shackle and a 3-link coupling.

George Stephenson was persuaded to become involved, and Robert Stephenson was appointed Engineer, with the Railway's Act being passed in 1830. Despite the Rainhill Trials and the opening of the Liverpool & Manchester Railway, the directors saw little likelihood of passenger traffic, and what Stephenson designed was a 16-mile coal line on the same principles as in the North East, albeit including a 3-mile long tunnel, Glenfield Tunnel. The first section, 10¾ miles long from Leicester, was opened on 17th July 1832 and included at its end the Bagworth Incline.

This was a self-acting incline, with the load coming down from what was to be the summit level. It was 946yds long on a gradient of 1 in 29. At the top there was a 6ft diameter return wheel in a pit below rail level; however, it did not have a brake fitted to it, braking being done by men travelling on the wagons applying the wagon brakes. The incline itself was laid out on the 3 rails/4 rails/2 rails plan, and it was supplied initially with a hemp rope 5in in circumference weighing two tons. This was replaced in October 1833 by a wire rope, one of the first used on a railway. Communication between the bottom and the top of the incline was by means of wire-operated bells. A descending set comprised between ten and twelve wagons, and took between eight and nine minutes to travel the distance.

Human nature being what it is, the brakesmen did not always wait for a counterbalancing load, but ran wagons down the incline without the rope, braking as before – except that sometimes they lost control. The directors had provided a handful of passenger carriages, and on 28th August 1844 one of these was part of a train of wagons when the rope broke; fortunately the carriage was empty. The directors wrote to the Railway Department of the Board of Trade for advice and were told that the passenger carriage should always be at the rear of a descending train. It would also seem that some passengers could not be made to wait for a carriage, but instead travelled in the empty coal wagons – which did not belong to the railway!

The remainder of the railway opened in 1833, with the second incline, the Swannington Incline, probably beginning work towards the end of November. This was 726yds, less than half a mile, at 1 in 17, and as coal had to travel uphill from near the end of the railway, it had to be worked by a stationary engine. This was designed by Robert Stephenson, but was a very different design from anything used elsewhere on railways at the time. It had a single horizontal cylinder, not then regarded favourably, as it was believed that the weight of the piston would wear the cylinder oval. To counter this believed effect, the piston was fitted with a long tail rod, supported by slippers running inside a second pair of guide blocks. The cylinder had an 18¼in bore and a 42in stroke, had a flywheel 9ft 4in in diameter and took steam at 80

p.s.i, a very high pressure for these early engines. Another interesting feature was the incorporation of a piston type of steam control valve, something which did not come into general use until much later in the 19th century. Whether Stephenson regarded this as an opportunity to experiment in design is not known. A full description of the engine can be found in chapter 6.

Despite being designed by Stephenson, his firm did not build it. The directors put the construction out to tender, receiving three replies, from Thomas Banks & Co of Manchester, the Horsley Coal & Iron Co of West Bromwich in Staffordshre and W. Baldwin & Co, possibly connected with the ironfounders Baldwin, Son & Co of Wolverhampton. The Horsley company received the order, delivering the engine for £750. The initial wire rope, from Webster's Patent Ropery in Sunderland, cost £78 and the engine house cost a further £400; curiously, the boilers stood in the open until 1856. The connecting of the rope to the wagons was unusual; Clinker[22] describes it as a 'slip coupling, [designed] so that [the] wagons might automatically disengage from the cable and run forward on the level line beyond the drum'; exactly how it did this is not known. The drum was located outside the engine house, the normal practice at the time, but placed between and below the rails alongside the engine house wall because the design of the engine meant the crank shaft was at this level. In the tradition of the time this was square in section, which was easier to forge and made it easier to secure the flywheel on the shaft.

The incline was single line, so that fulls and empties were worked alternately. The engine was soon in trouble. The crankshaft fractured in the first week of operation and then the boiler sprang a leak, leaving the engine out of commission for 4½ months and causing horses to work the traffic. In the event this did not prove as much as hoped and the engine was used only two or three times a week.

The Midland Railway purchased the railway in 1845 and before long extended it north to Burton-on-Trent, leaving the link to Swannington and its incline as a branch line. As noted above, it soon introduced communication on the incline and enclosed the boilers in a large boiler house. Little else changed until 1877, when the local colliery companies combined to build a central steam-driven pumping station at the Calcutta Pit at Swannington, near the bottom of the incline, to prevent the local collieries from being flooded underground. At first this was not significant, but when the Calcutta Pit closed in 1894 the incline, instead of closing, had to remain open in order to lower down coal from Coalville for the five boilers which supplied the pumping station. The maximum number of wagons allowed was three fulls or six empties, in either direction.

5-32. *The buildings of the Swannington Engine in November 1923. The building housing the engine is the flat-roofed building on the right, with the drum alongside its wall. The boiler house lay beyond this, near the chimney. The semaphore signal was operated by the men at the foot of the incline and replaced the wire-operated bells which were used originally.*

5-33. *Looking up the Swannington Incline from the bank foot in November 1923. Note the combination of vertical rollers and slides nearest the camera.*

The Engine continued working this traffic until the pumping house pumps were replaced by electric pumps in 1947. The last loaded wagons were lowered down on 20th September 1947 and the last empties were raised on 14th November 1947. The incline was officially closed in February 1948. However, the historical importance of the engine was realised and in October 1951 it was dismantled for preservation, being removed to the York Railway Museum in January 1952.

Although collieries on the southern bank of the River Tyne shipped their coal on the river, the Ouston Waggonway (see chapter 4) and the Springwell Colliery Railway were the only lines up to 1830 which brought coal from further inland to be shipped east of Newcastle. This changed with the construction of the **Stanhope & Tyne Railway**. The initiative here came from a small group of entrepreneurs who saw the opportunity to combine the extensive limestone deposits around Stanhope in upper Weardale with the coal around Pontop for the manufacture of agricultural lime, but this was soon extended into a much more ambitious scheme to take the line to staiths at South Shields, a distance of 33 miles, with a further 4½ miles of branches. In May 1832 the 'Stanhope & Tyne Railroad' was formed, with Sunderland shipbuilder William Harrison (1778-1848) as its leading promoter, his son Thomas Elliot Harrison (1808-1888), later to become the Engineer of the North Eastern Railway, as Engineer, and Robert Stephenson as consulting engineer.

However, desperate to keep its plans as secret as possible, the company decided against obtaining an Act of Parliament and compulsory powers, and instead set out to obtain wayleave agreements for the whole route. At first the wayleave charges were not remarkable, but the company's plans had become known by the time it began negotiations for the eastern section, and huge prices were charged here. Of the total 37½ miles, 14½ were to be worked by horses, 11 miles by stationary engines, 3 miles by self-acting inclines and 9¼ miles, between Fatfield and South Shields, by locomotives. Construction began in July 1832, with the section between Stanhope and Annfield, a distance of 15½ miles, opening on 15th May 1834 and the remainder following on 10th September 1834.

At Stanhope lines serving a limestone quarry, lime kilns and a lead smelter brought wagons to the beginning of the railway, with two fearsome inclines being needed to lift the line out of Weardale. The Crawleyside Incline, 942yds and worked by the 50 h.p. Crawleyside Engine, had gradients of 1 in 7¼ and 1 in 12, and passed through the short Hog Hill tunnel, another example of a tunnel on an incline. Fulls and empties were run simultaneously, albeit only two at a time. Next the Weatherhill Engine, also 50 h.p., brought the wagons up 1 mile 128 yards on an average gradient

of 1 in 13 to a summit of 1,445ft, the highest point ever reached by a public railway in England. Once again fulls and empties could be worked at the same time. Horses worked the next 1½ miles, bringing the waggons to the Park Head wheel house. Here the tail rope of a main-and-tail system was attached, worked by the Meeting Slacks Engine (40 h.p.) to bring the wagons down to the engine house. This Engine also worked the incline, 1 mile 453 yards, on its eastern side, lowering wagons down over gradients from 1 in 26½ to 1 in 58 to the top of the Nanny Mayors Incline (named after an eccentric woman who kept an ale house alongside the line). This was a self-acting incline 1,122yds long on a gradient of 1 in 14. For the next 1¼ miles the wagons were again hauled by horses, which were then taken round to the rear of the train to be put into 'dandy carts', so that the wagons could coast down by gravity for two miles to the edge of the Hownes Gill, a dry ravine about 160ft deep and about 800ft wide. Instead of crossing this with a viaduct, it was decided to locate the Hownes Gill Engine (20 h.p. according to Holmes, but 25 h.p. in the Robert Stephenson company records; 'Howns' is also recorded) in the bottom of the ravine, to lower the wagons down one side and raise them up the other. Tomlinson (p.244-45) describes the system as follows:

> 'The sides of the Gill being so precipitous, 1 in 2½ and 1 in 3 respectively, it was considered necessary, in order to keep the waggons in a horizontal position, to provide cradles or trucks - one for each incline – having front and hind wheels of unequal diameter; upon these the waggons travelled side foremost. Only one waggon could be taken at a time. On arriving at the edge of the ravine, it was placed at right angles to the line by means of a turntable, moved forward and fixed upon the incline truck, passing beneath the sloping walls on which the rails were laid, to the bottom of the Gill. Here, adjoining the engine, was a rectangular platform having turntables at its four corners. Pushed off the truck towards one of these turntables, the waggon was slewed round to its ordinary position and worked forward to a turntable at another corner, which placed it once more at right angles to the line. It was then run forward on to another truck and raised to the top of the Gill, where, after being turned round a fourth angle, it was able to proceed in a more direct fashion. The number of waggons that could be taken across the Gill in an hour was twelve. Both inclines were worked at once, so that the weight of the descending waggon might assist the engine. The truck appears to have run on two pairs of rails, with the width of the outer pair being 7ft 0⅛in [probably simply 7ft] and of the inner pair 5ft 1¾ in.'

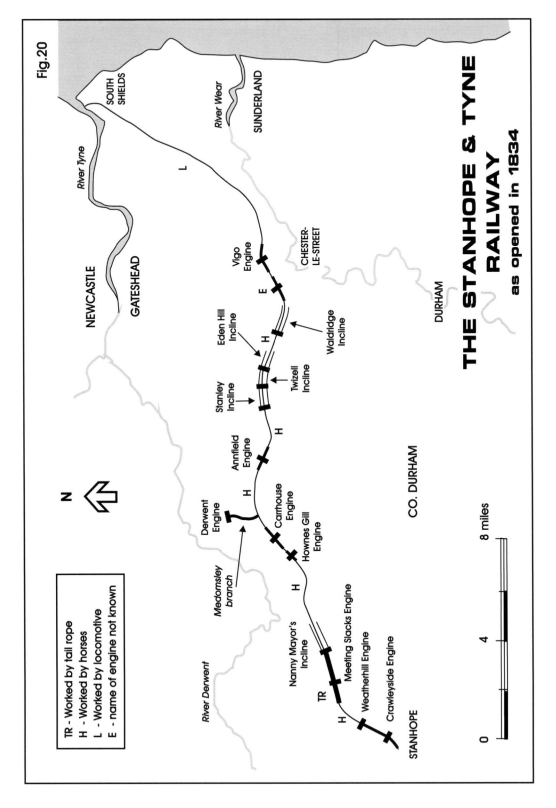

Fig.20

THE STANHOPE & TYNE RAILWAY as opened in 1834

TR - Worked by tail rope
H - Worked by horses
L - Worked by locomotive
E - name of engine not known

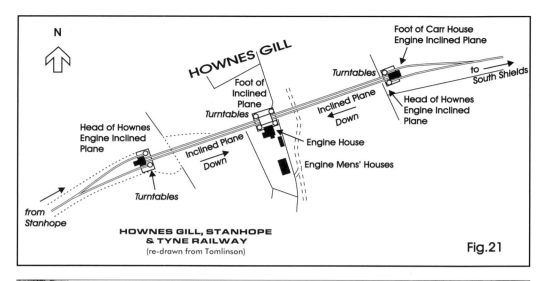

HOWNES GILL, STANHOPE
& TYNE RAILWAY
(re-drawn from Tomlinson)

Fig.21

5-34. Hog Hill Tunnel, Stanhope, on the Crawleyside Incline of the Stanhope & Tyne Railway, about 1914, after the tunnel was widened to accommodate double track. Tunnels on inclines were not common, but several are mentioned in this chapter.

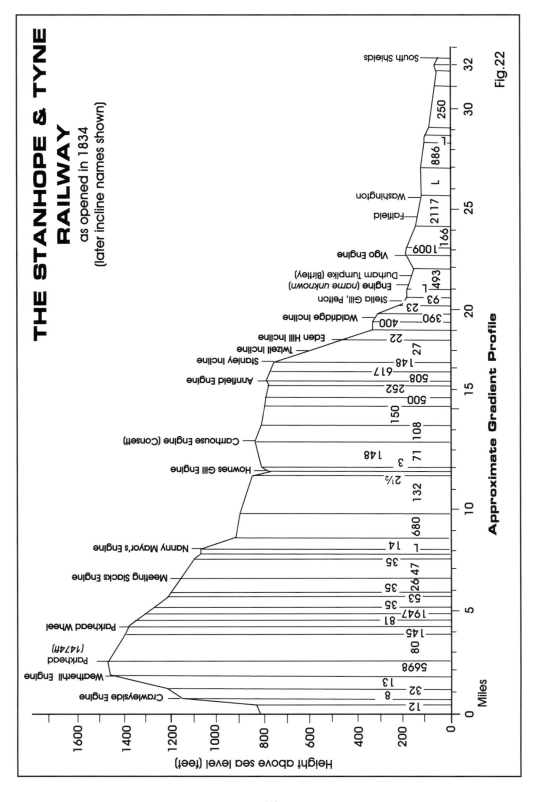

THE STANHOPE & TYNE RAILWAY

as opened in 1834

(later incline names shown)

Fig.22

Presumably there were large wheels, probably mounted vertically, around which the ropes went to operate the cradles. Although the fame of Hownes Gill attracted many visitors – one described it in 1843 as 'one of the most wonderful railway rarities in existence' – no one ever seems to have sketched it.

Three times in fifteen years, in 1836, 1844 and 1853, there was a proposal to build a viaduct across the ravine, but none of these produced any action. After the third proposal was abandoned, the cradle system carrying one waggon at a time was replaced by two standard gauge inclines, presumably retaining the return wheels, which could handle two or three waggons at a time, although not without spilling their loads on numerous occasions. This raised the daily capacity from 140 waggons to about 600 in twelve hours.

From the eastern side of the ravine the Carrhouse Engine hauled the waggons up the Carrhouse West Incline, 1 mile 779 yards at 1 in 71, before lowering them down the Carrhouse East Incline, 812yds at 1 in 108. The sale notice for this engine in 1859 records three 'rope rolls', or drums, here, one 9ft 7in in diameter and two 6ft in diameter, which might suggest that the eastern side was worked by some form of main-and-tail haulage. Horses worked the next 2¼ miles, and then the Annfield Engine, on the top of a ridge near Pontop Pike, drew the waggons up the Annfield West Incline, 662yds, and then lowered them down the East Incline, 1,056yds. The line was now 15¼ miles from Stanhope.

Not surprisingly, given their very varying gradients and operating systems, the number of waggons handled by each haulage differed quite markedly. The Crawleyside Incline could manage only two or three, the Weatherhill Incline between four and six. The Parkhead-Meeting Slacks haulage and the Meeting Slacks Incline are credited with sets of eight, while as noted above, the Howns Gill inclines could handle only one at a time. It would thus seem likely that on this western section of the railway, some of the inclines suffered periods of idleness.

Fortunately, some basic details survive of the stationary engines which subsequently passed to the Stockton & Darlington Railway, and these are quoted in *The Stockton & Darlington Railway, 1825-1975* by P.J.Holmes. Some of them also feature in a sales list published in the Darlington press in July 1859 (see 2-17). From these sources the table below has been drawn up.

It is interesting that apparently two manufacturers each built two of the engines. Given that the construction of the line began in July 1832 and that it was opened in May 1834, it would seem likely that two was the maximum order that could be accepted, given only 18 months for construction and erection. However, there is curious problem apparently affecting the Annfield Engine. A RWH engine, Works No.159, is given in the RWH Engine Book (Tyne & Wear Archives, DS.HL/4/48/1) as for 'Pontop', which would strongly suggest it was intended for here. It is recorded as a 30 h.p. machine. However, the Robert Stephenson & Co works list shows that they built a high pressure

Incline	Gradient	Maker	h.p.	Cylinder (diam. by stroke)
Crawleyside	1 in 7¼ to 1 in 12	Hawks, Son & Co Gateshead	50	28in by 72in
Weatherhill	1 in 32 to 1 in 10¼	Hawks, Son & Co, Gateshead	50	28in by 60in
Meeting Slacks	(1) main and tail at 1 in 80 (2) 1 in 26½ to 1 in 47	R.& W. Hawthorn, Newcastle Works No.156	50[23]	24in by 60in[23]
Howns/Hownes Gill	(1) 1 in 2½ (2) 1 in 3	Robert Stephenson & Co, Newcastle Works No. 39	25[24]	20in by 60in
Carrhouse	(1) 1 in 71 (2) 1 in 108	Robson & Co, Gateshead[25]	50	28in by 72in[25]
Annfield	see	above		

5-35. Crawleyside Bank Head, near Stanhope, about 1914. The outline of the Weatherhill Engine can be seen on the skyline and its rope can be seen attached to the set on the right.

engine for the Stanhope & Tyne destined for 'Pontop Ridge', works no.57. It was the largest stationary engine the firm ever built, a 100 h.p. engine with twin 28in by 60in cylinders, a very different machine from the Hawthorn engine. Interestingly, the order was not received until September 1833, exactly a year after the order for the Howns Gill Engine, and it would take time for it to be built, transported, erected and tested, this perhaps being the reason why the Annfield – South Shields section was not ready to open until 10th September 1834. The problem of there being two engines destined apparently for the same location cannot now be resolved.

The next section, rather more than 2½ miles, was known as the 'Stanley Level' and was worked by horses. Then followed three self-acting inclines, the Stanley Incline, 1,276yds at gradients varying between 1 in 21 and 1 in 41; the Twizell Incline, 880yds at gradients between 1 in 17½ and 1 in 25, and the Eden Hill Incline, 1,122yds at between 1 in 17 to 1 in 71. This brought the line down to the 'Pelton Level' of 1,331yds, after which there was a fourth self-acting bank, the Waldridge Incline, 1,518yds at gradients varying between 1 in 20½ and 1 in 24½. The various levels, and the area around the foot of the Waldridge Incline, known as Stella Gill, attracted the sinking of collieries close by and also branch lines and colliery railways from collieries further afield.

From Stella Gill there were two sections, both about ¾ mile long, the first comparatively level and the second a descending gradient of 1 in 493 down to the Durham Turnpike Road. Both were worked by a stationary engine, the first by main-and-tail haulage, as was possibly the eastern section, given the shallow gradient. From the Turnpike, the waggons were hauled up to the Vigo Engine on the short West Bank and then lowered down the East Bank, most of which was on a gradient of 1 in 166. These two inclines handled sets of twenty-four, apparently in a similar way to the method at Etherley described above, where 'it was customary to run twenty-four loaded waggons against twenty-four light ones' (Tomlinson, p.377). Overall, in 1837 the Engine normally handled four sets of twenty-four in an hour, equal to 1,153 waggons in a day of 12 hours. The Vigo East Incline took the waggons down to Fatfield, from where for the last 9¼ miles locomotives worked the traffic.

The traffic receipts on the Railway did not come up to anticipation, and the losses were aggravated by the high wayleave payments. Due to the expense of working the section between Stanhope and Carrhouse, the company was forced to close it in 1840 and give up the making of lime, and in December 1840 it was revealed to be bankrupt. To try to avoid the personal ruin of all the shareholders, including Robert Stephenson, it was proposed to set up a new company, with the

5-36. A set of empties arriving at Stanley Bank Head, about 1933. The set rider is just about to 'kick the quoit' (see chapter 3) to release the rope. The 'long end' of the rope can be seen on the right.

5-37. The bank foot of the Stanley Incline, with the bank head of the Eden Hill Incline in the distance, about 1933. In the distance empties can be seen in the dish, with the rope attached to them. The previous set of fulls went down the left hand road, taking the rope outside the 'four foot' between the rails. This also happened on the right hand side, where the groove gouged by the rope in the wooden slides can be seen. Note the measures that therefore have to be taken to accommodate this huge lateral movement of the rope.

5-38. The brakesman at Eden Hill Bank Head about 1933; William Nollith, standing in his cabin in charge of his brake wheel. Note the absence of instruments; control of the speed of the set was achieved purely by experience.

shareholders unable to continue being allowed to drop out with the loss of their shares. However, the new company only felt able to take over the 24½ miles between Carrhouse and South Shields. The Stanhope & Tyne company was dissolved on 5th February 1841, and the Pontop & South Shields Railway, the new name for the section east of Carrhouse, received its Act on 23rd May 1842. It was acquired by the Newcastle & Darlington Junction Railway and became part of the North Eastern Railway on 31st July 1854.

In 1840 an ironworks had been established at Berry Edge, later called Consett, and a year later its owners set up the Derwent Iron Company. This done, the only way in which the iron company could safeguard supplies of limestone was to buy the section of railway between Stanhope and Carrhouse, probably early in 1842, calling it the Derwent Railway. The Stockton & Darlington Railway was gradually extending towards Weardale using subsidiary companies, and under a complicated agreement the S&DR acquired the Derwent Railway and merged it with their 'Weardale Extension Railway' between Crook and Waskerley (at the foot of the Nanny Mayors Incline) to form the Weardale & Derwent Junction Railway, which was opened on 16th May 1845.

In 1844 the S&DR had asked their engineer, William Bouch (1813-1876), to survey the operation of the Derwent Railway, and on his recommendation the Iron Company replaced the horse working between Weatherhill and Parkhead by a second main-and-tail system utilising the Weatherhill Engine and (presumably) a second return wheel at Parkhead. The operation of the line then remained unchanged until the late 1850s. The Hownes Gill inclines were finally replaced by a 730-yard viaduct opened on 1st July 1858, with the Carrhouse inclines being replaced by locomotives on the same day. The rope haulage between Weatherhill and Hownes Gill was gradually replaced by new deviation routes operated by locomotives from a shed at Waskerley; the last incline to be replaced was the Nanny Mayors Incline, which was closed on 4th July 1859.

Improvements were also put in hand on the section owned by the NER, although they were spread over 35 years. Probably the first of these, although no precise date seems to have survived, was the merging of the Stanley and Twizell Inclines into one incline of 2,250yds at 1 in 17 (see chapter 1). The next section to be tackled was that between Stella Gill and Fatfield, where a double track railway was installed and the two stationary engines replaced by locomotive working from 8th June 1857, thus allowing locomotives to work all the way between Stella Gill and South Shields. Locomotives also replaced horses on the Stanley and Pelton Levels.

Nothing more was done until the 1880s, when a new double track line was built to avoid the two Annfield inclines. This included gradients of 1 in 64 and 1 in 103, and was opened on 1st January 1886, allowing the inclines to be dismantled. This done, the NER turned to the section between South Pelaw and Annfield, where pressure for local communities to be served by passenger services had been growing for some time. In 1890 work began on the 'Annfield Deviation', a 6½ mile

double track line between South Pelaw, about half a mile east of Stella Gill, to what was now called Annfield Plain. The new line included gradients as steep as 1 in 35 and 1 in 50, and very little of it was less than 1 in 100, so it presented some challenging locomotive working. It was opened for freight on 16th October 1893 and for passengers on 1st February 1894. But this time the inclines did not close; they were too important for coal traffic. As noted in chapter 1, in the late 1890s the Stanley Incline was handling an average of 428 sets of six per week, or nearly 1,400,000 tons of coal per year. So of the original haulages from 1834, by the end of the nineteenth century the only inclines to survive were the two powered inclines out of Stanhope, Crawleyside and Weatherhill, kept open by the limestone traffic, and the modified Stanley, Eden Hill and Waldridge self-acting inclines, carrying a large volume of coal traffic. Crawleyside was given a new engine in 1886-87 and its bottom section was rebuilt to double track, including through Hog Head Tunnel, to accommodate increased limestone traffic from Ashes Quarry at Stanhope, this traffic to the Consett Iron Works keeping these inclines open.

The opening of the Stanhope & Tyne Railway had created additional shipping capacity on the southern bank of the River Tyne close to its mouth, but in the early 1830s the only lines bringing coal to the southern bank of the River Wear at Sunderland were the Newbottle Waggonway (1815) and the Hetton Railway. Since 1820 the coalfield in central and eastern Durham had begun to be developed, and supporters of railways saw potential traffic beginning to choose Hartlepool as a shipping port. To counter this, the **Durham & Sunderland Railway** was promoted, obtaining its Act in 1834. Its Engineer was Thomas Emerson Forster (1802-1875), a North-East man but an unusual choice as he was much better known as a colliery engineer. In October 1834 he was asked by his directors to report on the comparative merits of locomotives or fixed engines for their railway. He recommended the latter, for reasons unknown, and so the whole line, initially about fifteen miles long, was to be worked by stationary engines.

Construction of the line began in February 1835 and the first section, rather more than 9½ miles between Sunderland and Murton Junction, together with the Haswell branch, was opened on 5th July 1836. The branch from South Hetton Colliery first carried coal on 6th October, and the next section of the main line, between Murton Junction and Pittington, followed a week later. The final sections seem to have been completed early in 1837; the sinking of Whitwell Colliery was finished on 21st June 1837. The line was amongst the first to be laid on wooden sleepers, rather than stone blocks.

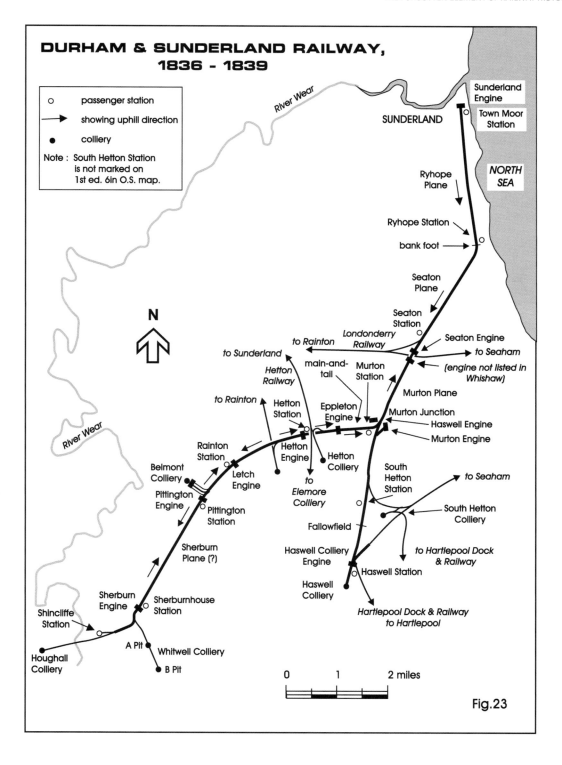

DURHAM & SUNDERLAND RAILWAY, 1836 - 1839

○   passenger station

→   showing uphill direction

●   colliery

Note : South Hetton Station is not marked on 1st ed. 6in O.S. map.

Sunderland Engine

Town Moor Station

River Wear

SUNDERLAND

NORTH SEA

Ryhope Plane

Ryhope Station

bank foot

Seaton Plane

Seaton Station

N

to Rainton

Londonderry Railway

Seaton Engine

to Seaham

to Sunderland

main-and-tail

Murton Station

(engine not listed in Whishaw)

Hetton Railway

Murton Plane

to Rainton

Hetton Station

Eppleton Engine

Murton Junction

Haswell Engine

Murton Engine

Rainton Station

Hetton Engine

Hetton Colliery

Belmont Colliery

Letch Engine

to Elemore Colliery

South Hetton Station

to Seaham

Pittington Engine

Pittington Station

South Hetton Colliery

Fallowfield

Sherburn Plane (?)

Haswell Colliery Engine

to Hartlepool Dock & Railway

River Wear

Sherburn Engine

Sherburnhouse Station

Haswell Station

Haswell Colliery

Shincliffe Station

A Pit

Whitwell Colliery

Hartlepool Dock & Railway to Hartlepool

Houghall Colliery

B Pit

0   1   2 miles

Fig.23

Unfortunately, the Railway has attracted hardly any historians, perhaps because it was rope-worked throughout, and little has been published about it. No attempt has previously been made to describe or explain the haulage working. Thus the description below is based upon juxtaposing the accounts in Whishaw and Tomlinson, together with the evidence revealed by the 1st edition of the Ordnance Survey, surveyed in 1857 and published in 1861.[26] It should be read in conjunction with Fig.23.

The railway was about fifteen miles long, built to standard gauge, and was divided into seven haulages, all worked by stationary engines. No details are known about these, except for their horse powers. The first was the Sunderland Moor Engine (70 h.p.), which worked the gradually rising section, with gradients of 1 in 230 and 1 in 190, as far as the bank foot of the Seaton Incline at Ryhope, a distance of about 2¾ miles (Whishaw gives 5,616yds, apparently incorrectly). This used three ropes, all 4,900yds long, or slightly more than 2¾ miles. The first rope went from the engine out to a set of fulls; the second, rather smaller rope, went from the back of the fulls, round a large horizontal return wheel at Ryhope and back down the other side of the incline to a set of empties; from the other end of the empties the third rope went back to a second drum in the engine house. So as the engine hauled in the full wagons it was also hauling out the empties, with their tail rope winding off the second drum which was out of gear. The use of three ropes on one haulage appears to be unique.

This haulage was not without its problems. On the opening day, 5th July 1836, one of the drums collapsed and the engine was out of action for a fortnight while new and stronger drums were fitted, only for one of these to crack on 17th September and have to be renewed.

The next section was 4,485yds, or rather more than 2½ miles, with rising gradients of 1 in 43½ at the bottom easing to 1 in 60 on the upper part. This was worked by the Seaton Engine (42 h.p.) at Seaton Bank Head. This was worked by a single rope on a single line. As the fulls were travelling downhill, they descended by gravity, taking the rope with them, with the engine then hauling up the empties.

The next section took the line down a gradient of 1 in 212 for 2,427yds to Murton Junction, where the Haswell branch diverged. Tomlinson calls this the Murton Plane and states that it was worked by a 52 h.p engine near the crossing with the Londonderry Railway at Seaton Bank Top, but that the set dragged a tail rope from another engine at Murton Junction, an example of the reciprocating haulage advocated by Benjamin Thompson and described earlier. Whishaw does not mention the

first engine, but states that the Murton Engine (70 h.p.) had two ropes, one of which was 2,500yds long, clearly the tail rope that Tomlinson describes. It would appear therefore that the incline was single line, with the un-named engine at Seaton Bank Top hauling fulls uphill and the Murton Engine winding the empties in coming downhill.

A similar system using two ropes but with only one engine was employed on the Haswell branch. At Haswell itself a stationary engine owned by the Haswell Coal Co hauled the full coal wagons out of the pit and lowered them underneath the line owned by the Hartlepool Dock & Railway Co, which also served Haswell Colliery, and down part of the Durham & Sunderland branch to a point about half a mile further on, known as 'the bank head' at Fallowfield (Tomlinson). Here a rope 3,000yds long was attached to the front of the set for them to be drawn to Murton Junction by the Haswell Engine (42 h.p.), which was situated near the Murton Engine but at right-angles to it. The wagons dragged after them a great tail rope 6,000yds long, which went back to Fallowfield, round a horizontal grooved wheel and then back to a second drum on the engine. This rope, nearly 3½ miles long, which Tomlinson states was made without a single splice, was hauled in to pull the empties back to Fallowfield. How operating arrangements for the two engines at Murton Junction were handled is unknown.

As noted above, the Murton Engine (70 h.p.) at Murton Junction had two ropes, with one assisting the operation of the section eastwards to Seaton Bank Top. The other worked the next section westwards, as far as the Eppleton Engine, a distance of just under ¾ mile at a descent from the engine of 1 in 61. So this was a conventional single line incline, with the engine hauling up the fulls and then lowering the empties, presumably on the brake. The next incline, 1,585yds on a descending gradient from the engine of 1 in 60, was operated in the same way, with the Eppleton Engine ('Appleton' in Whishaw) (83 h.p.) using a single rope to raise the fulls and lower the empties alternately. However, the Ordnance Survey map shows the 'landing', the section comprising two lines for the sets on the inclines to interchange, to be located east of the Eppleton Engine, rather than in front of the Engine, on its western side. This might suggest that the Eppleton rope came out of the rear of the engine house and went round a return wheel to go down the Eppleton Incline. This incline brought the railway down to the village of Hetton-le-Hole, the headquarters of the Hetton Coal Co and the location of Hetton Colliery, with which there was a link.

The next section westwards, between the Hetton Engine (42 h.p.) and the Letch, or Moorsley, Engine (52 h.p.) was 2,850yds, rather more than 1½ miles, with a descending gradient of 1 in 530 from Hetton, followed by a rising gradient of 1 in 462 to the Letch Engine. Whishaw states that this length was worked by one rope, but that would be difficult over an undulating route. However, it must be significant that the Letch Engine is described with two ropes and that one of them is identical with the rope assigned to the Hetton Engine. Two ropes of the same weight and length would suggest that this Hetton Incline was worked by yet another version of main-and-tail haulage, with one engine hauling and the other paying its rope out out with its drum out of gear, much the same as the system between the western engine at Seaton Bank Top and the Murton Engine.

The sixth section, between the Letch Engine and the Pittington Engine (Whishaw has 'Piddington') was 1,400yds long, descending on a gradient of 1 in 68. This would again seem to be a single line, with the Letch Engine hauling up fulls and lowering empties alternately. Near the foot of the incline the main line was joined by a ¾ mile branch from Belmont Colliery. This was a self-acting incline, so presumably the Letch Engine ran in empties here and removed fulls as required.

The final section is the most difficult to interpret. Whishaw says that there were two planes and gives details of two ropes, both of which were 4,900yds, or slightly more than 2¾ miles, while Tomlinson does not mention this length at all. At its eastern end was the Pittington Engine and at its western end the Sherburn Engine, with both engines being 85 h.p. The Ordnance Survey 6in map shows a slightly rising gradient away from the Pittington Engine, followed by a slight fall to the Sherburn Engine. Whishaw states that the Sherburn Plane was 3,712yds, or slightly less than 2¼ miles. This would appear to refer to the section between Pittington and Sherburn. However, Thomas Hair's watercolour of Pittington, reproduced here, shows the engine having two drums, one larger than the other. This, together with the undulating track, would to the author suggest that this section was worked by main-and-tail haulage, using a rope from each drum.

This would in turn mean that the Sherburn Engine worked traffic west of it. The Ordnance Survey map shows the line to Houghall Colliery as owned by the North Eastern Railway (Durham & Sunderland), with Shincliffe Station on this line a short distance from the bridge over the River Wear. Although there is as yet no supporting evidence, a possible interpretation might be that the Sherburn Engine worked this line, certainly as far as Shincliffe Station and perhaps as far as the river bridge. The Whitwell Colliery branch is known to have had its own stationary engine.

How many wagons formed a set on these various inclines is not clear. On the two and three rope haulages probably at least a dozen wagons were run at a time, perhaps more, while on the direct haulage inclines perhaps half the number elsewhere. Hair's painting of a coal and passenger train passing Broomside Colliery, west of Pittington (see 3-23), shows twelve chaldron waggons.

This was not only one of the most complex applications of rope haulage during this period; a timetabled passenger service was also run over it. Fortunately, this has been the subject of a detailed investigation by Michael Quick, a member of the Railway & Canal Historical Society's Railway Chronology Group and published in the group's Co-Ordinating Newsletter No.69, January 2012. Quick believes that the first passenger service began in April or May 1837 and operated between Sunderland and Haswell, where passengers could change to catch a train on the Hartlepool Dock & Railway. On the H&DR this service was provided by a contractor using horses, but this would seem unlikely on a solely rope-worked railway, and almost certainly the carriages on the D&SR were provided and operated by the railway company itself. According to Whishaw, the carriages were built by a Mr. Usher of Newcastle upon Tyne and were of two types, mixed and second class. The former had a central first class section which was enclosed, flanked by two open second class sections, while the second class carriages had three sections all the same. Eventually, presumably after the 1844 Act,[27] there was third class provision too. The main line was also provided with a passenger service, apparently reaching Shincliffe in June 1839; presumably horses pulled the carriages west of Sherburn. With the centre of Durham City about a mile away from Sherburn, a connecting stage coach service was provided for passengers wishing to travel there. There was no lack of demand for the passenger service; Whishaw states that 77,421 passengers were carried in 1838.

Originally passenger carriages were attached to the rear of coal trains; Whishaw states this, and one of Thomas Hair's drawings shows this. But in Board of Trade reports on accidents in 1844 and 1848, it seems that different practices had taken over. Passenger carriages were forming their own trains and being allowed to run behind coal trains supposedly no closer than 100 yards, though in one accident this had been reduced to 20 yards (Hair's illustration of Pittington (5-39) shows a set of passenger coaches without any coal wagons). To make this possible the guard had access to what was termed a 'towing bar, which enabled him to pick up the rope from the rollers and attach it to the carriage'. Moreover, on descending gradients the guards could detach the rope and allow the carriages to travel 'by force of gravity'. To readers

5-39. *A lithograph of the Pittington Engine about 1838 looking north east, after a water colour by Thomas Hair. It shows the engine with two drums, discussed in the text, and what appears to be a five-carriage passenger train, with a tail rope attached. To the left of the drum house, chaldron waggons can be seen at the foot of the self-acting incline from Belmont Colliery, while to the right of the engine house the Letch Engine can be seen.*

today such practices will seem unthinkable, but the Board of Trade's railway inspectors raised no comment. It would seem that about four minutes was allowed for the transfer of a passenger train from one haulage to the next.

The 1st edition 6in O.S. map shows the following stations, replicated on Fig.23. On the main line these were Town Moor (at Sunderland), Ryhope, Seaton, Murton, Hetton, Rainton, Pittington and Sherburn, all of them of course adjacent to stationary engines, with the western terminus at Shincliffe. Some of these, like Rainton, were quite a distance from the villages after which they were named. On the Haswell branch only the station at Haswell is shown, though one timetable also shows a station at South Hetton; the branch line bisected this village. On 1st May 1858 the Town Moor Station at Sunderland was replaced by a new station at Hendon, about a mile to the south.

Timetable evidence is sketchy and incomplete. By the mid-1850s the weekday service between Sunderland and Hartlepool comprised three trains per day in each direction, averaging an hour between Sunderland and Haswell and 40 minutes between Haswell and Hartlepool. The D&SR stops are shown as Sunderland, Ryhope, Seaton, Murton, South Hetton and Haswell. On arriving here the carriages were run a little way down the line towards Haswell colliery and then back into a siding at right-angles to the H&DR station. The siding ended in a turntable with the H&DR line, and it seems, curiously, that 3rd class carriages were worked through to Hartlepool by using the turntable but that 1st and 2nd class passengers had to get out and walk to their coaches at the H&DR station. At some point a link was put in between the two lines to make through passenger working possible – both lines were owned by the North Eastern Railway after 1854 – but when this was done is uncertain.[28] In February 1858 trains for Hartlepool left Sunderland at 8.30am, 1.00pm and 6.30pm. Three months later trains for Shincliffe left Sunderland at 8.30am, 1.00pm and 4.30pm, calling at Murton, Hetton, Pittington and Sherburn and taking approximately an hour for the complete journey. Given that in two cases the departure time for both Haswell and Shincliffe were the same, it may be that the carriages were combined into one train, but no evidence of this survives. The three trains in the reverse direction left Shincliffe at 6.50am, 10.50am and 3.00pm. Whether by this time the trains were still rope-hauled is uncertain; the date(s) when the inclines were abandoned in favour of locomotive haulage are not known. The conversion would seem unlikely before the creation of the NER in 1854, but might have been carried out soon afterwards, perhaps in stages; Quick argues that improvements in the passenger timetable can perhaps be linked to the introduction of locomotives. It was almost certainly completed by 1858.

The Durham & Sunderland Railway was the longest public railway in Britain worked entirely by stationary engines, and, claimed Whishaw (p.74), 'exhibits clearly the inefficiency of this plan for passenger traffic. The difficulty of starting the trains, the numerous detentions on the way and the great uncertainty of the time a journey will occupy, added to the jolts experienced by passengers when reaching a bank head, or when making a false start - a thing of very frequent occurance – all present themselves as serious objections to the stationary system'. He does not mention perhaps the greatest difficulty – that if one incline stopped working, all the others had to stop working too, a major problem if the stoppage was caused by a rope breaking.

Yet it took time for railway engineers to dismiss rope haulage for passenger services entirely from their minds, and indeed several very sophisticated haulages were installed after 1836, even on lines much more important and famous than the Durham & Sunderland Railway.

The first railway to link two great cities after the Liverpool & Manchester Railway was the **London & Birmingham Railway**. It obtained its Act in May 1833 and its Engineer was Robert Stephenson, then 29 years old. From London its route included Rugby and Coventry and terminated at Curzon Street in Birmingham. The Act designated Camden as its London terminus, but it was soon decided that a terminus closer to the centre of London would be preferable, and in July 1835 an Act was obtained to authorise an extension from Camden to Euston Square. At the same time Isambard Kingdom Brunel (1806-1859) was surveying the route of the proposed Great Western Railway from London to Bristol, and the Great Western directors hoped to come to an agreement with the London & Birmingham to share the Euston terminus.

From Euston up to Camden was a distance of slightly more than a mile. It rose by almost 46ft with successive gradients of 1 in 66, 1 in 110, 1 in 132 and 1 in 75, which was steep but not unprecedented on locomotive-worked lines at that time. There was a mile and a half at 1 in 82 on the Bolton & Leigh Railway, which opened in 1830, and a mile at 1 in 85 on the Warrington & Newton Railway, which opened in the following year, and these gradients were handled by locomotives. However, the ownership of the land needed was shared between Lords Southampton and Bedford, who in April 1835 required the L&BR Board not to erect any steam engines, workshops, etc. on their land south of the Regent's Canal at Camden. In the event, Stephenson adopted rope haulage to bring trains up to Camden, probably as a result of a private agreement between the L&BR and the landowners in order to retain the latter's support. This decision was not taken because the L&BR Act of 1835 forbade the use of steam

5-40. The beautiful water colour by John Cooke Bourne (1814-1896) of the construction of the Camden Engine House dated 26th April 1837. The quality of the finer detail can be clearly seen. The vaulting for the stationary engine can be clearly seen; it should be remembered that the railway had to go over the top of these vaults.

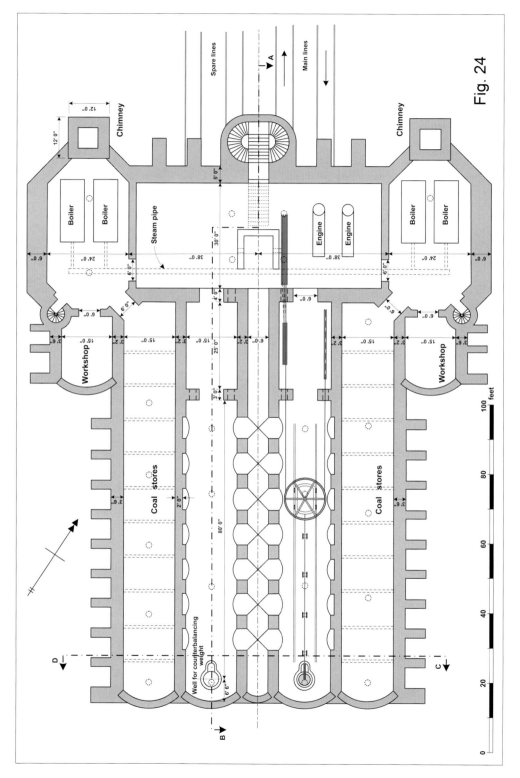

Fig.24 The plan of the Camden Engine House, London & Birmingham Railway, 1837.

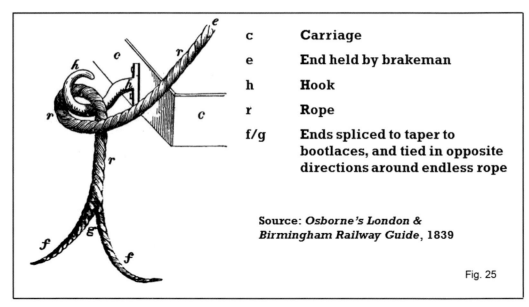

c	**Carriage**
e	**End held by brakeman**
h	**Hook**
r	**Rope**
f/g	**Ends spliced to taper to bootlaces, and tied in opposite directions around endless rope**

Source: *Osborne's London & Birmingham Railway Guide*, 1839

Fig. 25

Fig.25 Diagram showing the 'messenger rope' used on the carriages on the Camden Incline of the London & Birmingham Railway, and also previously on the Liverpool & Manchester Railway.

5-41. The top of the Camden Incline, with rope haulage now operating. Trains to and from Euston used the two right hand tracks, with the left hand side devoid of both machinery and sheaves. Looking from left to right, Hampstead lies to the left of the left chimney, with Parliament Hill in the distance, while on the right stands the Locomotive Shed with the Regent's Canal curving round in the foreground.

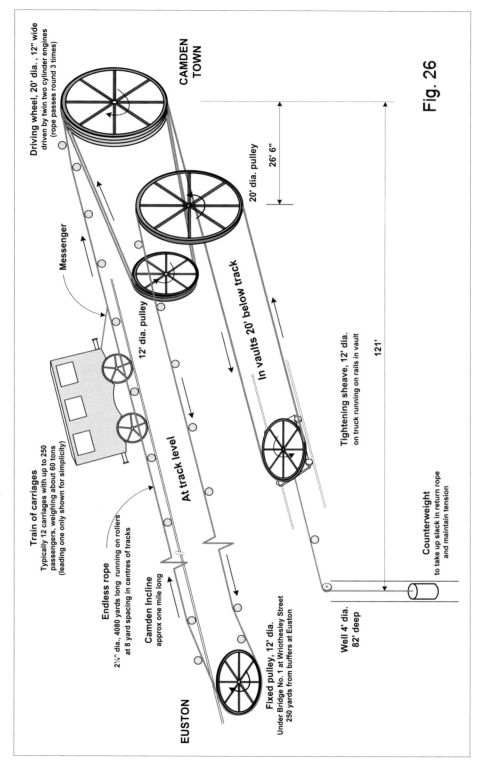

Driving wheel, 20' dia., 12" wide driven by twin two cylinder engines (rope passes round 3 times)

CAMDEN TOWN

20' dia. pulley

26' 6"

12' dia. pulley

Messenger

In vaults 20' below track

Tightening sheave, 12' dia. on truck running on rails in vault

121'

At track level

Train of carriages
Typically 12 carriages with up to 250 passengers, weighing about 60 tons (leading one only shown for simplicity)

Counterweight to take up slack in return rope and maintain tension

Endless rope
2¼" dia., 4080 yards long running on rollers at 8 yard spacing in centres of tracks

Camden Incline approx one mile long

Fixed pulley, 12' dia. Under Bridge No. 1 at Wriothesley Street 250 yards from buffers at Euston

Well 4' dia. 82' deep

EUSTON

Fig. 26

Fig.26 Diagram showing the endless rope haulage system adopted by Robert Stephenson on the Camden Incline.

5-42. There is a considerable collection of illustrations of the incline both by Bourne and also by Robert Schnebbelie (d.1849?). This shows Schnebbelie's painting of Hampstead Road Bridge looking towards Euston, a rare view of locomotives working over the sheaves, which must date it to between July and October 1837. It also shows a horse-drawn train on the western side, inaccurately showing sheaves; perhaps this was a case of an artist finishing his work from memory in his studio, although it is interesting to see a train on this side too.

locomotives on it; it did not, despite a common belief at the time.[29] Still less was the reason because the locomotives bought for the line were considered by some since to be underpowered, latterly sometimes specifically linked to the appointment of Edward Bury (1794-1858) as locomotive superintendent and the allegedly underpowered locomotives that he designed – a myth which has been perpetuated for well over a century in some popular railway literature.[30]

To operate the haulage Stephenson adopted an endless system similar to that already planned for the Wapping Incline on the Liverpool & Manchester Railway. There trains in winter would comprise five carriages, doubled in the summer, so it was felt that twelve would be sufficient here. These would descend from Camden by gravity under the control of the brakeman; the engine would be used only to haul. The haulage would be driven by stationary steam engines housed in an underground vault measuring about 170ft long by 135ft wide. This huge engine house was necessary to accommodate two sets of engines, equipment, boilers, workshops and coal stores, the western side provided for the Great Western Railway and the eastern side for the L&BR. The engine rooms were 72ft long by 30ft wide, with in the centre, opposite the main staircase, a structure supporting the driving wheels. The boiler rooms were 44ft long by 24ft wide, with workshops of 20ft by 15ft on their southern sides. Then came four parallel longitudinal vaults, each 15ft wide, 114ft long and 20ft high, their floors being inverted vaults. The inner vaults housed the pulley and the sheave, trolley, rails and wells, 82ft deep, for the counterweight carriage that maintained the tension on the rope, while the outer vaults were coal stores. The central vaulted passage between the two inner vaults was 6ft wide, with seven arched openings into the rope tightening vaults (Fig.24).

The construction of the Extension had not begun when in October 1835 Brunel's proposal that the Great Western Railway should be built to a gauge of 7ft 0in was accepted by his directors. Shortly afterwards the Great Western directors broke off negotiations with their London & Birmingham counterparts. Accommodating the broad gauge at Camden and Euston would have meant a great many changes to the plans, although in their report to their shareholders in February 1836 the Great Western directors claimed that they had withdrawn because of the refusal of the L&BR Board to part for any reasonable and definite period the land necessary for the Great Western premises.[31]

Despite the withdrawal of the Great Western Railway, the construction of the Extension and its engine house went ahead unaltered, perhaps because this was easier than to re-draw plans and re-negotiate contracts. The line involved a cutting up to 19ft deep in places and seven over-bridges. For the incline the London & Birmingham ordered two 60 h.p. condensing beam engines from the Lambeth firm of Maudslay, Sons & Field. These had cylinders of 43in diameter with a 48in stroke, working side by side to a common crankshaft. They took steam at 4½ p.s.i., initially from two marine boilers 18ft long by 7ft 6in wide by 8ft high. Two circular boilers measuring 20ft 6in long by 6ft 8in diameter were added in the western boiler room in 1838, the only part of this area to be utilised. Neither boiler room was roofed. The two chimneys were 133ft high and mounted on pedestals 12ft 8in square by 23ft high, taking the smoke well away from neighbouring housing. The original hemp rope was manufactured by Messrs. Huddart & Co of Limehouse and was 4,080yds, rather more than 2¼ miles long, reputedly the longest unspliced rope up to that time; it cost £476-19s-0d, was 2¼in diameter and 7in in circumference and weighed 11¾ tons.

L ONDON AND NORTH-WESTERN
RAILWAY COMPANY.
STEAM-ENGINES FOR SALE BY AUCTION,
On Tuesday, the 15th of June, at Camden Station, on the London and North-Western Railway, if not previously disposed of, TWO LOW-PRESSURE STATIONARY ENGINES, 60-horse power each, made by Maudslays. These Engines are in good working order, and have duplicate Pistons, also Five Fly and Rope-Wheels and a Travelling-Frame ; Two Circular Boilers, 20 ft. 6 in. long, 7 ft. 8 in. diameter, with two tubes in each, 2 ft. 8 in. diameter ; Two Marine Boilers, 18 ft. long, 7 ft. 6 in. wide, and 8 ft. 9 in. high ; 100 feet of 9½ in. Steam-Pipe, Safety-Valves, Dampers, Frames, &c. complete.
Office, Euston Station, April 17, 1847.

5-43. The newspaper notice advertising the proposed sale of the Camden engines by auction on 15th June 1847, giving full details. They were bought for re-use in Russia.

All the equipment for the engines had to be brought to site via the Regent's Canal, but repairs to the canal delayed the engines' completion; so on 12th July 1837 the Railway was opened between Euston and Boxmoor – using locomotives! On 27th September the rope haulage began partial operation, taking over fully on 14th October 1837.

The stationary engine was located as close to the top of the descending gradient as possible, so that trains for Euston could be detached from their locomotive near the bridge over the Regent's Canal and then continue down to Euston at 10 m.p.h. under the control of a brakeman. From the platforms at Euston Station the first 264yds was downhill on a gradient of 1 in 156 to allow trains to roll down and run on to the beginning of the rope-worked section, where there was a level section of 286yds. Here the train was attached to the rope by a 'messenger', illustrated in Chapter 3. When the train was ready, a signal was sent to instruct the engineman by depressing a plunger at the Euston end of an air tube. Four seconds later air pressure displaced a coloured liquid in a glass indicator in the engine room, accompanied by what was described as a 'low melancholy moan'; see Fig. 9 in Chapter 3. Cooke & Wheatstone experimented with their electric telegraph system here, the first use of this system, but it was not adopted. In order to be able to start the machinery immediately the signal was given, a small 6 h.p. engine was used to exhaust the condenser. The haulage went beyond the summit of the ascending gradients and is believed to have been 77.3 chains in total, or almost exactly 1,700yds. In his book Lecount[29] found that the average speed over 14 trains, pulling 70 tons, or 14 carriages and 148 passengers, was 15 m.p.h., although up to 20 m.p.h. was achieved on occasions. Whishaw states that the time spent drawing up the trains was between 3½ and 5 minutes, depending on the load.

In the event the incline was short-lived. From November 1843 locomotives began hauling some prestige trains from Euston; in fact, locomotives had already been used when the engines were laid off for maintenance or the rope was being changed. As with the Liverpool & Manchester Railway, so here too the demand for passenger travel had vastly exceeded the directors' expectations. Trains needed to become longer, and soon grew to 18 or 20 carriages, meaning that they had to be divided to go up the incline. Trains also needed to become faster and more frequent, while suburban services and trains for third-class passengers had been introduced. Longer, heavier trains could be hauled by two locomotives coupled together. The incline had thus become an impediment. From 15th July 1844 the rope haulage was abandoned altogether.

The engines lay disused for over 2½ years, during which, in 1846, the London & Birmingham Railway became part of the new London & North Western Railway. The new owners lost no time in ridding themselves of the redundant equipment. All of the engine house equipment was advertised for sale on 17th April 1847. The engines were sold for use in a flax mill in Russia, leaving the boiler vaults to be roofed over and the huge underground vault to be shut up. The chimneys were demolished two years later.

The final major use of rope haulage on a public railway in Britain also happened in London, but for very different reasons from Camden. This was on the **London & Blackwall Railway** in east London, which obtained its Act in July 1836 under the title of the Commercial Railway. The original engineer was John Rennie (1794-1864), second son of the famous Scottish engineer of the same name; but after the Act was passed, with Rennie's route, he was replaced by Robert Stephenson, with George Bidder (1806-1878) as his resident engineer.

The line as authorised was 3 miles and 843 yards long, promoted purely to provide a passenger service, initially between the Minories and Blackwall with five intermediate stations. To avoid the wholesale demolition of property, the first 2 miles 500 yards between the Minories and the entrance to the West India Dock was carried entirely on a viaduct, with 285 arches, and iron girder bridges across the principal roads and streets, with the stations also being elevated. But this was no ordinary passenger line. It was envisaged as a self-contained unit, and so the gauge was fixed at 5ft 0in, to allow for wider carriages to carry more people. The aim was to provide a fast passenger service every fifteen minutes from both ends, but it was felt that, given the number of stations, locomotive haulage, with its slow acceleration, could not achieve this, while equally coke sparks from the chimneys could cause fires in the properties below. So Stephenson recommended the adoption of rope haulage - not the endless system used at Camden, but a reciprocating system. There were to be two parallel tracks, known as the 'north line' and the 'south line', worked independently of each other but co-ordinated. The haulages would operate at speeds up to 25 m.p.h., with the carriages gripping the rope whilst it was stationary and then being detached at speed to serve the stations. At both ends there would be pairs of stationary engines, the intention being that one pair would be in service while the other was receiving maintenance or repairs. At the Minories the engines were built by Maudslay, Sons & Field; they are described in detail in a paper given by Andrew Robertson to the Institute of Civil Engineers in January 1846.[32] Each engine would provide 112 h.p., or 224 h.p. for the pair (per Robertson; Whishaw gives 115 h.p.), given the generally uphill gradient towards London. Similarly, there were two pairs of marine

THE BLACKWALL RAILWAY.

5-44. The Minories Station, probably soon after the opening in 1840. Note the brakesman on the platform at the end of the nearest carriage. The Cooke & Wheatstone electric telegraph instrument stands on a pedestal on the far left, while the two arms operated by the 'clipper' to guide the rope on to the nearest drum can be seen to the left of the shoulder of the rope brakesman on the right (see text).

"CLIPPER" OF THE BLACKWALL RAILWAY.

5-45. The 'clipper', illustrated in THE PICTORIAL TIMES of 22nd November 1845. The rope drum, not shown, was mounted in front of him. This must have been a tedious job.

arches which carried the railway over the engine house. These tanks were 24½ft square by 6ft deep, each connected by pipes. This system was soon found not to cool the water quickly enough, and the number of tanks was subsequently increased to eight. The hot water was then carried to the most distant of the eight tanks. From there it passed into successive tanks, cooling as it went, because the top of each tank was exposed to the air. In the final tank it was mixed with cold water pumped from a well by the 12 h.p. engine. The distance between the engine houses was 5,466yds, or rather more than three miles.

The ropes were each about 3½ miles long, probably the longest ever made, and were again manufactured by Messrs Huddart & Co of Limehouse at a cost of about £1,200. Each was 1¾in in diameter and weighed about 40 tons. The rope drums were coned, being 23ft in diameter outside and 16½ft in diameter inside, and 3ft 2in wide at the top and 1ft 6in wide at the bottom. With the rope on the smaller diameter side when the drum was put into gear, the engine could accelerate the train more quickly than if a normal cylindrical drum was used. However, Stephenson and Bidder foresaw that there might be problems with operating a haulage at such a length, speed and in a way never previously attempted. They regarded it as essential that the rope should wind on to the drum evenly. So at the Minories a vault was installed just in front of the drum where a man was positioned. He operated a device similar to a large pair of scissors, which had a large roller fixed to each of the upper arms, and using this he guided the rope on to the drum. He was known as a 'clipper', presumably because he made people think of hair-cutting. Bidder was also worried that the rope might unwind too quickly off the drum when the Blackwall engines were hauling, causing it to become tangled on the sheaves, or that it might be 'snatched' when the slack was taken up, causing the rope to break. So on the side of each drum was a brake wheel, 14 ft in diameter and 12in wide. Each wheel had a brake lever alongside the track, operated by a brakeman, who applied the brake as required to keep the rope under tension. In the discussion following Robertson's paper, Bidder said that originally the brake blocks were made of wood, but these caught fire; lead had been tried but had proved unsatisfactory, so now copper was being used.

At Blackwall the engines, also a side-lever design, were located at ground level, offset from the track and a short distance from the station. The cylinders were 45½in in diameter with a 48in stroke, averaging 25 strokes to the minute. The large spur wheels were 17ft in diameter, while the drums were also coned, being 16½ft diameter when empty and 22ft diameter outside. It is not known whether a 'clipper' was used here, although presumably a brakeman was needed.

condensing engines at Blackwall, but these provided only 70 h.p. each, or 140 h.p. per pair (Whishaw gives 74 h.p.). Whishaw credits their construction to the 'Horsley Company, under the immediate supervision of Mr.Barnes'; Robertson gives John Barnes and one of the newspaper cuttings gives Messrs. Barnes and Miller. As on the Camden engine, a small auxiliary engine, 12 h.p. at the Minories and 8 h.p. at Blackwall, was used to exhaust the condensers to allow the engine to start immediately the steam valve was opened. Each set of engines was reported to have cost £30,000.

The engines at the Minories were situated in a vault beneath the track measuring 48ft long by 72ft wide. The cylinders were 56in in diameter with a 60in stroke. The spur wheel on the main shaft was 17ft in diameter and weighed 16½ tons. The hot water from the condensers was conveyed to the first of three water tanks mounted in the

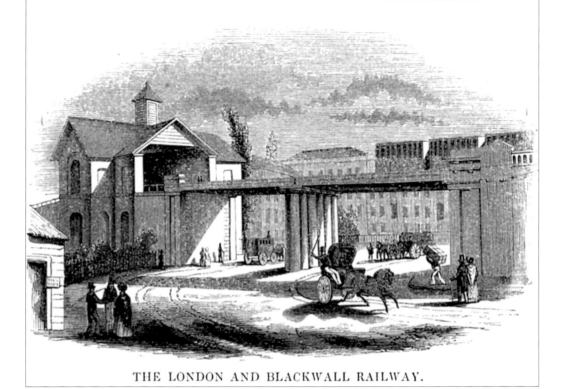

The Literary World:

A JOURNAL OF POPULAR INFORMATION AND ENTERTAINMENT.

CONDUCTED BY JOHN TIMBS, ELEVEN YEARS EDITOR OF "THE MIRROR."

No. 68.]   SATURDAY, JULY 11, 1840.   [Price 2*d*.

THE LONDON AND BLACKWALL RAILWAY.

5-46. The West India Dock Station, from THE LITERARY WORLD of 11th July 1840, four days after the opening. Like many of the London & Blackwall stations, it was elevated. The West India Dock Station was at the other end of the long elevated section of railway from the Minories.

The operation of the trains was almost certainly unique in railway history and underwent a number of changes. Whishaw describes what was almost certainly the initial operation, in which nine carriages were used on both ropes. At the start of the sequence there would be seven carriages at the Minories Station, which from the rear of the train comprised separate vehicles for Shadwell, Stepney, Limehouse, West India Dock and Poplar Stations, with two carriages at the front for Blackwall. Passengers had to be careful to get into the correct carriage for their destinations. Out on the route there were also single carriages at Shadwell and Stepney Stations. As each carriage was attached to the rope, the needle on the electric telegraph was moved to 'Ready' by the policeman on the platform, which repeated on the instrument in the Minories Engine House, as did a similar needle for the Minories Station. While this was being done, the drum on the Minories Engine for this rope was taken out of gear, to allow it to revolve freely. When all the needles showed 'Ready', a signal was given to the Blackwall Engine to haul and the journey began. A complete haul took between eight and nine minutes, travelling at about 26 m.p.h. As each carriage approached its station, one of the two brakemen in each carriage detached it from the rope and braked it to a halt at its platform. The carriages from Shadwell and Stepney were in turn detached near the Blackwall Engine and then ran up a gradient of 1 in 150 into Blackwall Station, to be subsequently followed by the two carriages which had travelled all the way from Minories Station. Once all the carriages were detached from the rope, the Blackwall Engine was stopped, that drum was put out of gear and the drum for the other side was put into gear, ready for the next haul. At the same time, on the other side for the Minories, the single carriages standing at Poplar, West India Dock, Limehouse, Stepney and Shadwell were each attached to the rope, while the four from Blackwall were run down the gradient from the station to the rope for them to be attached. Once ready this train set off, with the rear two carriages being released at Stepney and Shadwell respectively and the other seven carriages continuing to the Minories station. In 1840 there were fifty Up trains and 51 Down trains every day, so that each rope travelled over 150 miles a day.

The carriages were built by Joseph Wright of London, who had previously built carriages for the London & Birmingham Railway. They were all six-wheelers, of three types. The first-class carriage had four enclosed compartments, each seating up to ten people on wooden benches. It was 20ft long and 7ft 6ins wide and was fitted with 'improved' springs. Then came composite coaches, which had two enclosed central compartments for first-class passengers, again with bench seating for up to ten people each, whilst the two end third-class, or 'stand-up' compartments, held twenty people. No seats were provided here, and although there was a roof, these passengers were otherwise exposed to the weather. Finally there were carriages for third-class only, measuring 18ft long by 7ft 6in wide. Once again there were no seats and no protection from the weather other than the roof. The interior was divided into four equal areas by wooden bars and could hold up to 70 people. All the carriages were painted dark blue and had the company's arms emblazoned on the side panels. How these various carriages were used within the traffic pattern described above is not known. The fares were 6d for first class and 3d for third class, subsequently raised to 4d, so that travelling on the train became known as 'taking the four-penny rope'. For tickets the railway used another recent invention, the card tickets of Thomas Edmondson (1792-1851).

The electric telegraph was essential to enable such an intensive service to operate and keep it running to time. But human ingenuity immediately saw other possibilities. The operators of the instruments met and devised a code of their own by utilising certain movements of the needle, enabling them to send messages to each other. As early as the first week of operation, *The Literary World* reported that not only 'notice of any impediment or casualty may be conveyed along the entire line within three

5-47. One of the original Cooke & Wheatstone electric telegraph instruments for the London & Blackwall Railway. The stations on the instrument from left to right are Limehouse, Minories, West India Dock, Poplar and Stepney, curiously not in order along the line. Shadwell Station, not opened until August 1840, is omitted, suggesting that this instrument was in use at the opening of the railway in July 1840. Incredibly, it was retained when it ceased being used and in 1862 passed into the ownership of the Post Office. Fifty years later it was loaned to the Science Museum, which subsequently acquired it, though it is not currently (2012) on display.

seconds', but that ships coming up river could communicate by signals with the terminus at Blackwall, so that messages could be sent via the Minories station to their friends in business, who could then meet them in town, without waiting for hours at docks or wharfs! However, a later report says that the superintendent of the line heard about this, as did the telegraph's inventor, William Cooke (1806-1879); the two men were questioned and told never to do it again under threat of dismissal – while Cooke went on to develop and patent the alphabet for which the telegraph soon became famous.

The hemp ropes soon began to cause major problems and it is clear that a combination of their extreme length and the very demanding operating conditions had taken rope technology into the unknown, baffling both engineers and manufacturers. The diameter of the original rope was soon reduced. Breaks were frequent and some ropes lasted only two months. It was believed that the frequent tensions in opposite directions were a factor, as were jolts from the drums. Even more serious was the constant twisting of the rope in use. Unable to diagnose the cause, which Robert Stephenson thought might be due to the rope winding on the top of the Minories drums but the bottom of those at Blackwall, as early as November 1840 engineers had attempted to reduce this by inserting swivels into the rope. At first these were riveted into the rope, but then

fractures occurred at the rivets, leading to swivels being spliced into the rope. Then it was found that the swivels affected how the rope wound on to the drum. Ropes from which the tar had been expelled under pressure were tried, but were soon worn out. So the hemp ropes were replaced by wire ropes. These were 1¼in diameter and had a central hemp core, around which were woven six strands of six wires each, again with a hemp core. Latterly ropes manufactured by Messrs. Newall of Gateshead were purchased. These reduced the breakages, but still needed swivels, with one inserted every half mile. By 1845 fractures had been reduced to one or two per month. When these occurred, the passengers had to push their carriage to the next station, although there were also stories of sailors playing football whilst waiting for the rope to be repaired.

Even the sheaves caused trouble. These were positioned about eleven yards apart, but as elsewhere different designs had to be used for the curves and to allow for the lateral movement of the rope, which was thought to be damaged by running along the wooden sleepers between the sheaves. The company also received many complaints about the noise of the sheaves as the rope rattled over them, to the extent that serious consideration was given to a plan to cover the sheaves with hard leather, which it was also hoped would reduce fuel costs.

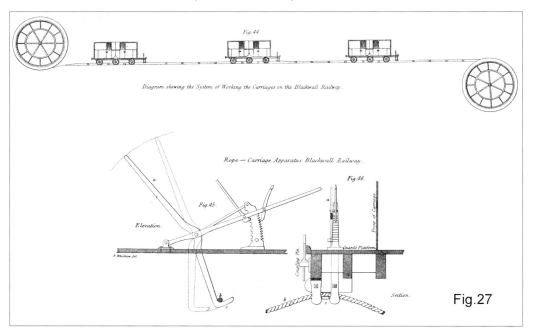

Fig.27 The London & Blackwall Railway diagrams in RAILWAYS OF GREAT BRITAIN & IRELAND by Francis Whishaw, 1842. The upper diagram shows carriages attached to the rope, with their platforms for the brakesman. The Blackwall drum is on the left and the Minories drum on the right. The 'grip iron' apparatus is shown in the lower diagram, a simple device for gripping the rope and holding it tight till it needed to be released.

Meanwhile, the railway company soon decided that it needed a terminus nearer to London than the Minories, and on 20th July 1841 it opened a quite a small station at Fenchurch Street, not far from Tower Bridge and the Tower of London. Like Blackwall Station, this was approached up a gradient of 1 in 150 and was served similarly. Carriages were slipped near the Minories Engines and continued up the gradient into Fenchurch Street, while carriages from the terminus were run down by gravity to the Minories to be attached to the rope. In 1842 a further station was opened, at Cannon Street, between the Minories and Shadwell. These new stations meant that train operation had to be re-organised. Now eleven carriages were normally used, with trains from Fenchurch Street/Minories slipping carriages for Shadwell, Stepney, Limehouse, West India Dock and Poplar, with six carriages going through to Blackwall, whilst on the return journey carriages were slipped at Stepney, Shadwell, Cannon Street and Minories, with six going through to Fenchurch Street. However on occasions this was varied considerably. In the discussion following Robertson's paper, Bidder said that the minimum number of carriages was six, but this number could rise to 23 or 24. He added that the train usually averaged 100 tons, but sometimes reached 200 tons, whereas the average weight of a locomotive train 'did not much exceed 50 tons.'

In terms of passengers the line more than fulfilled expectations. In 1844 it carried over 2½ million passengers, two-thirds of them boarding at the intermediate stations. In 1845 the rope haulage operated 38,325 trains, running every fifteen minutes from both ends. In the winter trains began at 8.30am and ended at 9.00pm, while in the summer they began at 8.00am and ended at 10.00pm. The traffic was said to be 'immense' in the summer, with 'the great bulk of passengers requiring to be carried by the evening trains'. Passenger vessels coming up the River Thames could disembark their passengers at the pier at Blackwall, where the station had special premises for Customs officers. The cost of operating the railway was given as 1s 6¾d per mile.

Despite the huge numbers of passengers, the railway was said to be unprofitable. The fatal blow came in 1848, with a proposal to build a link between Stepney and the Eastern Counties Railway at Bow. This could not be done unless the London & Blackwall Railway was converted to 4ft 8½in gauge, so this was done in 1849, with locomotives replacing the rope haulage at the same time. The engines and their equipment were advertised for auction in the *Morning Advertiser* of 11th February 1850; three years later the Minories engines were re-erected in the City Corn Mills to drive the machinery there.

The next major railway to be opened was the Great Western Railway, 120 miles between London and Bristol and designed by I.K.Brunel for a gauge of 7ft 0in. The only steep section on the route was the Box Tunnel near Bath, 3,212yds at 1 in 100 and dead straight. In 1839 Charles Saunders, the GWR Secretary, 'told the Parliamentary Committee on Railways that it was intended to work the Box Tunnel Incline by a stationary engine, or possibly by water power'.[33] A double track incline of about two miles to the 7ft gauge would truly have been one of the wonders of the railway age. But when the line was opened, on 30th June 1841, there was no stationary engine; Box Tunnel was worked by locomotives. In the previous September the Birmingham & Gloucester Railway had opened its section north of Bromsgrove which included the Lickey Incline, just over two miles, again dead straight, at 1 in 38 - with locomotive-hauled trains assisted by banking engines. The demands of railways had moved on, as had technological development; the period of new, passenger-carrying rope haulages, at least on main line railways, was nearly over.

But not quite; even after 1840 two public railways each constructed a rope haulage to carry passengers. The **Manchester & Leeds Railway** was superintended by George Stephenson, although its resident engineer was Thomas Gooch (1808-1882), older brother of Daniel Gooch (1816-1889) of the Great Western Railway. It was opened in stages between 1839 and 1841, and one of its branches was to serve Oldham, via a branch from Middleton Junction down to the Werneth area of the town. This was done using a rope incline 1 mile 1,383yds long, of which about a mile was on a gradient of 1 in 27, making it the steepest passenger-worked railway line in Britain. It was opened on 31st March 1842.

This incline is hardly mentioned in railway histories, and the only contemporary account of it was recorded almost by accident. Following a serious accident to a passenger train on their Bagworth self-acting incline in August 1844, the directors of the Leicester & Swannington Railway decided that the man in charge of the incline, Francis Stather, should go to inspect the Werneth Incline at Oldham and report if the method of working could be applied at Bagworth. Fortunately, his rather quaintly-worded report to the directors survives, and is given in full in Clinker's history of the railway:[34]

'It is very simple, safe, Effective, and expeditious. It is put in motion by the Locomotive Engine and a balance weight of about 30 tons attached to one end of the Rope as a permanent thing – there is no hooking or unhooking it is always

ready, there is no delay, they run from 10 to 18 Miles per Hour with the greatest safety and command over the Trains – they have a double road, the plane is nearly a Mile Long and the Engine always runs up and down one side – they have a Wire Rope about 4½ inches they use no Brake Sticks.
October 31st, 1844

Francis Stather

Even this brief description shows what may well have been a unique incline. It was a self-acting incline, but used a locomotive on one side as a counter-balance and what appears to be a weighted wagon of about 30 tons on the other side, both permanently attached to the ends of the rope. This system allowed for both full and empty vehicles to travel both uphill and downhill, with the locomotive putting the haulage in motion and then controlling the speed. It was similar to the Pwllyrhebog Incline in South Wales (see chapter 8), but there a locomotive was attached to the downhill end of each train. Exactly what equipment was installed at the top of the Werneth Incline remains to be discovered.

When the rope was replaced by locomotives is uncertain, but it was probably during the late 1850s. A new route avoiding the steep gradient was not opened until March 1880.

What was probably the last new rope haulage built in Britain to carry passengers was opened in 1847. This was in Edinburgh on the **Edinburgh, Leith & Granton Railway**, the second railway to serve the city after the Edinburgh & Dalkeith Railway discussed earlier. This line linked the city with various locations to the north, with its terminus being at Scotland Street, but the company sought a new terminus closer to the city centre. It engaged Thomas Grainger (1794-1852), who had been involved with various railway projects in both Scotland and England, to design a tunnel from its Scotland Street Station to a new station at Canal Street. This was 1,000yds long, with its severest gradient being 1 in 27, and carried the line under Edinburgh's New Town. At Scotland Street it was only just below street level,

but at St.Andrew's Street it was 49ft below ground and was 37ft below ground at Princes Street. No doubt partly because of the gradient but also because of the problem of using steam locomotives in a 1,000-yard tunnel, it was decided to work the line by a stationary engine. This was built by R.& W. Hawthorn of Newcastle upon Tyne, works no. 560 and was ordered on 13th June 1846. It was a 60 h.p., two-cylinder horizontal engine, a reflection of how the design of stationary steam engines had developed. The cylinders were 20in in diameter with a 24in stroke and took steam at 50 p.s.i. The incline is said to have been operated by an endless rope, but precise details of how the trains were worked appear to be lacking. The station at Canal Street was opened on 17th May 1847.

The railway subsequently passed to the control of the North British Railway in 1862. Six years later the NBR connected it to what became the 'East Coast Main Line' and developed Edinburgh Waverley Station, demolishing Canal Street Station in the process and closing the Scotland Street Tunnel, which is thought to have remained rope-worked until then.

The 25 years between 1822 and 1847 had seen railways develop in Britain beyond all expectation. The Hetton Railway of 1822 had been a colliery railway, not carrying any passengers; the London & Birmingham and Great Western Railways were national main line railways, carrying many thousands of passengers a year. The same period had seen the rise of rope haulage in increasingly complicated and sophisticated forms as engineers saw it as a solution to the challenges which they faced. Then came its decline, partly because technical development was unable to meet the operating demands placed upon it, but mainly because its operating disadvantages became increasingly obvious as the 'Railway Age' developed. Most of the rope haulages described here had disappeared by 1870, but they were the passenger haulages; rope inclines continued to be used, and new ones built, on mineral lines, private and public, and were to survive for more than another century.

1   For details of the background to the Hetton Railway, and a discussion of Stephenson's involvement with it, see *The Hetton Railway – Stephenson's Original Design and its Evolution* by Colin E.Mountford in *Early Railways 3*, Sudbury, 2006.

2   Dodds, 15.

3   Dodds, 4.

4   Dodds gives complete details of every incline rope, its length, weight, diameter, initial cost, the precise number of chaldron waggons which it hauled, the cost per chaldron per rope and the exact dates when it was fitted and removed.

5   von Oeynhausen and von Dechen, translation in 1971, 39.

6   Northumberland Archives, 725/F/17, 57-61. 62-67, 68-72.

7   NEIMME, 3410/Wat/2/23 and NA, 725/F/17, 304.

8   von Oeynhausen and von Dechen, translation in 1971, 38.

9   The details of the four inclines are those given to Oeynhausen and Dechen by the Railway authorities, and the same figures are recorded by Walker and Rastrick; subsequently other figures have been quoted.

10 Robert Stephenson & Co records give 36in, but both the Prussian visitors and Rastrick give 38in.

11 NEIMME, Buddle-Atkinson Collection, 3410/Bud/32/326.

12 Courtesy Dr. Michael Bailey from information gleaned from the Robert Stephenson & Co. works ledger, 1823-1831, retained in the National Railway Museum, York.

13 *Railways of Great Britain and Ireland* by Francis Whishaw, London, 1842, 43.

14 The report is quoted in full in *A Century of Locomotive Building by Robert Stephenson & Co, 1823-1923* by J.G.H.Warren, 1923, 166-170.

15 The Stockton & Darlington Railway had the same motto, with the differently-nuanced translation 'Private risk for public profit'

16 *The Cromford & High Peak Railway* by John Marshall, Leeds, 1996, new edition 2011.

17 Marshall, 41.

18 Marshall, 53-55.

19 A detailed account of these trials and of locomotives fitted with Handyside's patent equipment is to be found in *The Industrial Railway Record No.53*, by Trevor J.Lodge, 205-219.

20 The men actually working on the inclines were known as 'planemen', not a term found in North East England. Marshall discusses other workmen's titles also in use on the line.

21 There is no supporting evidence that this catch pit was actually built; if it was, it had a very short life, with the incline being closed in the following year.

22 *The Leicester & Swannington Railway* by C.R.Clinker, Leicester, 1954, 95.

23 R.& W.Hawthorn built two stationary engines for the Stanhope & Tyne Railway, Works Nos. 156 and 159, the second being attributed to 'Pontop'. The first is listed as 50 h.p., and is also shown thus on the Stockton & Darlington Railway sale notice in 1859 (see 2-17); Holmes gives 40 h.p. So almost certainly the Meeting Slacks engine was No.156. The cylinder size is given as shown in Holmes; the sale notice gives 28¼in by 60in, although this could of course be a replacement cylinder. For No. 159, see below. No.159, shown as 30 h.p. in the RWH Engine Book, was almost certainly the Annfield Engine, which was close to Pontop. See also p.144.

24 The Robert Stephenson & Co works list and Holmes both give 25 h.p. and 20in by 60in; the 1859 sale notice gives 20 h.p. and 20in by 71¾in.

25 This manufacturer appears otherwise unknown. The 1859 sale notice gives 28in by 60¾in, very possibly in error.

26 Many stationary engines in Durham were removed towards the end of the 1850s, and it is fortunate indeed that the first Ordnance Survey in Durham was undertaken just before this, giving us information and detail that would otherwise have been lost.

27 The Railway Regulation Act of 1844 compelled railways to provide one train a day for third-class passengers, in each direction and stopping at all stations, at a fare of 1d per mile, in carriages with seats and protected from the weather, at an average speed not less than 12m.p.h.

28 The link has been previously dated to 1877, but in the RCTS paper referred to, Quick argues for an earlier date, possibly not long after 1854.

29 The belief that rope haulage was adopted because of restrictions on smoke is mentioned in *The Iron Road Book* by Francis Coglan (1838); *History of the Railway connecting London and Birmingham* by Peter Lecount, an assistant engineer on the London & Birmingham Railway (1839) and by John Britton in John C.Bourne's *Drawings of the London & Birmingham Railway* (1839).

30 This myth is first stated in *Railways of England* by W.M.Acworth (1889) and has been continued through into the 21st century in *Robert Stephenson: Railway Engineer* by John Addyman and Victoria Haworth, Newcastle, 2005, 73.

31 *The History of the Great Western Railway*, Part 1 by E.T. MacDermott, London, 1927, 35-6.

32 *Description of the Machinery erected by Messrs. Maudslay, Sons & Field at the Minories Station for working the London & Blackwall Railway.* This includes much more information than simply details of the engines, and the discussion afterwards, in which both Stephenson and Bidder took part, is also very interesting.

33 MacDermott, 135.

34 Clinker, 92.

Chapter 6 Stationary engines

From even the briefest details in the previous chapters, it will be clear that dozens of stationary engines were built on railways. Most did not survive the end of the nineteenth century, but some survived into the second half of the twentieth century. Yet detailed work on the thousands of stationary engines used in British industry in general has been limited. The great pioneer here was George Watkins (1904-1989), who travelled Britain for some fifty years and published several books in the 1970s; his extensive collection of photographs and notebooks is now in the National Monuments Record Centre at Swindon. An excellent little book by Geoffrey Hayes entitled *Steam Stationary Engines* was published by Shire Publications in 1979; but he included only one example of a stationary engine serving a railway, and Watkins himself covers only a handful. To attempt to describe and illustrate their development across well over a hundred years is thus a major challenge, because so little primary material survives.

This chapter will look at thirteen stationary engines. Ten of these were steam, built between 1829 and 1915, and the chapter will attempt to draw out the main features of their development. Details of early advertising are included, with rare published specifications for the construction of two engine houses. Two engines are used as exemplars: one, for the rare detailed costs of its construction which survive; another for the complexity of its operation. The last three were electric, built between 1947 and 1950, and illustrate the contrast with the earlier engines. Many stationary engines were long-lived; between them these thirteen engines worked in commercial service for over 1,000 years, five of them for over a hundred years.

Unlike the designers of locomotives, almost nothing is known about designers of stationary engines. Very many of them were probably designed by the senior engineer employed by the manufacturers, working to a general specification supplied by the customer. Even when 'main line' railway companies operated stationary engines, they seem always to have been built by private manufacturers, rather than the companies themselves. Equally, most of the designs were 'one-offs', drawn up to meet a particular set of circumstances; there is no evidence to suggest that stationary engines were mass-produced, with the exception of those on the Cromford & High Peak Railway. A few of the larger private locomotive manufacturers accepted orders for stationary engines, but from what little is known, quite a number of stationary engines were built by firms of general engineers. Many of these concentrated on other versions of stationary engines, for winding, pumping and driving machinery, and some also built a handful of steam locomotives, like J. & G. Joicey & Co Ltd of Newcastle upon Tyne, while others like Robey & Co Ltd of Lincoln began by building portable engines and threshing machines and then moved into traction engines and stationary designs.

At the beginning there were three main sections to steam stationary engines – the engine itself, the drum house (or drum wheels where these were used) and the boiler house. Initially these were each in separate units. Strictly, an 'engine' was the unit driven by one cylinder; so if the design incorporated two cylinders, there were two engines. Although it cannot be proved definitively, almost certainly all the stationary engines built for railways before 1830 were vertical-cylindered beam engines, developed from the eighteenth century designs of Thomas Newcomen (1664-1729) and James Watt (1736-1819). As the return wheels at the top of self-acting inclines were at this period in roofed buildings but open to the weather, so also were the drum houses of stationary engines. If the track changed direction at the bank head, then the engine could be built offset to the curve; but if the track continued on straight, the released rope had to be taken clear of the wagons, either by dragging it out of the way or by elevating it. There seems to have been little agreement at this time regarding the ideal position; in his examination of the Hetton Railway in 1823, the engineer William Chapman (1749-1832) criticised the siting of the Warden Law Engine, which was 150yds from the bank head instead of the more usual 50-60 yards.[1] Because of the height of vertical engines, their engine houses are usually recognisable in illustrations.

Incredibly, four engines for railways built before 1840 survive, three of them in working order. Because many engines had long working lives, some were thus still working in an age which recognised their interest and historical importance and thought that they should be preserved for posterity. The oldest is the

Middleton Top Engine, 1829; a twin vertical-cylinder beam engine, built for the Cromford & High Peak Railway

This engine comprises a pair of single cylinder rotative beam engines driving a common crankshaft. The engines, like the other seven on the original Railway, were built by the Butterley Company at their works near Ripley in Derbyshire.

6-1. The Middleton Top Engine from the bank head in June 1961. The three-sided front elevation, used on all the Cromford & High Peak Railway's engine houses, can easily be seen. The uphill track is in the foreground, with the single chock beyond the summit to prevent wagons from running back down the incline. A large wheel in the boarded pit beyond the second roller alters the angle of the rope for it to enter the engine house below the middle window.

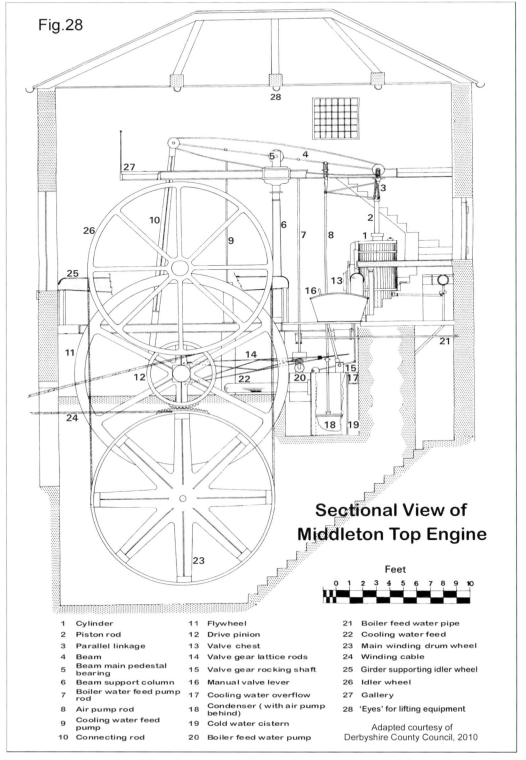

Fig.28

Sectional View of
Middleton Top Engine

Feet

0 1 2 3 4 5 6 7 8 9 10

1	Cylinder	11	Flywheel	
2	Piston rod	12	Drive pinion	
3	Parallel linkage	13	Valve chest	
4	Beam	14	Valve gear lattice rods	
5	Beam main pedestal bearing	15	Valve gear rocking shaft	
6	Beam support column	16	Manual valve lever	
7	Boiler water feed pump rod	17	Cooling water overflow	
8	Air pump rod	18	Condenser (with air pump behind)	
9	Cooling water feed pump	19	Cold water cistern	
10	Connecting rod	20	Boiler feed water pump	

21	Boiler feed water pipe
22	Cooling water feed
23	Main winding drum wheel
24	Winding cable
25	Girder supporting idler wheel
26	Idler wheel
27	Gallery
28	'Eyes' for lifting equipment

Adapted courtesy of
Derbyshire County Council, 2010

Fig.28. Side view plan of the Middleton Top Engine today, amended from previously-published diagrams.

6-2. *A view of the left-hand engine in October 1960, showing its valve chest mounted on the vertical-cylinder behind it, with the piston rod connected to the parallel linkage above it. The controls visible are as follows : 1. manual lever for reversing the valve gear; 2. Regulator handle; 3. condenser cold water spray; 4. Gab disengaging lever for lifting the eccentric rod off the valve gear; 5. brass disc and pointer showing the position of the wagons on the incline. Once set in motion the engine would be allowed to operate without the intervention of the driver.*

6-3. The view from the oiling gallery in the summer of 1961, showing both beams, the idler wheel, 14ft in overall diameter, and to the right the top of the 16ft 2in diameter flywheel.

It should be remembered that all of the powered inclines on the C&HPR were operated by an endless chain, later a steel rope, which came into the engine house and went round a wheel before going out again. These wheels are always termed 'drums', but to avoid confusing the reader, in this book they will be termed 'drum wheels'. Because wheels were used, the geometry of the machinery was different, and so the engine and the drum wheel were housed within one building. The Butterley Company also designed all of the engine houses, probably employing sub-contractors to build them, using ashlar gritstone with a slate roof. These buildings, which all seem to have been constructed to the same plan, were unusual in having a three-sided front elevation, believed to be unique in engine house design.

The two engines are identical, each being of the low pressure condensing double acting type, each rated at 20 horse power. Each has a cylinder of 25in bore and 60in stroke.[2] The slide valves have a 6½in travel and are operated by fixed eccentrics on the crankshaft, but the cranks are set at 90 degrees. This design of valve gear meant that in forward gear motion was automatic, but to reverse the engine the driver had to manipulate the valves. Steam was supplied at 5lbs p.s.i. The piston rods are coupled by means of Watt's

parallel linkage to cast iron beams 16ft 3ins long. The beam gudgeon pins pivot on pedestal bearings mounted on an iron transom built into the side walls and supported by cast iron columns. The cylinders are located on stone platforms and held down by bars pinned deep in the masonry, as is usual with a 'house-built' engine, where the building forms an integral part of the machine. The crankshaft carries the valve gear eccentrics, a 16ft 2in diameter flywheel, essential for the smooth operation of these early engines, and a 5ft diameter pinion which drives the winding drum wheel below. This pinion can be disengaged from the drum wheel by mean of a gear and circular rack designed to slide it along the crankshaft out of mesh.

The drum wheel in the bottom of the wheel pit is 15ft in overall diameter and carries 150 teeth. The drive pinion has 50 teeth, so that the reduction ratio is 3:1. In addition to the gear teeth, the wheel has two rope grooves and a band brake fitted with wooden brake blocks. Subsequently an idler wheel, 14ft in overall diameter, was mounted above the original wheel, very probably when the incline reverted to endless cable haulage, but using steel rope, in 1894. The present wheel was fitted early in 1962, as the steel rope had caused considerable wear on the guides of the old one.

The endless rope hauling the upward wagons entered the engine house below the centre window in the front wall and passed around the drum wheel for three-quarters of a wrap. It then passed up around the idler wheel, back around the drum wheel and finally up over the idler wheel again before leaving the engine house, thereby providing a further half-turn of contact on the drum wheel and preventing slippage.

Each side of the engine has its own controls. In addition to the regulator valves on either side of the stairs leading down to the main floor, the large levers pivoted below the floor control the valve. The front-mounted levers, when swung across simultaneously on each engine, disconnect the eccentric valve rod, allowing the slide valves to be operated by the floor hand levers to facilitate the reversing of the engine and non-automatic starting. Also on the floor are pedestal-mounted controls with pointers to provide direct water injection into the condensers when a fast vacuum was needed. At two corners of the handrail surrounding the wheel pit is a small brass dial, driven by a worm drive and shafting from the drum wheel axle; on the dial is a pointer to indicate the number of turns it has made and marked to show the position of wagons on the incline. Other indicators are located on the right hand wall,

including a telegraph showing instructions from the bank foot and two, added later, which showed when the catch points moved on the bank head.[3] A second man, provided with a seat at the front of the engine house, pulled on the chain which operated a large lever to apply the brake. Nearby was a sloped desk on which the engineman recorded the sets, or 'runs', which he handled.

The boiler house is sited immediately behind the engine house. The original building had no roof, a feature also found elsewhere in this early period. According to Watkins, who recorded the engine in 1935, there were originally three Butterley 'whistle mouth' boilers here, 'a primitive type, with the firegrate in front of the boiler with a water casing over the top and two flues through the boiler shell'; one of these was, he noted, still in situ when he visited. As there was no reliable water supply available, a reservoir was built near the engineman's cottage and kept supplied by old locomotive tenders converted to water carriers and filled from the tank supplied by the spring near the workshops at Cromford.

The brick chimney nearby is 80ft high. Sometime between 1861 and 1869 the London & North Western Railway installed two Cornish boilers, which have only one firetube instead of the two in Lancashire

6-4. *The former boiler from a London & North Western Railway Ramsbottom DX 0-6-0 tender engine, which provided steam for the engine in its latter years. Note the large pile of wooden off-cuts, brought regularly from the Carriage & Wagon Works at Derby for mixing with the coal to fuel the boiler. Beyond are the chimneys of the engineman's cottage.*

6-5. Every day the inclines handled full tenders carrying water from the spring at Cromford for places along the railway. Here alongside the Middleton Top loco shed in June 1961 a former LNWR tender discharges its load into the trough which led down to the reservoir.

boilers. The second of these was condemned about 1960, and British Railways London Midland Region then sent a stationary boiler from a former LNWR Ramsbottom DX 0-6-0 goods engine, mounted on the frame of an old tender, which was installed at the rear of the loco shed here. This supplied steam at 150lbs p.s.i. to a 2½in reduction valve to bring the pressure down to the 5lbs required.

The Middleton Incline was closed on 12th August 1963 and the rope was cut outside the engine house. However, the loco boiler continued to be used to drive a scotch-crank engine which pumped water from the reservoir to the tank at the loco shed, and on occasions when the boiler was lit up for this pump, the engineman would take the opportunity to demonstrate the beam engines. But at Christmas 1966 vandals broke in and smashed all the brass fittings, making the pump unusable and it never worked again. The stationary boiler was cut up in March 1967. A small petrol-driven pump was provided for the loco shed, which itself closed at the end of April 1967.

The engine and the remaining associated buildings were subsequently acquired by Derbyshire County Council and restored, though the engine is now operated by compressed air (see chapter 10). More comprehensive engineering details can be obtained from the site.

The next engine was built only four years later but was a very different design from the Middleton Top Engine:

Weatherhill Engine, 1833, a single vertical-cylinder beam engine, built for the Stanhope & Tyne Railway near Stanhope, Co. Durham

To lift the Stanhope & Tyne Railway out of Stanhope in Upper Weardale on to the Durham moors two fearsome inclines were needed. Weatherhill was the second, one of the longest inclines of the period at 1 mile 128 yards on a varying gradient averaging at 1 in 13, with a summit at 1,445 ft, the highest point ever reached by a public railway in England. Ascending and descending sets were run simultaneously, using the 3-4-2 rail system and two drums, with of course nearly 1½ miles of rope on each drum.

James Watt's patent on the design for his parallel motion on steam engines expired in 1800 and in the same year Phineas Crowther (1763-1818) of Newcastle upon Tyne patented his design. It is believed that many engines of Crowther's basic single vertical-cylinder design were produced in the North East, for pumping, winding in a shaft and hauling, and the Railway's engineer, Robert Stephenson, specified a 50 h.p. version here. As at Middleton, the engine house building was an

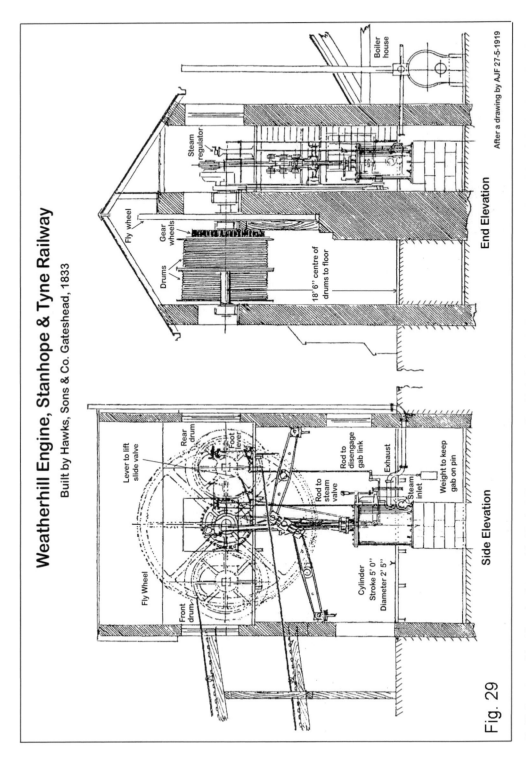

Weatherhill Engine, Stanhope & Tyne Railway

Built by Hawks, Sons & Co. Gateshead, 1833

End Elevation

Steam regulator

Fly wheel

Gear wheels

Drums

18' 6" centre of drums to floor

Boiler house

After a drawing by AJF 27-5-1919

Side Elevation

Lever to lift slide valve

Rear drum

Foot lever

Rod to disengage gab link

Exhaust

Rod to steam valve

Steam inlet

Weight to keep gab on pin

Fly Wheel

Front drum

Cylinder Stroke 5' 0" Diameter 2' 5"

Fig. 29

Fig.29. Drawings of the side and end views of the Weatherhill Engine, originally published in the NORTH EASTERN RAILWAY MAGAZINE for July 1919 and partially re-drawn.

integral element of the design, which included mounting two small beams on brackets on the walls of the engine house linked to a vertical piston rod, at the top end of which was a crank. In the early 1880s the Engine's original cylinder burst and was replaced by a cylinder from a recently-redundant stationary engine on the Tanfield Branch near Sunniside, Gateshead, possibly the Bowes Bridge Engine. This replacement, with its steam chest and valve gear, was made by the Chester-le-Street firm of Thomas Murray about 1838 and was 29in in diameter with a 60in stroke. The dimensions of the replacement cylinder must have been close to the dimensions of the original, because otherwise the geometry of the engine would have been affected.

On the crankshaft, which is 18ft 6in above the original floor level, was a flywheel – the present wheel, a replacement, is 20ft in diameter – and a drive pinion, 5ft in diameter, to mesh with the pinions on the drums, which were 9ft in diameter. The operating platform was about 3ft lower than the crankshaft. With both drums in gear, the drive pinion turned them in the same direction, but with one drum having the rope coming off the top and the other drum having the rope coming off the bottom, one rope was hauled in while the other was paid out. This synchronisation of the drums kept the position of the sets constant in relation to each other, especially critical when they passed at the meetings. At the end of each haul the engine was reversed, so that the drums, which did not need to be taken out of gear, then rotated in the opposite direction to previously. However, each drum could be taken out of gear when required using a handwheel mounted on a pedestal at each end of the operating platform. This operated reduction gearing with a cam on the lower shaft which slewed the drum out of mesh.

Also on the crankshaft was the eccentric for working the slide valve on the steam chest on the side of the cylinder. The eccentric sheave was loose on the shaft and the reversal of the engine was achieved by means of a hook, or 'gab', on the end of the eccentric rod. To reverse the engine the gab had to be removed from a pin on the end of a weigh bar by means of a lever operated by the engineman. This allowed the eccentric to drop, and the valve was then put into the corresponding position by another lever and the gab pushed back on by a foot lever. When the regulator valve was opened to re-start the engine, the engine crank took hold of the eccentric sheave by a projecting catch which met a similar catch on the sheave. This was fairly heavy work for the engineman, who had to be careful when handling the regulator valve. Virtually all early stationary engines, and indeed early steam locomotives, had to be reversed by this method. Braking was

applied via a band brake on the flywheel. There were latterly emergency brakes on the drums, but whether these were fitted subsequently is not known.

The engine was built in 1833 at the Gateshead Iron Works of Hawks, Son & Co. William Hawks had manufactured parts for a steam locomotive assembled for Wallsend Colliery near Newcastle in 1815 and later, as Hawks, Crawshay & Sons, the firm manufactured the ironwork for Robert Stephenson's High Level Bridge in Newcastle. Crowther had also built a steam locomotive for Whitehaven in 1816.

The massive engine house was constructed of ashlar stone, with an interior wall to support the inner end of the crankshaft and to divide the engine from the drums. The wagons, two or three at a time, passed under the drums at the bank head. The engine started work on 1st May 1834, only for there to be a tragic accident that day. A set of four waggons, crammed with passengers, was released from the Weatherhill bank head before the engine had been set. At the resulting jolt, the rope broke and the four waggons ran away down the incline. They might have gone right down to Stanhope had not a young man at Crawleyside bank head altered some points to divert the runaways into a siding where four loaded wagons were standing. In the collision several people were injured, three people fatally.

The original Crawleyside Engine, also built by Hawks, Son & Co, was replaced in the mid-1860s, but the Weatherhill Engine continued to work into the twentieth century, with only the gear wheels being replaced as well as the cylinder. Then in 1918 the North Eastern Railway decided that a newer and more reliable engine was needed and so a replacement was installed,[4] with a new engine house and bank head. The NER recognised the antiquity and interest of the old engine, which was dismantled and preserved. However, the engine as now preserved and displayed in the Great Hall of the National Railway Museum is very different from the engine built in 1833; this is described and explained in chapter 10.

For many years the Great Hall has housed a second stationary engine, but yet again it is a very different machine.

The Swannington Engine, 1833, a single cylinder horizontal engine, built for the Leicester & Swannington Railway, Leicestershire

This is a horizontal cylinder engine, probably the oldest still in existence. A few of this type were made about 1800 by Richard Trevithick (1771-1833), the inventor of the first steam locomotive, and the format was taken up again after 1825 by

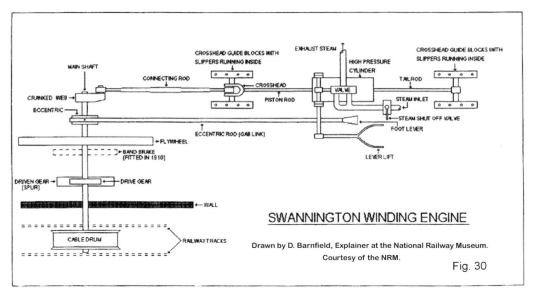

Fig.30. The plan view of the Swannington Engine.

6-6. A view of the Swannington Engine from the cylinder end, showing the tail rod and crosshead guides, in its original engine house, taken in November 1923. Note the band brake on the wheel to the left of the fly wheel, and the large lever needed to operate it.

Messrs. Taylor & Martineau of London. But many engineers thought that in this design the weight of the piston would wear the cylinder oval, hence the inclusion in the Swannington Engine of the long tail rod, supported by slippers running inside crosshead guides. The extra length of the rod also equalised the volume of steam admitted to each side of the piston, giving a more even distribution

6-7. The exterior of the Swannington Engine House (left), with its boiler house, also taken in November 1923. See also 5-30 to 5-33.

of power. Another innovative feature was the fitting of a piston valve to control the admission of steam into the cylinder, instead of the usual slide valve. This was said to have been included because of the ease with which it could be manipulated for reversing, although this feature too took many years to gain more general favour. The cylinder itself is 18¼in in diameter with a 42in stroke and the original flywheel was 9ft 4in in diameter. Like many of these early engines, it was fitted with a condensing cylinder.

It was ordered for working the Swannington Incline, 764yds at 1 in 17, on the Leicester & Swannington Railway, and was designed by the Railway's Engineer, Robert Stephenson. However, his works did not build it; instead it was constructed by the Horsley Coal & Iron Company of Tipton in Staffordshire. The flywheel was cast in two halves for ease of manufacture, transport and assembly, and it was held secure by pins at the rim and shrunk-on hoops at the centre boss. The main shaft was made from wrought iron forged square, again for ease of manufacture and the mounting and centralisation of the flywheel. But here the crankshaft was below ground level and went out through the foundations of the engine house to the drum, mounted between the rails of the adjacent railway. The engine cost £750, with a further £78 for the rope and £400 for the brick engine house, and it was commissioned on 1st September 1833.

Its early days were not without problems. The main shaft fractured within a month and had to be replaced. The first boiler burst in 1834 and was repaired, only to have to be replaced by a new boiler in 1839. The lubrication of the crosshead guide blocks also proved very palatable for the local rats.

The engine continued to haul coal until the mid-1870s; but just as coal production was ending, a large engine was installed at the bottom of the incline for pumping water from the mine workings, so that the incline had to be retained, but with coal now being lowered down to serve the pumping engine. Its normal load was three fulls down. This task it fulfilled for 70 more years, until the steam engine was replaced by electric pumps. The last wagons descended the incline on 20th September 1947.

Once again the historical importance of the Engine was recognised and it was subsequently included in the National Railway Museum collection. Meanwhile interest in its local area and resulted in the formation of the Swannington Heritage Trust, which in 1985 excavated the foundations of the engine house and subsequently undertook considerable conservation work on the route of the incline, with help from Leicestershire County Council. With the NRM's plans for a major re-organisation of the Great Hall at York, the Swannington Engine may well be returned to the care of the Heritage Trust.

It might be appropriate at this point to discuss another early stationary engine that is preserved in full working order, and indeed operated by steam – the 'Haydock Engine' at the Manchester Museum of Science & Industry (MOSI). This is a beam engine with a single cylinder, 25in stroke and 60in in diameter, driving a beam 16ft long, which in the past has been alleged to be one of the engines installed on the Liverpool & Manchester Railway for the operation of the incline from Edgehill down through Lime Street Tunnel to the new Lime Street Station at Liverpool, the extension to which was opened in August 1836.

Amongst the papers held at the Museum relating to this engine is an article by W.R.Watson in the *Meccano Magazine* for June 1950, in which the author states that this engine was built for Edge Hill in 1832 and was subsequently sold in 1860 to Richard Evans, the owner of Leigh Colliery at Haydock in Lancashire. It wound at one of the shafts until 1911, when it was re-located to drive machinery in the colliery workshops, a job it undertook until 1943, when it was replaced by electric motors. After various vicissitudes it was erected in what is now MOSI's Power Hall in 1983.

However, subsequent research, summarised in the excellent *The Liverpool & Manchester Railway* by R.H.G.Thomas (Batsford, London, 1980), shows this belief not to be supported by fact. The order from the Liverpool & Manchester Railway to Messrs Mather & Dixon for the two stationary engines for the Lime Street Tunnel was placed in April 1834 [not 1832] and was for two-cylinder [not single] non-condensing engines of the side-lever type, similar to the paddle steamer engines of the period. The cylinders were indeed 25in by 60in, but the beams were 18ft long [not 16ft]. Rope haulage in the tunnel was not replaced by locomotives until 1870, which would make its sale in 1860 seem very unlikely. There is scope for further research, but whilst Richard Evans may well have purchased a second-hand beam engine in 1860, it seems very unlikely that it had any connection with the Liverpool & Manchester Railway.

The misgivings about the horizontal design of engine meant that the vertical-cylindered beam engine dominated the first half of the nineteenth century. But there were gradual changes in design. Mounting the drums overhead above the track gave way to moving the engine house alongside the track, with the drum(s) brought down to ground level over a shallow pit. The drum house continued to be open to the weather, but those of these early engines that survived into the twentieth century gradually had the ends of the drum houses bricked up, with small apertures left for ropes to come in and out. Both developments were no doubt welcomed by the men who had to maintain or repair the drums and their gearing.

One entrepreneur who saw the growing market for manufacturing vertical-cylindered stationary engines was Thomas Murray of Chester-le-Street between Durham and Newcastle uponTyne. Begun by his father and older brother, the business passed to him in the mid 1830s, and he expanded it to supply both the North East and further afield. Murray died in 1860 and the business faded away after the death of his nephew in 1878.

Only a few miles from Murray's works was the Hetton Railway, discussed in chapter 4. In 1836 he supplied a winding engine for the summit of the line atWarden Law, three miles north of Hetton-le-Hole. The first engine here, built in 1822, was a 60 h.p. condensing engine with two 30in by 60in cylinders driving one drum with one rope and operating on a single line incline one of the strangest methods known. The engine rope was attached to a set of waggons at the foot of its incline, 775yds at an average of 1 in 20, while attached to the back of the set was a second rope running back a further 775yds to the top of another incline, where it was attached to another set of wagons. The Engine hauled both sets of wagons, bringing the nearer set up to the summit. The ropes were then attached to sets of empties, which were lowered similarly, a procedure which must have required great care. The Engine itself was criticised in a report byWilliam Chapman in 1823, not least for being 150yds from the bank head, a distance which seems extraordinary. Perhaps not surprisingly, this method of operation was altered in 1826-7 by the installation of a stationary engine atWarden Law bank foot; but this left theWarden Law incline still single line. So it was rebuilt to an orthodox 3-4-2 rail system to run fulls and empties simultaneously and a new engine and engine house were built alongside the line. Originally it was built as a double-acting condensing engine, but latterly the condensing apparatus was discontinued.

2nd Warden Law Engine, 1836, a single vertical-cylinder beam engine, built for the Hetton Railway near Hetton-le-Hole, Co.Durham

In 1956 J. Free, a 3rd year student for the Mechanical Engineering degree at what was then King's College in the University of Durham, chose to study this 120-year old Engine for his degree dissertation, and incredibly this work survives in the archives of what is now the University of Newcastle.[5] This not only gives an informed and accurate description and analysis of the Engine, but a rare account of what had had to be replaced over the years. The cylinder, believed to be still the original, was 3ft 3in in diameter with a 6ft 2in stroke and Free calculated that the mean brake horse power was 97.5, making this a considerably more powerful engine than any of those studied hitherto. Steam was supplied from two Lancashire boilers at 65lbs p.s.i., reduced to 35lbs p.s.i.The slide valve which admitted steam to the cylinder had an 8in stroke. Like many engines, it had to work coal into its boiler house

6-8. Looking at the front of the Warden Law Engine, with the front door open, as is the upstairs window for the oiling gallery. To the right is the drum house with its sloping roof and the front drum visible; both ropes came off the bottom of the drums, avoiding the problems if they came off the top. On the far left can be seen the steam exhaust pipe. The boilers lay behind these buildings.

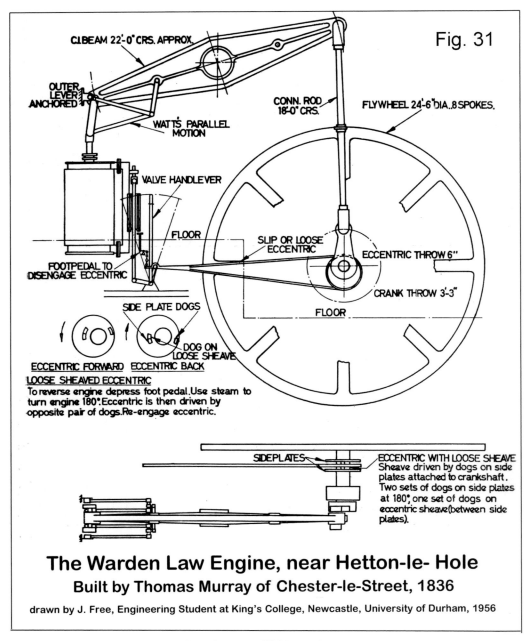

Fig. 31

CL.BEAM 22'-0" CRS. APPROX.

OUTER LEVER ANCHORED

WATTS PARALLEL MOTION

CONN. ROD 18-0" CRS.

FLYWHEEL 24'-6" DIA.,8 SPOKES.

VALVE HANDLEVER

FLOOR

SLIP OR LOOSE ECCENTRIC

ECCENTRIC THROW 6"

FOOTPEDAL TO DISENGAGE ECCENTRIC

CRANK THROW 3'-3"

FLOOR

SIDE PLATE DOGS

DOG ON LOOSE SHEAVE

ECCENTRIC FORWARD   ECCENTRIC BACK

LOOSE SHEAVED ECCENTRIC

To reverse engine depress foot pedal.Use steam to turn engine 180°.Eccentric is then driven by opposite pair of dogs.Re-engage eccentric.

SIDE PLATES

ECCENTRIC WITH LOOSE SHEAVE
Sheave driven by dogs on side plates attached to crankshaft. Two sets of dogs on side plates at 180°, one set of dogs on eccentric sheave(between side plates).

The Warden Law Engine, near Hetton-le- Hole
Built by Thomas Murray of Chester-le-Street, 1836

drawn by J. Free, Engineering Student at King's College, Newcastle, University of Durham, 1956

Fig.31. Parts of the Warden Law Engine, drawn by J. Free, 1956 (see text)

siding using a fly rope. Photographs show that in later years the boilers were not roofed, though where the men fired may well have been.

The beam was a one-piece casting which Free estimated weighed 6½ tons. The flywheel, like the beam, still the original, was 24ft 6in in diameter and fitted with a band brake operated by a foot pedal, not to brake the engine but to maintain the piston at mid-stroke when not working, so that in turn the crank would give maximum turning moment when winding started. The usual gab gear was fitted in order to reverse the engine. The drums were mounted in a separate lean-to building on the side of the engine house. They were originally made of cast iron and were 8ft in diameter and only 2ft 6in wide; narrow drums were a feature of Durham engines in the nineteenth century. The pinion on the

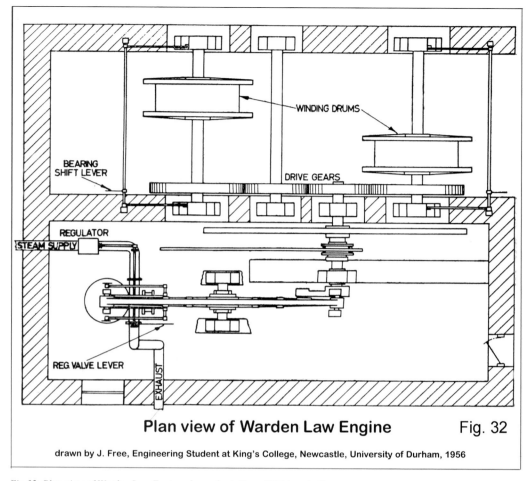

Plan view of Warden Law Engine   Fig. 32

drawn by J. Free, Engineering Student at King's College, Newcastle, University of Durham, 1956

Fig.32. Plan view of Warden Law Engine, drawn by J. Free, 1956 (see text)

end of the crankshaft meshed with one drum pinion directly and, via a separately-mounted idler pinion, with the rear drum. Pull-rods linked to both bearings of each drum meant that operating a lever could either separate a drum's gear or force it into mesh. All of the shafts were originally of square section but were replaced by circular section steel between 1933-1935. Also replaced in this period were the piston and the piston rod, the crank and the drums (all by steel components), while by 1946 three of the four gears had been replaced.

The engine was started by disengaging the eccentric, working the slide valve by the hand lever and operating the regulator valve. The gab was held disengaged by the right foot, the regulator was controlled by the right hand and the slide valve was worked by the left hand. As operations began, it was essential to keep the paying out rope taut. This was

monitored by the second man in the engine house, standing by the drums, who blew a blast on a whistle when the rope went slack, so that the engineman could restrict the speed of the rope but still allow a gradual overall acceleration. When the empty set had gathered speed, the whistling stopped, the gab was engaged and the regulator opened fully, allowing the engine speed to attain its maximum, about 30 revolutions per minute.

Latterly owned by the National Coal Board, the engine ceased work, after 123 years' service, on 9th September 1959 because the coal from the two collieries still sending it along the Railway was diverted underground to a new combined mine. It and its engine house were subsequently dismantled for preservation and today the parts are stored at Beamish Museum, hopefully one day to be re-erected.

6-9. Mr. Alf Swinhoe, the final driver of the Warden Law Engine, with his hand on the regulator handle. To the left is the foot pedal for disengaging the gab and to the left of that is the long hand lever, which oscillated when the engine was in motion. Behind it can be seen the steam exhaust pipe.

6-10. From left to right can be seen the connecting rod from the beam – behind it the driver is standing in front of the cylinder - then the crank, the crankshaft, bearings, the eccentric and the 24ft 6in flywheel. On the other side of the wall, at the end of the crankshaft, was the drive pinion for the gears.

6-11. The four gear pinions, looking from the rear of the drum house. The third pinion from the right is the drive pinion at the end of the crankshaft. All four pinions are in mesh during normal operating.

6-12. The weighted safety valve on one of the Warden Law boilers, with its flared exhaust.

6.13. *The engine's beam, estimated to weigh 6.5 tons. Below it is its works plate, reading 'MURRAYS CHESTER-LE-STREET 1836'.*

6-14. *The Engine with the bank head of its incline, in the summer of 1959, just a few months before closure. The Engine has just hauled up a set of fulls, the first wagon of which is being run back into the boiler house siding. The Engine's other rope emerges from underground alongside the kip to go down to the foot of the incline. To the right is the 'short end' of the rope for No.1 self-acting incline, with the 'long end' passing around the return wheel behind the photographer and back underground in the shuttered gully in the foreground and under the kip to go down to the bottom of its incline. Note the short length of rope (a 'fly rope') in the foreground used for local shunting. Alongside the cabin on the far left is one of the white discs raised by the men at the bank foot to indicate that their set was ready to be run.*

NEWCASTLE ON TYNE.

6-15. This picture is believed to be by Thomas Hair (c1810-1875). It is included in Hair's VIEWS OF THE COLLIERIES IN THE COUNTIES OF NORTHUMBERLAND AND DURHAM, first published in 1844. Newcastle upon Tyne can be seen in the background, notably the Lantern Tower of what is now St.Nicholas' Cathedral, with to the left the recently-erected monument to Earl Grey, the Prime Minister from Northumberland who had promoted the great Reform Act of 1832. Nearby to the right is the keep, the only surviving remains of Newcastle's castle, whilst on the far right is the Georgian church of All Saints.

But in the foreground, on the southern bank of the River Tyne in Gateshead, is a railway and to the left is the Redheugh Engine, with its unusual short chimney. This was situated on a connecting line, owned by the Brandling Junction Railway, between the Redheugh Quay Station at the end of the Newcastle & Carlisle Railway's branch from Blaydon and the Gateshead Station of the BJR. The engine drew up waggons of coal and other merchandise to the top of the incline, from where locomotives, seen on the drawing, took them across bridges over the principal streets of Gateshead. There was no passenger traffic. The incline had a gradient of 1 in 27 and was opened on 15th January 1839. The rope haulage was replaced by locomotives about 1875 and the line itself was closed about 1907.

The engine was ordered from R.& W.Hawthorn of Newcastle on 6th May 1837, works no.233. Their works was at Forth Banks, and may even be shown on the picture. The engine had two cylinders, 30in diameter with a 72in stroke, presumably vertical given the height of the engine house. It was nominally 60 h.p. and took steam at 25lbs p.s.i.

Eight years later Murray supplied another engine that has been recorded, this time to the north-west of Chester-le-Street:

Bank Top Engine, c1844, a single vertical-cylinder beam engine, for the railway between Burnhope and Craghead, Co.Durham (with a horizontal cylinder subsequently added)

The sinking of Burnhope Colliery in Co.Durham was begun by the four sons of William Hedley, of Wylam and *Puffing Billy* fame, shortly after his death in 1843. The site was in largely-deserted farmland, so the Hedleys had to build their own railway line to serve it. The only realistic route was to Craghead Colliery, another colliery in which they had an interest, 2¼ miles to the north east, from which there ran a link down to the Pontop & South Shields Railway, which in turn gave access to shipping on the River Tyne. Because this route climbed steeply up to the top of a ridge at nearly 900ft before descending to Craghead, the obvious method of operating the whole line was by installing a stationary engine at its summit. This divided the line into 69 chains/1,518yds up from Burnhope and 1 mile 39 chains/858yds down to Craghead. The engine needed to be capable of working both inclines simultaneously, and for much of its existence it also had to help to shunt wagons at the colliery.

For this location Murray supplied a single cylinder vertical beam engine, the cylinder being 27in in diameter with a 5ft stroke, noticeably smaller than at Warden Law. The drums were again narrow, only 2ft 10in wide, the Burnhope side being 7ft in diameter and the Craghead drum 9ft in diameter, to accommodate the longer rope (3,000yds latterly). The flywheel was 20ft in diameter, made in two halves bolted together; the part of the rim opposite the crank was made solid to act as a balance weight. The rims were keyed together. As can be seen in Photo 6-16, the engine house itself was similar to Warden Law, with the drums enclosed in a brick lean-to building and the boilers on the left. The railway's operation required one drum to haul whilst the other simultaneously lowered wagons down on the other side; but here to disengage a drum, a large lever had to be pulled which bodily slewed the drum but not far enough to prevent it being used for gravity working. The drums were slightly offset and the outer bearings were pivoted to allow the individual engagement of the required drum gear wheel with the drive shaft gear wheel (see 6-20).

However, it is the next stage of this engine's history that makes it very unusual. The original engine must have proved inadequate for the weight of the traffic, for in 1868 a single horizontal-cylinder engine was installed in the northern end of the building, with its piston rod connected to the original crank, creating a very unusual combined unit. This engine was almost certainly built by J. & G. Joicey & Co Ltd of Newcastle upon Tyne. The cylinder was 24in in diameter with a 5ft stroke. For many years the piston's tail rod drove a pump for supplying the boilers from a well about 10ft behind the slidebars, connected to a small pond about 175yds away. In the 1920s the pond became affected by mining subsidence and had to be replaced by a large cast iron tank, built up in sections. The driver continued to drive both engines from his original position, whilst his second man operated the drums and controlled the gravity working.

The colliery manager's 'day book' covering the years 1912 to 1936 survives in private ownership in the village, and records that various accidents occurred, both to the men and the machinery. In 1908 a pin fell out of the parallel motion on the vertical engine; it stopped but the horizontal engine did not, and the beam was fractured just above the cylinder, so that a new beam had to be made. In 1921 a piece the size of a dinner plate blew out of the vertical cylinder, just missing a man having his lunch. However, when the new cylinder was being unloaded outside the engine house a timber support broke and the cylinder fell on to the railway line, causing a crack about 18in long from the upper end in a Vee shape. The cylinder had cost £800, but the colliery blacksmith said he could repair it. He beat some boiler plate to fit the shape of the cylinder, studded it on and then held it in place with two steel clamps around the cylinder; the engine ran successfully like this until it ceased work. The horizontal cylinder was re-bored in 1931.

In 1922 the engineman was killed in a terrible accident. At the rope entrance for the Burnhope drum was a horizontal shaft on which a pulley slid as the rope wound on to the drum, and because of this the shaft needed to be kept well greased. Unfortunately, on this occasion the pulley stuck while the engine was running, and the engineman left the engine, still hauling, to go and free it. He put a prop in the ground to help him lever the pulley over; but the prop slipped, he fell on to the moving rope and was wound on to the drum. Another death occurred in 1945, when the bank rider was crushed between a wagon and a corner of the engine house, where there was very little clearance.

In a letter to the *Model Engineer* on 15th October 1976, the engine's last driver, Jack Thompson, described the difficulties of driving the engine:
'The engine would only run in forward gear with the gab engaged, and when you had to reverse the engine, the engineman had to go between the two cast iron pillars supporting the centre of the beam and walk about 30ft along a steel gantry, then

6-16. The front of the Burnhope Bank Top Engine in 1950, after closure. From left to right are the boiler house, with its 120ft chimney, the engine house (made of stone) and the lean-to drum house (added later, made of brick), the fulls road and then the empties road on the far right, with its kip.

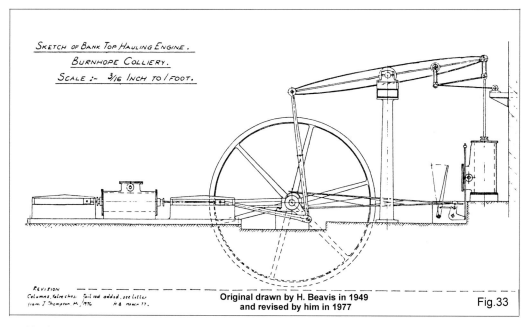

Fig.33. The measured drawing of the combined engine, done by Harry Beavis of the North Eastern Society of Engineering Historians in 1949. A note was appended that the drawing was revised in 1977 in respect of the columns, valve chest and tail rod following a letter from Mr. J. Thompson, the engine's last driver.

6-17. The view looking from the driver's position at the northern (Craghead) end of the engine house, with the vertical-cylinder on the left (part of the beam can be seen above it), the crank pin between the roof support and the handrail, and the horizontal cylinder beyond.

6-19. The view of the engine from the end housing the 1868 horizontal cylinder, with its valve chest on top and the crank pin in the centre of the picture behind the guard mesh.

6-18. The patch on the vertical-cylinder, put on by the colliery blacksmith in 1921 when it was a new cylinder and was dropped and cracked outside the engine house. It lasted until the engine ceased work in 1949.

6-20. The Burnhope drum, 2ft 10in wide, with its brake band and spur wheel, and on the left the lever used to slew the drum and spur wheel out of mesh with the pinion on the crankshaft.

descend six steel steps to get on to the floor level of the horizontal engine, walk past the cylinder and the tail rod and then back to the reversing gear placed to the side and slightly to the front of the cylinder; then he would walk back to the vertical-cylinder and after depressing the gab pedal, he would simultaneously operate the slide valve by the hand lever and operate the throttle valve.'

He went on to describe another difficulty:
'When landing a set of wagons from Craghead, you had to stand in the doorway between the engine-house and the drum house and look over the top of the drum, and you could just see the wagon-rider lift his foot to kick the lock-chain off the set; when it was dark, or the exhaust steam was blowing across the rope hole, you simply had to listen for the chain dropping on to the boards. Then you dashed into the engine-house, slammed the throttle shut and clapped the brake on.'

In the spring of 1949, with the colliery facing closure, what proved to be a short-lived group of industrial historians called the North East Society of Historical Engineers obtained permission to measure and record the engine, and again the documents survive, albeit in private hands. The engine ceased work on 22nd July 1949, again after over a century of work. Although the engine house was demolished, its base and foundations survive, together with about 25ft of the chimney, engulfed and forgotten in trees and undergrowth.

Despite the domination of vertical-cylinder designs in the first half of the nineteenth century, it would seem that a small number of horizontal engines were also built. Probably the main reason for their development was the need for greater power, as longer trains and heavier wagons came to be introduced. The logical answer to this problem was to design stationary engines with two cylinders, and here it soon became clear that single-cylinder vertical engines had major limitations, while with two cylindered horizontal engines the cylinders lay on their sides on the floor, latterly on a bedplate. With everything at a much lower level than on vertical designs, maintenance, repairs and the replacing of ropes and other major components became much easier.

What appears to be a rare example of a two cylinder horizontal engine was built in the first half of the nineteenth century but retained the layout of the engine and the drums being in adjacent buildings separated by a dividing wall:

Kibblesworth Engine, 1840, a two cylinder horizontal engine for the colliery railway to Kibblesworth Colliery, Kibblesworth, Co.Durham

This was a 80 h.p. engine built by Messrs Robert and William Hawthorn at Forth Banks in Newcastle upon Tyne, Works No.346. This firm is better known for its steam locomotives, but it also built a considerable quantity of other machinery, including, latterly, marine engines. Why the horizontal design was chosen for this engine is not known. No drawings are known for it, and there are only two authenticated photographs.

The Kibblesworth Incline was part of an extension of the Springwell Waggonway (opened in 1826) from Mount Moor, south of Gateshead, across the valley of the River Team to a new colliery at Kibblesworth, on the western side of the valley. Leaving the colliery the gradient was 1 in 16, but lower down the gradient reduced through 1 in 90 to almost level near the bottom. The incline, just over a mile long, was single line, so that fulls and empties had to be worked alternately. Although the fulls were to travel downhill, it was thought necessary to install a stationary engine and fit this with a flywheel, to provide braking at the top of the bank and for the flywheel to maintain the speed of the waggons over the lower section. The line was opened on 30th May 1842, but soon afterwards the crankshaft fractured and the flywheel went through the engine house roof. Although a new one was made, it was found that the incline could be worked perfectly well without it, so that it lay uninstalled outside the engine house for many years. Later the colliery and its incline were incorporated into the Pontop & Jarrow Railway, re-named the Bowes Railway in 1932, one of the major colliery railways in County Durham.

Originally coal from the colliery was loaded into wagons at the bank head. In 1914 a drift mine was opened alongside the incline about half way down, so the engine then also had to work wagons in and out of here. This closed in 1932, but in 1936 a second shaft was sunk at the colliery and both shafts sent their tubs by endless haulage down to new screens built on the site of the drift, so that the Engine once again had to work empty wagons in and run fulls out.

Fortunately, in 1946 some members of the Stephenson Locomotive Society's Newcastle Centre formed the North Eastern Historical Engineering & Industrial Locomotive Society, with the purpose of visiting, gathering information and recording local engineering and railway relics, which they rightly foresaw might not survive much longer. The group included two men who worked on the Bowes and Pelaw Main Railways and who had for many years researched the history of the two lines. The group recorded the Kibblesworth Engine on 27th October 1946.

6-21. The front of the Kibblesworth Engine House on 27th October 1946, with the engine section on the left and the drum house on the right, with the Bowes Railway's main line on the far right. The rope came off the bottom of the drum, running more or less at ground level to reach the bank head about twenty yards away. The pipe supplying steam from Kibblesworth Colliery's Robert Pit boiler house can be seen coming in on the left.

6-22. The Kibblesworth Engine from the driver's position in June 1947. The main glare is coming through the open door (compare with the previous picture); the drum is behind the wall on the left. Note the large valve chests and the two pairs of pinions on the drumshaft.

The two cylinders had a 23in bore and a 48in stroke and were supplied with steam at 35lbs p.s.i.. Each cylinder had its own throttle valve, allowing the engineman to use only one cylinder if he wished. Later the throttle valves were left open and a large single throttle, or regulator, was inserted in the main steam pipe. This was operated by a lever about 7ft long, put in about 1918. The pillar supporting the handle was adapted from the brake pillar of a steam locomotive. In 1928 new cylinders at 18in by 48in, taking steam at 100lbs p.s.i., were installed.

The valve chests were fitted on top of both cylinders. The valves, plain 'D' slides, were driven through rocking shafts by a single eccentric gab motion. Connecting rods with 10ft centres ran on crank pins which were cottered into the crank webs, a most unusual arrangement compared with later design. The crossheads ran in double guide bars which were bolted to brackets cast on the bedplate. Another later addition was a mechanical lubricator driven off the tail rod of the right hand cylinder.

A single eccentric was operated by each piston rod. These were 10ft long and fish-bellied in outline. In 1928 a T-section was added to strengthen the main rod. This was yoke-ended at the sheave end and the opposite end had a gab and bearing plate to engage with the valve rocking leavers and reversing gear. The gab motion was of the two-lever type. One lever lifted the eccentrics clear of the valve driving pins, whilst the valves were operated by the hand levers to reverse the engine. The single drum measured 14ft in diameter and was 2ft 9in between the cheeks, a typical narrow Durham drum of the period. The engine drove it through a spur gear giving a 2:1 reduction. It was disconnected from the drum by sliding one end of the drum shaft until the spur wheels were out of mesh, the outside end of the drum shaft being mounted on a pivot bearing for the purpose. The braking consisted of a full band brake on one side of the drum rim and a half strap on the other, both controlled by a screw-down hand wheel in the drum house. The spur wheels, made in two pieces, were bolted on square section crank and drum shafts.

Originally steam was supplied from what were described as 'independent old cylinder type boilers', but later the engine took steam from the boiler house serving the nearby Robert Pit. This latterly held seven Lancashire boilers, but by 1946 only two of them were still in use, in steam alternately. By this time the engine was of course over 100 years old, and with the railway expected to carry coal for many more years, plans were drawn up to replace it. The old engine ceased work in July 1947 and was quickly demolished.

****

All of the engines above were built in the fifteen years between 1829 and 1844, a period when two major industries, railways and heavy engineering, were very much in their development period. Railways had begun to move away from being constructed purely for local use, though many hundreds more small railways were to be built. Engineering firms were very much 'general engineers', accepting whatever work was offered for a wide range of applications. But advertising as it is known a century and a half later did not exist; engineering firms did not publish brochures about their products. So how did demand meet supply?

Undoubtedly many contracts were placed as a result of personal contact; a director or engineer of a railway company would know people in the engineering world locally. This method could clearly be open to the charge of not achieving competitive evaluation of quality of design, manufacture and price. So from quite early some colliery companies and railways chose to advertise for tenders, using the only medium available to them – the local newspapers. Examples are not easy to find.

This simple advertisement appeared in the *Newcastle Courant* on 18th February 1826. Arthur Mowbray was the managing partner in the Hetton Coal Company, the owners of the Hetton Railway between Hetton-le-Hole and Sunderland (see chapter 5). Note that prospective bidders had to go to Hetton to see the plans and discuss the

---

TO ENGINE BUILDERS, &c.

WANTED, for Hetton Colliery, TWO high-pressure STEAM ENGINES, one of 30 and the other of 12-Horse Power, to be fixed on the Hetton Company's Rail-Road.

The Plans, Elevations, &c. may be seen on Application to Mr Joseph Smith, the Hetton Company's Engineer; and Proposals will be received by Arthur Mowbray, Esq., Hetton, not later than the 1st of March next.—Hetton Colliery, Feb. 14th, 1826.

engines, which almost certainly were to be vertical-cylinder beam engines. The advertisement is frustrating, because the Hetton company actually installed three engines at this time – one between Copt Hill and Warden Law (see the Warden Law Engine above) and two to operate a main-and-tail system near Sunderland, replacing the locomotives which had formerly worked on this section, so that the planned location for these two engines is uncertain.

In 1837 a much larger advertisement, covering nearly a whole page, also appeared in the Newcastle press, not for the supply of engines but for the construction of two engine houses. The Brandling Junction Railway, whose line ran from Redheugh, near Gateshead to Monkwearmouth (Sunderland), also wanted to rebuild the Tanfield waggonway, which dated from 1725, from Redheugh southwards to Tanfield in north-west Durham, where new collieries were being sunk or planned. The new line was to be operated entirely by rope haulage for coal traffic only, and two stationary engines were required. The BJR's Engineer was Nicholas Wood (1795-1865), long-time associate of George and Robert Stephenson and one of the judges at the Rainhill Trials in 1829. On 22nd July 1837 Wood drew up the following advertisement (see below), occupying more than half a page. It is too long to quote in full, but the initial paragraphs are headed Foundations, Walls, Boiler Seats, Cylinder Pillars, Quoins, Ashlar Walls, Heads and Sills of Doors and Windows, Tops of Chimneys,[6] Freestone Arches over Doors and near to the Fire Doors, and Ash Pits. Following the details for these stone buildings come the requirements of the Slater's Work (using best Welsh slates); Plastering ('the inside of the engine houses to be plastered with two coats of hair and lime, floated and stone finished with clean sharp rock sand and lime', with the boiler house receiving one coat), Carpenter and Joiner Work and Painting & Glazing. Then come rules for the contractor, and the advertisement ends with a Form of Tender listing 27 items for which the contractor had to enter his prices.

These tenders were for the Bowes Bridge and Causey Wood Engines, the latter working inclines on either side, and the line was opened on 26th November 1839. They were replaced by locomotive haulage in 1881, but the cylinder of the Bowes Bridge Engine near Sunniside was re-used in the Weatherhill Engine and its boiler house was converted into a locomotive shed, surviving as such into British Railways' days.

Accounts showing the cost of constructing a stationary engine seem to be very rare. Tomlinson,[7] quoting a summary made in 1841, says that on average the smaller engines (20 to 52 horsepower) cost, with engine house, ropes, etc., about £2,000 each and the larger ones (60 to 120 horsepower) about £4,000. Heavy traffic was conveyed at a cost of about ½d per ton per mile and the cost of working stationary engines on the Stanhope & Tyne Railway in 1839 was about £485 per mile, with self-acting inclines being £70 cheaper.

Accepting the figure of £4,000 for a larger engine, then less than twenty years later the cost had more than doubled. Detailed cost breakdowns for stationary engines are rare, but one outstanding example does survive, albeit by sheer luck. In 1974 descendants of a William MacNay deposited family papers with Shildon Town Council in County Durham, since moved to the Durham County Record Office. A folder of some of these, CP/Shl/11, includes specifications and the complete cost of the construction of the **Stanley Engine, near Crook, Co.Durham, a two cylinder horizontal engine, built in 1857**.

Three years earlier the Stockton & Darlington Railway had decided to build a 3½ mile link north-eastwards from its Crook-Tow Law line north-eastwards into the valley of the River Deerness, where one of its major shareholders, Joseph Pease (1799-1872) was planning to sink Waterhouses Colliery. This became known as the 'Stanley branch'. This name was taken from a nearby settlement, and should not be confused with the town of Stanley to the east, nor with the Stanley Incline on the Stanhope & Tyne Railway.

SPECIFICATION & DESCRIPPTION[6]
OF THE
TWO ENGINE HOUSES AND OTHER WORKS
CONNECTED WITH THE SAME
On the Tanfield Lea Railway

WHERE SITUATE: No.1 Near the Old Junction with the Tanfield Moor Railway
No.2 Near the Cross Wood End

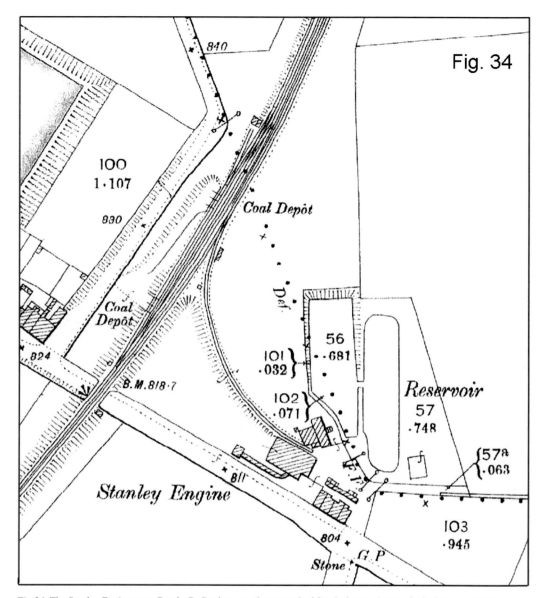

Fig.34. The Stanley Engine near Crook, Co.Durham, as shown on the 25in Ordnance Survey, 2nd edition, in 1896.

The new line would mean that Pease could bring his coal through to his huge industrial complex at Crook. This initiative stimulated the promotion of another line, under the auspicies of the North Eastern Railway, into this otherwise undeveloped valley from its Durham end. Both routes were planned as freight-only lines. The S&D route was the most direct geographically, but from Crook at 550ft it took the line up for 1¼ miles to a summit at 800 ft on gradients varying between 1 in 16 and 1 in 9.6 before falling 2¼ miles on a gradient at a maximum of 1 in 24 down to a junction, known as

Stanley Bank Foot, with the NER line about 1¼ miles north-west of Waterhouses Colliery, and these gradients made a stationary engine at the summit unavoidable. The S&D having approved the work late in 1856, Pease decided to sink Stanley Colliery near to the branch, which meant that the design of the stationary engine had to be modified so that it could also work the ¾ mile branch to the colliery. It was decided to locate a coal depot at the summit, and later this was joined by a goods depot, these too being worked by the Engine.

The site chosen for the Engine was unusual, in being set back nearly 80yds from the railway and at right angles to it, for reasons which are not known. This meant that to bring the ropes through 90 degrees at the bank head, two large sheaves (wheel pulleys) had to be provided. Following the normal practice of the period, the drum house was a separate building attached to the southern side of the engine house, while the boiler house, served by a siding from the bank head, was set obliquely south of it. Also rather unusually, the chimney was a little way from the boiler house.

The Stockton & Darlington directors decided that the engine house should be built by its subsidiary engineering company, the Shildon Works Company, but with parts of the work sub-contracted. The company had been set up in 1849 under the management of William Bouch (1813-1876), although he had been in charge there since 1840; he was to become Locomotive Superintendent in 1860. Bouch's estimate of the cost of the engine, its buildings and the associated works, dated 19th November 1856, was £9,187 [£396,510.92 at 2010 value], comprising £4,604 for machinery, £2,884 for buildings, £1,199 for earth work[s] and £500 for wire ropes.

The title of the expenditure is entitled 'Account for the construction of Stanley Engine, 4 May 1859' and comprises a summary, in sections, followed by a detailed breakdown of those sections;

Engine	£1,839-14s-10d	[£79,403.25]
3 Boilers	£436-11s-3d	
2 Drums	£599-17s-2d	
2 Rope Sheaves	£590-12s-11d	
Donkey Engine	£163-7s-3d	
Patterns	£120-5s-5d	[total = £161,869.06]

Buildings including		
chimney	£1,918-16s-7d	[£82,816.67]
Depot and gearing	£107-11s-9d	[£4,643.48]
[Total]	£2,026-8s-4d	[£87,460.15]
Reservoir	£373-19s-1d	[£16,139.86]
Wire ropes	£635-4s-11d	[£27,417.21]
Railway [see below]	£793-18s-10d	[£34,266.52]
Overall total	£7,580-0s-0d	[£327,152.80]

Thus the overall cost of the engine came in at £1,607 [£69,358.12] less than Bouch's original estimate. (All bracketed figures are values in 2010).

The breakdown of the details of the Engine shows that it had two cylinders having a 30in diameter and a 60in stroke.[8] These were not manufactured by the Shildon Works Co, but were sub-contracted to Gilkes, Wilson & Co of Middlesbrough. This may well have been because Shildon did not have patterns for such large cylinders. Gilkes, Wilson received orders for locomotives for the Stockton & Darlington Railway every year between 1852 and 1862, so they were the obvious choice for this work. Their account, dated 3rd June 1857, shows the cylinders cost £34-17s-8d. and £35-2s-1d respectively and that the

6-23. *The Stanley Engine on 29th October 1949. On the far left is the reservoir. Then in turn come the engine house, the drum house and the boiler house, its wagon road now protected by a lean-to corrugated iron shed. Note the chimney, unusually detached from the buildings.*

overall total for materials and work was £257-6s-11d, from which there was a 5% discount. The engine had a 20ft diameter flywheel and there were two cast iron drums both 6ft in diameter; the width is not given, but in another notebook kept by 'WM'[9] this dimension is given in 1863 as 4ft.

Three boilers were installed, each given as 34ft long by 6ft diameter, but these were not costed, as they were the Railway company's own, second hand from the Carrhouse Engine on the former Stanhope & Tyne Railway near Consett, which had been replaced by locomotive working in 1858.[10] The two large sheaves mentioned earlier were 25ft in diameter and were set in masonry-lined pits and supported by metal girders, presumably near to the bank head. Three round wire ropes were required. Two of them were 2,000yds long, made of six strands, weighed 5½lbs per yard and cost a total of £326-13s-5d; these were obviously for the Crook and Stanley banks. The third, obviously for the bank down to the Deerness Valley branch, was 3,700yds long and was also wound with six strands but only weighed 4½lbs per yard and cost £300-13s-6d.

The Engine needed a reservoir to store water for the boilers, and for this ground to the north of the engine house was used. This involved excavating 6,993 cubic yards which, with puddling and other work, cost £276-16s-1d. It would seem from the 2nd edition Ordnance Survey map shown here that the reservoir had been extended by the 1890s. To supply the reservoir a well was sunk and a donkey engine was provided, with 6in pump gear, at a cost of £121-2s-0d. The construction of all of the buildings was sub-let to various tradesmen, as follows (modern figures are as given in 2010):

Mason's contract for Boiler House (incl. extras)	£416-9s-4d	[£17,974.70]
Mason's contract for Engine House and pillars	£456-12s-6d	[£19,707.94]
Mason's contract for Drum House and pillars	£65-14s-4d	[£2,836.33]

6-24. Because of the Engine's unusual location, the two ropes had to be brought from the drum house at just above ground level to the bank head (behind the photographer), where two large sheaves were mounted to turn the ropes through 90 degrees to being them to the tops of their respective inclines.

Bricklayer's contract for Firebrick Chimney	£230-0s-0d	[£9,926.80]
Carpenters & joiners, painting, glazing and sundry other work	£305-0s-2d	[£13,164.16]
Slating	£104-13s-3d	[£4,517.23]

The specification for the construction of the engine house, dated [27] May 1857,[11] specified that ashlar [lime]stone was to be used and that this could be obtained from Brusselton, Westerton, Hutts, Witton-le-Wear or Stocksfield Fell [Quarries]. A similar specification covering the boiler house[12] included provision for inspection by officials of the Shildon Works Co and a fine of £1 [£43.16] per day for any overrun. The construction of the chimney involved 49 cubic yards of excavation, 29 cubic yards of cement, 61,000 firebricks at a cost of £1-16s-0d [£77.69] per 1,000, together with seven wagonloads of lime from Aycliffe Quarry near Ferryhill in Co.Durham, and twenty wagonloads of sand.

Finally, under the heading 'Incline', presumably all three inclines, the incline sheaves, rollers, signals, safety switches and chocks cost £611-18s-6d [£26,410.68].

The engine house carried an engraved date of 1857. Both the S&D and NER lines were opened in 1858; the exact dates are unknown. How the two northern inclines were worked from only one drum but with two ropes of different lengths is unknown, as is how the depot(s) were shunted, though for the latter it is likely that fly-ropes were used. The note of 29th January 1863 referred to above states that the Engine drew twenty-four loaded chaldron waggons from the Stanley Pit to the bank head in seven minutes, making 206 strokes, and raised eight loaded chaldron waggons from Crook bankfoot to the bank head identically. The engineman stated that there were no waggons going down the opposite side in either case, but presumably whilst the engine was hauling on one side waggons could be lowered by gravity on the other with the drum being braked.

In 1866 Joseph Pease & Partners opened Wooley Colliery near to Stanley Colliery, but on the eastern side of the branch. This appears to have meant that the rope which served Stanley Colliery was used in addition to serve Wooley Colliery, so that the Engine was serving three routes northwards from its bank head. Beehive coke ovens were also built at both collieries. The Engine also had an additional short branch to work on its southern side, when a short link was built from the incline to reach the Lucy Pit near Crook, apparently to enable coal from Stanley and Wooley Collieries to travel directly into the Pease's West complex, However, the S&D had

amalgamated with the NER in 1863, and the enlarged company seems soon to have felt that the cost of maintaining the link between Stanley Bank Head and the Deerness Valley branch was consequently not justified; the line may well have been closed by as early as 1885.

Stanley Colliery was laid in during 1900-1901, its workings almost certainly being merged with Wooley Colliery. By 1949 the two remaining inclines were operated alternately, the usual full load to Crook being four 10½ ton wagons or two 20 ton wagons. On 1st April 1951 the National Coal Board merged Wooley Colliery with Roddymoor Colliery at Crook, and the branch and its engine were closed.

****

By the final quarter of the nineteenth century some of the early engines needed to be replaced, as the traffic began to exceed their capabilities, and thus the final developments in steam stationary engine design for railways can be seen. These included two horizontal cylinders, mounted on either side of the engine, with the drum or drums positioned between them but forward of them, the distance determined by the length of the piston rod. With the continuing need to put the drum(s) in and out of gear, the gearing became more sophisticated, as did the accompanying apparatus to aid the driver – indicators driven from the drum shaft to show the position of a set on an incline, a bell system with signals giving a range of instructions and, later, telephones. The use of two horizontal cylinders, with the valve gear on one side set at 90 degrees to that on the other side, meant that there was no longer any need for a flywheel. Such an engine would require at least three men to operate it, a driver, a second man in the engine house and a boiler house man, in addition to those outside operating the inclines. Rope haulage men became a tight-knit community, not least because of the specialist skills they developed, with men spending a lifetime on the inclines and a driver often holding the job for twenty years or more.

It was a very skilled and responsible job to be a driver of one of these engines. It was also an increasingly complex job, and it seemed appropriate that this chapter should include one detailed account of the operation of one of these later engines as an exemplar of this.

2nd Byer Engine, 1876, two cylinder horizontal engine for Hetton Railway, Co.Durham

As noted elsewhere, in the description of the Hetton Railway in chapter 4 and the account of its Warden Law Engine above, the original Byer Engine at Copt Hill was built in 1822 by an unknown maker. This was a double beam engine with cylinders 30in diameter by 60in stroke which worked an 882-yard

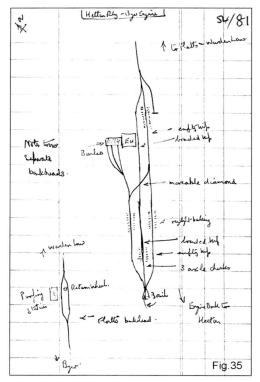

Fig.35. C.H.A.Townley's sketch of Copt Hill on 4th March 1950.

incline on its southern side, with an average gradient of 1 in 16, known as the Engine Bank. On its northern side it passed on fulls to, and received empties from, the Flat Engine, another beam engine, installed in 1826 but with a single cylinder 22in diameter with a 56in stroke. This worked sets of sixteen waggons alternately over the 775yds between the two engines, on an average rising gradient of 1 in 90. These two engines may well have survived until 1876, when the Flat Engine haulage engine was replaced by a pump to supply water to the reservoirs for the engines and a new engine was installed at Copt Hill.

The new engine, said to have been 350 hp, may well have been unique in that it was designed to work two uphill gradients on either side of it. It was also provided with four drums, which again may well be unique. It was built in 1876, Works No. 125, by The Grange Iron Co of Belmont, near Durham City. This was a firm of general engineers, of which there were several in North-East England, building stationary engines and a handful of steam locomotives, as well as handling a wide range of smaller engineering work. Its records do not survive, and there is no full contemporary description of the engine. However, a series of excellent photographs of both its exterior and interior were taken in the 1950s and from them it has been possible to produce the following understanding of how it was driven and how its design enabled it to carry out the operation of the two inclines simultaneously.

6-25. The view from in front of the Byer Engine, but looking towards the Engine Bank bank head. Note on the left, partly hidden by the cabin, the white disc formerly raised by the bank foot men to indicate that their set was ready to run. The semaphore signal was used only during the changing of a rope, in a process too complicated to describe here. On the right are the cottages where the engineman and one other worker lived, together with the line serving the boiler house. Note the absence of any guard around the moving rope on the right.

6-26. The view from almost the same position, on 26th August 1959, showing the front of the engine house and looking north towards the Flatt and Warden Law in the distance. With the bank head of the Engine Bank behind the photographer, on the far left is the boiler house, in the middle the engine house with its four drums and on the right the bank foot of the incline rising up to the Flatt, also worked by this engine.

6-27. The Byer Engine from the driver's position, although with his seat removed. The various parts of the engine and its controls are explained in the text.

The exterior views in the pictures above (Nos. 6-25/6-26) should be considered together with the plan of the area (Fig.35). In 6-26 the boiler house on the left is believed to have housed three, or possibly four, Lancashire boilers. To the right of the engine house is the bank foot for the section up to the Flat, sometimes called the Flatts, with fulls on the left and the kip for empties on the right. The rope for the western side of the Engine bank can be seen emerging through an aperture at ground level below the window. The rope for the eastern side is not visible, but was carried from the engine house underground to emerge near to the kip. Looking through the open door of the engine house, it may be observed that the drums were in pits partially below ground level. The picture No. 6-25 opposite shows the view facing the other way, with a set of fulls just coming over the kip at the top of the Engine Bank.

The full page interior view (No. 6-27) illustrates the engine from immediately behind the driver's platform, but with his wooden chair, normally positioned centrally on the platform, removed. Immediately in front of him is the steam control valve - the throttle or regulator – for admitting or reducing the steam to the horizontal cylinders which flank the engine. Fixed to the steam pipe serving the left hand cylinder is the circular steam pressure gauge. To his right but located slightly higher is the forward/reverse lever, capable of being slid up and down in its quadrant but here in neutral. At a higher level again, only operable by the driver standing up, are the two long cranked handles which operated the brakes on the two drums at the front of the engine. Note that the left hand handle guide has been filled with a wooden block to prevent it being operated, as by this time the front left hand drum was no longer in use. On the right hand guide there is a chain with a pin, so that the handle could be pulled down and the pin inserted to keep it in position. Immediately to the left of where the driver's chair would be is the electric bell signal apparatus for receiving and giving signals to the bankhead man. Between this and the main steam pipe to the left hand cylinder, lagged to insulate the heat, can be seen the Engine Bank indicator, which by means of a moving pointer, here near the bottom, showed the driver the position of the sets on the incline. Note that this pointer is wired to a bell, which it rang when passing certain points. Below the 'X', about half way up the indicator, are two horizontal white bars, with the words MEET INGS above them, indicating the places where the sets passed.

The two wheels immediately in front of the platform are the clutch wheels for the two rear drums, enabling them to be wound in and out of mesh with the drive pinions via the long shaft running across the back of the engine. These could only be operated at floor level and may have been the responsibility of the second man in the engine house. The large lever on the right, angled at 45 degrees and kept in position by another pin is the brake lever for the right hand rear drum and is mounted on a sleeve on the clutch shaft; the brackets for the ends of the semi-circular underslung band brakes can be seen on the same sleeve, either side of the brake lever. The lever for the left hand rear drum is hidden behind the mounting for the electric bell apparatus, although the top of the handle and the bottom section of the guide can just be seen. The rims of the drums – the brake paths - are shiny because of the band brakes tightening on them. Each drum can be braked separately, but in practice most of the braking would have been almost certainly done by using the engine itself.

As this view shows, the two cylinders were located slightly backward of the rear drums. Unfortunately, the size of the cylinders is not known. Clearly visible in No.6-28, the main steam supply from the boiler house was carried in the large overhead pipe, with connections down to both cylinders. The main steam control valve can be seen located immediately behind and above the driver, the operating linkage passing from his throttle lever, under his driving position and up to the valve. When C.H.A.Townley visited here in March 1950 he noted that the engine was fitted with Gooch curved link valve gear, invented by Daniel Gooch of the Great Western Railway in 1847. Both cylinders drove a common crankshaft positioned midway between the front and rear drums. Judging by the relative size of the drive and drum pinions, the gearing would be about 2:1, the drums rotating about half as fast as the crankshaft. The two handwheel clutches for putting the front drums out of gear were positioned at the front of the engine in similar positions to those at the rear, another job for the second man in the hauler house. Thus all four drums could be independently moved physically in and out of mesh with their respective drive pinion. The gearing pinions and eccentrics are clearly visible in No.6-29.

Note that the drums still follow the traditional narrow Durham practice, being probably not more than 3ft wide. As viewed from the driver's position in picture 6-27, the left hand rear and right hand front drums carry the ropes for the Engine Bank. To make their work possible, both drums had to be the same diameter and to revolve in the same direction, so that as one rope on one drum wound on, the rope on the other wound off. On the front drum the rope came off the top, while on the rear drum the rope came off the bottom and passed under the drum in front of it, remaining underground until outside the engine house and coming to the surface to reach the bank head.

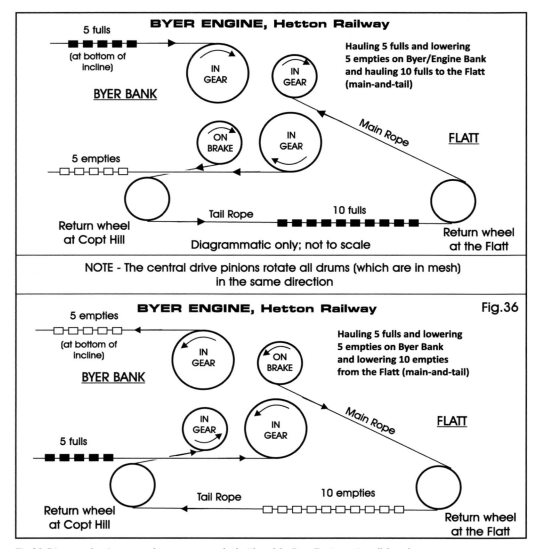

Fig.36 Diagram showing a complete sequence on both sides of the Byer Engine, using all four drums.

Because on the Flat side the engine had still to haul uphill, the basic design here was direct haulage over a single track. The main rope on the rear right hand drum came off the bottom and out of the engine house underground, passing round two sheaves to bring it through two right-angles and so enable it to run in a covered gulley alongside the track up to the Flat bank head. Here there was a return wheel in a pit between the tracks at the northern end of the pass-bye, which brought the rope round 180 degrees and out again, to run down between the rails back to the bank foot, where its fulls were waiting. This layout kept the outward and inward ropes from fouling each other.

For normal working just three drums were used, the right hand front (RHF) and left hand rear (LHR)

for the 882-yard Engine bank, both the same diameter but with the rope coming off the top of the former and off the bottom of the latter, and also the right hand rear drum (RHR) for the 775-yard Flat side, with the rope also coming off the bottom. Latterly sets of five 10-12½ ton wooden hopper wagons were run on the Engine and Warden Law inclines, and also on the four self-acting inclines north of Warden Law. To avoid the single-line Copt Hill-Flat section becoming a bottleneck, sets of ten were run here.

With a set of ten fulls on the west side of the Flat bank foot, ten empties on the kip next to them divided into two sets of five, and all four drums were out of gear, the operational sequence would begin with:

1. The rope from the RHR drum, running up to the return wheel at the Flat and then back down, is attached to the set of ten fulls. The first of the two sets of five empties is run by gravity from the Flat bank foot to the Engine Bank bank head and the rope from the LHR drum attached. The rope from the RHF drum at the bottom of the Engine Bank is attached to a set of five fulls. While this was being done the engine house men were putting all three drums into gear. Then

2. Simultaneously:

   (i) on the Engine Bank the empties descend from the bank head (LHR drum) and the engine hauls the fulls from the bank foot using the RHF drum. On arrival these fulls are run by gravity to the Flat bank foot.

   (ii) The engine hauls the set of ten fulls up to the Flat. Both rear drums are rotating in the same direction.

   (iii) The second set of five empties from the Flat bank foot is run by gravity down to the opposite side of the Engine Bank bank head kip.

   (iv) Meanwhile the Warden Law Engine to the north has completed the running of two sequences of five fulls up and five empties down, so that there are now ten empties waiting at the Flat ready to descend.

3. On the arrival of all three rope-worked sets, the rope from the LHR drum is attached to the next set of fulls at the bank foot and the rope from the RHF drum is attached to the set of empties now arrived by gravity at the opposite side of the bank head kip, while at the Flat the rope end is attached to the set of ten empties. While all this was happening, the haulerman reversed the engine and the RHR drum was taken out of gear. Then simultaneously:

   (i) on the Engine Bank the empties descend from the bank head (RHF drum) and the engine hauls the fulls from the bank foot using the LHR drum. On arrival they are run by gravity to the Flat bank foot to join the five already there;

   (ii) on the Flat side the ten empties descend by gravity, controlled by braking the RHR drum.

At the end of this sequence the position of fulls and empties on the Flat is the same as at the beginning above.

However, the nineteenth century engineers knew from experience that there were occasions when the power of the wind made it difficult to bring the ten empties down from the Flat. So the Byer Engine was provided with a fourth drum, the left hand front drum. This was the same size at the RHR drum and

6-28. The Byer Engine from the front, with the disused Flat drum on the right and its partner at the rear on the left, with the left hand front and right hand rear drums being for the Engine Bank.

6-29. Looking down the left hand side of the engine, with the cylinder, piston rod, crank pin and crankshaft and the LH rear drum, with its gearing. Note the various oil cups for lubrication.

the rope also came off the bottom, but going forward, emerging from the engine house underground and then going round a sheave to change its direction to reach the Flat Bank bank foot. When the wind was strong, this 4th drum rope was attached to the rear of an ascending set of fulls to convert the operation of the Flat bank from direct haulage to main-and-tail haulage. The sequence was the same as above for 1 and 2, except that the ascending set of fulls to the Flat was now hauling the LHF drum's rope as a tail rope, with this drum out of gear. On arriving at the Flat this rope was attached to the front of the fulls waiting to descend, while the rope from the RHR drum was attached to the back of the set and the drum taken out of gear. Now both the LHF and RHF drums had to haul, rotating in the same direction, while the RHR drum was braked and the LHR drum was in gear, again with both rotating in the same direction. Using the engine in this way, to haul and brake on both inclines simultaneously, meant that the two operations had to be completely synchronised, achieved presumably by having marks on the drum. Almost certainly the engine was unique in Britain in having this facility.

However, in photo 6-28 the LHF drum has had its rope removed, so clearly main-and-tail working had been abandoned sometime after 1950. In his notes C.H.A. Townley mentions that roller bearings had been fitted to the rollers between the engine house and the Flat, enabling them to run more freely, and perhaps because of this, when the rope on the front drum became due for renewal, it was decided that it was no longer needed.

In 1952 the National Coal Board began a major development near Murton, to the north east of Hetton. A large diameter shaft was sunk which was to handle the output of Elemore and Eppleton Collieries, then transported on the Hetton Railway, and also Murton Colliery, which was connected to the railway between South Hetton and Seaham Harbour. The new 'Combined Mine' would use extensive underground railway systems to bring the coal to the new shaft. Adjacent to the new mine, a large coal washery and coking plant were to be built. Once production at the new shaft was underway, the Hetton Railway between Hetton and Silksworth was to be closed, and so the Byer Engine ceased work on 9th September 1959. Today the whole site has been returned to farm land and nothing can be seen.

Even from the fragmented information currently known, quite a number of stationary steam engines continued in use into the twentieth century. They appear to have given few problems, and often those using them had good workshop facilities able to maintain them. Apart from the regular changing or replacing of ropes, the main components of the engine itself – cylinders, drums and even the boilers - could be expected to give fifty years service or more, extending the engine's

working life to a hundred years or more, and rarely, if ever, would all these components require renewal at the same time, thus spreading the cost of major maintenance out over many years.

A handful of stationary steam engines for railways continued to be built into the twentieth century:

3rd Black Fell Engine, 1913, a two cylinder horizontal engine, Pontop & Jarrow Railway, Eighton Banks, near Gateshead, Co.Durham

As noted earlier, the Pontop & Jarrow Railway was one of the important colliery railways in Durham, and to haul its coal up from the bottom of the valley of the River Team two stationary engines were needed. For the extension of the Springwell Waggonway from Eighton Banks to Kibblesworth (see above) in 1841-42, a standard single line incline on a gradient about 1 in 30 at the bottom, increasing to 1 in 15 for most of its 1¼ miles, was built, with an engine at Eighton Banks. This was another built by Thomas Murray, again a beam engine with a single vertical-cylinder measuring 36in in diameter with a 60in stroke. In 1854-55 a railway from Marley Hill in north-west Durham running south for 4½ miles to Dipton was linked to Kibblesworth in order for as much coal as possible from the western collieries to avoid the North Eastern Railway and be taken down to the colliery company's staiths at Jarrow on the River Tyne. To handle this increase in traffic the Black Fell incline was doubled in order to run fulls and empties simultaneously, and the engine had to be modified. As at Burnhope later (see above), a second cylinder was installed driving on to the same crank pin, while to accommodate two ropes, the drum was divided by a board, with the second rope coming off the top of the drum, out of the rear of the engine house and round a large vertical return wheel before going underground to re-emerge at the far side of the kip. This allowed the rope attached to the loaded full set to be wound in while the rope on the descending empty set unwound.

The drum shaft fractured twice in 1911-12, and with the engine generally showing signs of old age, it was decided to replace it. The new engine was built by Robey & Co Ltd of Lincoln and began work in August 1913. This had two 18in by 36in horizontal cylinders and was fitted with Robey's drop valve gear. There were two drums, both 8ft in diameter and much wider than had been traditional in Durham, with double helical gearing at a ratio of 2½:1. Both ropes came off the top of their drums, though because this was in opposite directions, one was wound in while the other was paid out. This engine lay immediately behind the old one and a new brick engine house was provided, although photographs suggest that the old boiler house, housing three Lancashire boilers installed between 1903 and 1906, was retained.

6.30. The haulerman on the Black Fell Engine on the Pontop & Jarrow Railway for many years was Mr. Bob Pallister, seen here at work in 1920, with his hand resting on the regulator. The two large handles are the reversing levers for each cylinder, whilst the foot pedal is the brake. Note that it is counterweighted and provided with a rachet. There would appear to be a second pedal on the opposite side, not fully visible, which has been depressed. Note also the provision of a governor, with its steel balls, to control the Engine's maximum speed.

6-31. The Black Fell Engine on what was now called the Bowes Railway on 19th July 1950, with the railway (on a curve) on the far left. The engine house was in the process of being converted to accommodate an electric hauler, hence the new front door, while the boiler house with its massive chimney, built between 1870 and 1880, was to be demolished.

3rd Blackham's Hill Engine, 1915, a two cylinder horizontal engine, Pontop & Jarrow Railway, near Springwell, Co.Durham

Two years later the owners of the Pontop & Jarrow Railway, John Bowes & Partners Ltd, decided to replace the stationary engine above Black Fell, at Blackham's Hill, the summit of the climb out of the Team Valley. This engine worked inclines on either side of it, which were always single track. The first, from Mount Moor Colliery/Black Fell up to the engine, was about 750yds, the grade varying between 1 in 18 and 1 in 13.7. The other, down to Springwell Colliery, east of Gateshead, was 1,170yds at 1 in 70. This section formed part of the Springwell Waggonway of 1826, but virtually nothing is known about the original engine here, other than it was believed to have been built by Robert Stephenson & Co. and to have been a vertical-cylindered beam engine with its drums over the track. In 1854 it was replaced, as part of the improvements mentioned earlier, by a second-hand beam engine, said to have been another built by Thomas Murray of Chester-le-Street. It had a single cylinder of 27in by 48in, with the usual gab motion described earlier to reverse it. The engine worked the inclines by means of two drums, which given the normal practice of the period were almost certainly 'outside' in their own drum house, with the smaller one on the west side. When one drum was in gear the other had to be out of gear, but could be worked by gravity.

This engine lasted until 1915, when it was replaced by a new engine built by Andrew Barclay, Sons & Co Ltd of Kilmarnock, Ayrshire (Makers No.7923), a firm much better known for building locomotives. This engine had two 18in by 36in horizontal cylinders, worked on 100lbs p.s.i. and was geared at a ratio of 3:1. Following the now standard practice, the drums were inside the engine house and wider than in the nineteenth century, with a 6ft diameter drum for the west side and an 8ft diameter drum for the east side. The drums could be operated independently of each other and were wound in and out of gear by handwheels mounted on pedestals, so that two men were needed to operate the engine, in addition to the firemen. As at Black Fell, a new brick engine house was provided. The adjacent boiler house contained two Lancashire boilers built by W. & J. Galloway & Sons Ltd of Manchester installed in 1904.

6-32. The interior of the Blackham's Hill Engine, half a mile from Black Fell, seen from the front on 19th July 1950. On this engine the connecting rods drove circular discs, seen best on the right, rather than crank pins. The 8ft drum for the East Incline can be seen, with the second man standing behind it next to the clutch wheels. The windows on the right have been enlarged to allow equipment to be moved in and out during the engine's imminent replacement by an electric hauler. At the back on the left can be seen the liquid controller and the electrical switch gear for the new engine.

6-34. The vertical clutch wheels for putting the two drums in and out of gear. To the right of the right hand wheel is the horizontal wheel for the brake on the East Incline, which the second man here operated. Note all the highly-polished oil pots.

The working of both inclines was complex, with on the western side a colliery and a depot for landsale coal to service and at the bottom on the eastern side Springwell Colliery, whose buildings after its closure in 1932 were converted into the Railway's Engineering and Wagon Shops.

* * * * * * * * * * * * * * * * * * * *

The extent to which steam stationary engine design could be developed is well shown in the five engines installed on the Serra Nova inclines on the Sao Paulo Railway in Brazil between 1898

6-33. The driver of the Blackham's Hill Engine for many years was Mr. John Humphrey, his left hand resting on the throttle. To his left is the brake for the West Incline drum with its guide and the pin to hold it in position, and on his right the simple reversing lever. Note above him on the shelf the two bells for the bell signals from the level crossings and bank foots on each incline.

6-35. The two Lancashire boilers for the Blackham's Hill Engine, taken about 1940. They were manufactured by W. & J. Galloway Ltd of Manchester, a firm founded in 1835. The man on the right, Mr. Tom Moore, became the final driver of the Black Fell Engine.

and 1901. This railway was British-owned, and so all the equipment and locomotives were ordered from Britain. These engines were built by Yates & Thom Ltd of Blackburn, with some work sub-let to Joseph Foster & Sons Ltd of Preston. Each was 1,000 h.p., designed to operate an endless rope incline of 1½ miles on a ruling gradient of 1 in 12½, with trains travelling on each incline in 7½ minutes. A fuller description is given in chapter 8, and one is illustrated in picture 8-21.

Despite some large colliery companies remaining faithful to steam, after 1900 others began to invest heavily in electricity, with the construction of electric winders, fans and compressors on the surface and even more so underground, where the provision of steam to drive haulers could limit their use. Some companies built their own power stations to supply their needs. Against this background, it is not surprising that some reviewed the use of stationary steam engines on

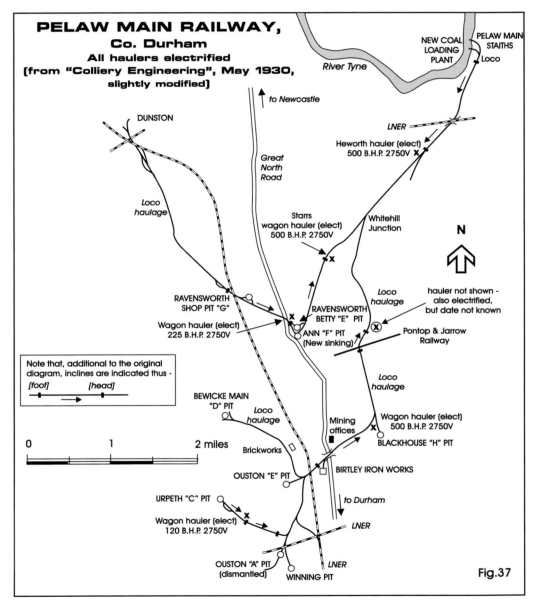

Fig.37 A plan of the Pelaw Main Railway in County Durham in 1930, taken from COLLIERY ENGINEERING, showing that all the haulers on the Railway had been electrified. In doing this, the owners, The Pelaw Main Collieries Ltd, were many years ahead of other private railways in Durham. Power was supplied from the company's own generating station at Ouston E Colliery.

their private railways. Many had begun the introduction of 10-12 ton wagons by 1910, and they also wanted to increase the haulage capacity of their inclines and the speed at which sets could travel to 20 m.p.h or more. Engines, especially beam engines, built before 1860 were rarely capable of meeting such demands, and where the coal reserves were estimated at millions of tons and the need for a railway stretched far into the future, the question of electric haulers came under serious consideration.

One of the pioneers to undertake this major investment was The Pelaw Main Collieries Ltd. This company was formed in 1926 to take over six collieries in the northern half of Durham, served by a sprawling railway system, and at that time producing only some 2,500 tons per day. The new owners wanted to double this, and by 1930 it had replaced all six of its steam stationary engines on its railway by electric haulers, with outputs varying between 120 and 500b.h.p.,[13] as part of a scheme to introduce larger wagons, newer locomotives and improved shipping facilities. Unfortunately, few details of these haulers have survived, although two are known to have been built jointly by Metropolitan-Vickers Electrical Co Ltd of Manchester and John Wood & Co Ltd of Wigan.

One of the engines considered earlier in this chapter was the Kibblesworth Engine of 1840, which operated the Kibblesworth Incline on the Pontop & Jarrow Railway, later re-named the Bowes Railway. This engine had passed its centenary during the Second World War, and once this was over plans were immediately put in hand to replace it with an electric hauler:

2nd Kibblesworth Engine, 1947, a 350 b.h.p. electric hauler, Bowes Railway, Co.Durham

The operating requirements for this hauler have been described earlier. The new 350 b.h.p. electric hauler was ordered by John Bowes & Partners Ltd from The English Electric Co Ltd of Preston in Lancashire. As can be seen from photo 6-21, the old engine house needed to be replaced too, the result being the penultimate stationary engine house built for a railway in Britain. This striking, rather art-deco, concrete building, painted white, straddled the track and became an icon visible for miles. The driver was provided with an elevated cabin at the front of the engine house some 30ft above the ground, giving him both a superb view of his incline and the comfort of electric heating. The hauler motor and the 14ft diameter drum were located behind the cabin.

6-36. The 1947 Kibblesworth Engine House, on 14th October 1965, with a full set from the Birkheads self-acting incline passing underneath. The old engine house stood on the waste ground to the left. Note how high the rope rises, and the angled tubular bars in the rope hole to stop the rope damaging the concrete. Note too how the plain front wall of the building has been relieved by the horizontal lines of decoration. The unusual 'ball-and-chain' rapper here can be seen on the right (see chapter 3).

6-37. The Kibblesworth electric hauler, taken in 1950. Nearest to the camera is the 14ft diameter drum, with the 350 b.h.p. motor behind it and the driver's elevated cabin behind that.

As noted above, the Engine had to run sets of empties in and fulls out of Kibblesworth Colliery's screens, alongside the incline about half way down. Latterly these were sets of twelve, the same as sets on the 'main line'. Because this incline was single line and situated between the self-acting Birkheads Incline and the double line Black Fell Incline, the Kibblesworth Incline had to be run fast, so as not to become a bottle-neck and restrict the flow of traffic. Thus the incline was said to be the fastest in the country, with the descending sets travelling at 27 m.p.h and the ascending sets at 22 m.p.h. (a speedometer was provided). Because of the high descending speed, the motor was used as a rheostatic brake, which made the resistances so hot that a constant supply of cold water was needed.

Three years later the National Coal Board's Durham No. 6 (North-West Durham) Area decided to replace the Bowes Railway's other steam haulers at Black Fell and Blackham's Hill.

4th Black Fell Engine, 1950, a 500 b.h.p. electric hauler, Bowes Railway, Co.Durham

This was the fourth stationary engine provided at this location, this one a 500 b.h.p. electric hauler from British Thomson-Houston Co Ltd of Rugby, Warwickshire, with the mechanical parts provided by Robey & Co Ltd of Lincoln, the makers of the engine this replaced. The 1913 brick engine house was retained, although new doors and windows were fitted and the walls were tiled from head height to the floor. The redundant boiler house was subsequently demolished, although one of the boilers was retained to provide a cold water supply. The bed of the old engine was reused, as were the drums, although they were eventually replaced in 1961. The motor was located behind the drums, which it drove through a double reduction gear and which were locked together in operation. A spacious driver's cabin was provided at the side of the engine and in front of the cabin window an indicator was mounted on a horizontal gantry to show the position of the sets on the incline. There was also a rope speed indicator and later a mirror was provided for each drum to allow the driver to observe the ropes as they wound on or off. The engine began work on 30th July 1950, and the sets took about seven minutes to cover the 1¼ miles.

6-38. *The rear of the 1913 Robey hauler at Black Fell on the Bowes Railway on 19th July 1950, with work already in hand to carry out its replacement by an electric hauler; the new brickwork to support the motor can be seen. Note how the rope from the right-hand drum comes off to go out of the back of the engine house – at head height.*

6-39. *The new 500 b.h.p. hauler in its noticeably cleaner engine house, on 3rd July 1951, a year after the engine started work. Note the steel girders that were installed to enable the new equipment to be moved into position. The driver's cabin and the back of the indicator showing the position of the sets on the incline can be seen on the extreme right – and that the rope coming off the right-hand drum is now guarded.*

6-40. The Black Fell Engine House from the front on 3rd July 1951, showing major changes from a year earlier (Photo 6-31). The front has a bigger door, with new steelwork installed to enable loads to be lifted off the delivery lorries, and all the windows are new. The boiler house and its chimney have been demolished, the ground levelled and trees planted. Even the rope frame has been moved.

4th Blackham's Hill Engine, 1950, a 300 b.h.p. electric hauler, Bowes Railway, Co.Durham

Although installed at the same time as the Black Fell Engine, the design was completely different, as was its manufacturer, Metropolitan-Vickers Electrical Co Ltd,[14] although the basic approach was very similar. The brick engine house was retained and again a new front door and larger windows installed. This time the heavy equipment was transferred from rail vehicles through the side windows, perhaps because access for road vehicles was only by an un-made track. As with the other Bowes stationary engines, the motor took current at 3,000 volts, transformed down from 20,000 volts at the substation. The East drum was 8ft in diameter and the West drum 6ft, and both were provided with indicators to show the position of the set on the bank and dials to show the speed of the rope in feet per second. As at Kibblesworth, the driver's cabin was raised on stilts, but at the rear of the engine, and the clutch wheels were moved into it, leaving the second man's job only to operate the brake on the set of fulls descending to Springwell. The driver was also provided with a brake handwheel for the West drum, as well as a foot pedal brake for an emergency stop. The brakes themselves were large clasp brakes tightening on to a path on one side of the drums. The motor was also used as a brake, and again the resistances could get so hot that the water they were in came close to boiling and needed to be constantly refreshed from the large tank outside along the north wall. Bells were operated by a plunger and a telephone system was installed, and the building was fully equipped with electric lighting and radiators.

Although the collieries which the Engine's inclines had once served closed in the 1930s, a short link between the Pelaw Main Railway and the East Incline was brought into use in 1959, so that the operation of both inclines had to allow time for the Pelaw Main locomotive to take its train of fulls into Springwell and come out again with its empties. Beginning with twelve fulls and twelve empties alongside the engine house, both inclines began by running sets downhill by gravity. A set of fulls, another set of empties and a second set of fulls was then run on the west (Black Fell) side, by which time the empties on the East Incline had reached Springwell. A set of twelve empties was then hauled from Springwell, and once it had cleared the junction with the Pelaw Main branch, the Pelaw Main train could enter for its trip to Springwell. After half an hour this sequence was complete and everything was ready to start again.

The Blackham's Hill electric hauler was not the last to be installed on an incline in Britain; this distinction is held by the hauler installed at the top of the Corkickle Incline at Whitehaven in 1955, which is described in chapter 9. However, it is worthy of note that the first engine described here, the Middleton Top Engine of 1829, and the last, the Blackham's Hill Engine of 1950, although 121 years apart, are both preserved and were for many years in working order, although the Blackham's Hill Engine is (2012) no longer used.

6-41. The Blackham's Hill Engine on 19th July 1950, during its conversion from steam to electricity. A steel frame for unloading equipment from rail vehicles through the south side windows can be seen, with another over the main door for unloading road vehicles. A temporary siding has been laid to accommodate the Railway's rail crane. The windows on the front and the north side are still to be enlarged and the boiler house and chimney on the left are still to be demolished.

6-42. The new Metro-Vickers 300 b.h.p. hauler at Blackham's Hill on 3rd July 1951, from almost the same position as photo 6-38. Behind the motor and alongside the East drum is the liquid controller for the motor. The elevated driver's cabin stands right at the back, with the electrical switch gear in the left hand corner. Note also the electric lighting and the radiators.

6-43. The Blackham's Hill Engine House on 11th December 1965. Both ropes come out of the front of the building. The West rope is slack, while the East rope is hauling the set of twelve empties from Springwell just arriving on the kip. Mr. Tommy McInness is about to strike the coupling to release the rope, which will then slide down the steel sheet ready for attaching to the waiting fulls, whilst his brother Matty is the set-rider.

1   Northumberland Archives, 725/F/17, 64

2   Given the disparity of measurements quoted in earlier sources and publications, I am very grateful to Mr. Colin Goodwyn for personally checking all the dimensions given here.

3   One indicator certainly does this and it is believed that the other, which is mounted alongside it, did the same for the points on the opposite side of the bank head.

4   The replacement was equally interesting – a second-hand three-cylinder compound marine engine, with the shaft driving a spur wheel instead of a propeller. Unusually the two drums were outside the engine house, mounted in sunken pits on either side of the kip at the new bank head.

5   Newcastle University, Robinson Library Special Collections, University Archive 11/5/2.

6   These spellings shown are as used in the advertisement.

7   W.W.Tomlinson, *The North Eastern Railway – Its Rise and Development,* Newcastle upon Tyne, 1914, 377.

8   The notes of Mr. C.H.A.Townley, who visited the engine on 29th October 1949, seem to suggest that the cylinders were vertical, in other words, that the engine was a twin cylinder beam engine; but nowhere in Mr. MacNay's records is there any record of beams being cast, and it is therefore assumed that this interpretation of Mr. Townley's notes is incorrect.

9   DRO, CP/Shl/17/6.

10 According to *Stockton & Darlington Railway, 1825-1975,* by P.J.Holmes, 142, there were only two boilers at Carrhouse, measuring 25ft long by 6ft diameter.

11 DRO, CP/Shl/11/9.

12 DRO, CP/Shl/11/11.

13 All of the haulers were supplied at 2,750 volts from the company's own generating station at Ouston 'E' Colliery, near Chester-le-Street.

14 British Thomson-Houston and Metro-Vickers were commercial rivals, although both were subsidiary companies of Associated Electrical Industries Ltd.

Chapter 7 Narrow gauge haulages

As the Industrial Revolution developed in Britain after 1820 and the knowledge of railways spread, not least information about chain and rope haulages, so engineers began to think about new applications. As noted in chapter 4, smaller gauges than what became the 'standard gauge' of 4ft 8½in were being used by 1800, and the introduction of 'narrow gauge' iron rails seems to have spread rapidly over the next forty years. A major area where this happened was underground in coal mines, where over time small wooden tubs with solid cast iron wheels running on iron rails – of a myriad of different gauges! – became the normal method of transporting everything. Near to the coal faces these were pushed by men and boys, but elsewhere ponies were introduced; and then with the development of wire ropes, coal owners saw the advantages of introducing steam haulages both underground and on the surface. On the latter they might link a drift mine, where coal was mined by opening up an outcropped seam on the side of a hill, for example, with the main colliery site some distance away. The haulage carried the output to the main site, where stone was removed from the coal and it was screened, or graded by size. Others carried the coal from the pit to a place where it was loaded into railway wagons or canal boats.

One of the first areas to develop surface narrow gauge tramways was the Lancashire coalfield, notably around Burnley and at collieries to the south near Bacup, where they were known as '**ginney lines**'. In some respects these looked back to the past, as they were laid with plate rails, flat rails with a flange, and haulage was by means of an endless chain. The first use of endless chain haulage in the area is said to have been in the early 1840s at Marsden Colliery, Briercliffe, owned by John Hargreaves. From there it is said to have spread rapidly to nearly every pit in the coalfield. These lines had the advantage of not needing to be very carefully laid or maintained.

These 'ginney lines' had two tracks, one for full tubs leaving the pit and the other for the returning empties. The wagon wheels, which were simple discs and not flanged, ran on the horizontal section of the rails. The endless chain, driven by a horizontal sprocket wheel on a vertical shaft and turned by gearing from the stationary engine, caught in a fork on top of the tubs and pulled them along at walking pace. They were always put on to the chain singly, at distances varying from ten to forty yards. Because the tubs carried the weight of the chain – no rollers were needed between the rails and the speed of haulage was only between 2 and 4 m.p.h. - only a small

stationary engine was needed to drive the system. At the far end of the ginney, the chain rose to pass around a return wheel, detaching itself from the tubs. Once emptied, these were returned on the other track, where again they automatically re-engaged with the chain.

An investigation into these lines, together with various experiments that were carried out, was undertaken by the North of England Institute of Mining & Mechanical Engineers in Newcastle upon Tyne and is reported in their *Transactions, Vol. XVII, 1867-68*. It stated that there were over forty miles of such lines around Burnley alone. The chain system allowed the lines to run over undulating ground, and many did this, often going into upland areas and linking more than one colliery. The report notes that a heavy gradient could be worked safely and efficiently, but notes that the chain would only work safely in a straight line and that where a change of direction was required, two pulleys were needed to achieve this and required the permanent attention of a man or boy.

Four collieries were investigated and described in detail, and a summary of one, chosen as an example, is included here. This was a system at Hapton Valley Colliery, on the outskirts of Burnley. In addition to two shafts sunk in 1853, a drift mine was begun, this being served by two ginney systems. The first was powered by a stationary engine on the surface at the colliery. This worked a main ginney which rose for 337yds at 1 in 20 and then fell for 286yds at 1 in 17, during which it entered the drift to the underground workings (Fig.38). At the underground station the drive was transmitted, through shafting and gears, to two further ginney lines. The vertical shaft for each line had a lever operating a clutch to enable it to be put out of gear. No.1 was 1,524yds long, with a gradient of 1 in 265 falling inbye[1] for 1,165yds, followed by 360yds on the level, while No.2 rose at 1 in 36 for 1,005yds before falling for 55yds at 1 in 9 to the working area. The track gauge was 1ft 10ins, laid on wooden sleepers 6ft apart, and the tubs held only 3 hundredweights. The whole system needed 258 full tubs and 260 empties, a total of 518. When the last full tub added passed a certain point it activated a rapper, telling the boy that the next tub could now be added. A wire rapper was also used to communicate with the haulerman.

The stationary engine was a twin cylinder vertical engine, erected in 1853 but converted from a winding engine (Fig.39). It had 12½in by 24in cylinders, 6ft 10ins apart, and was served by two

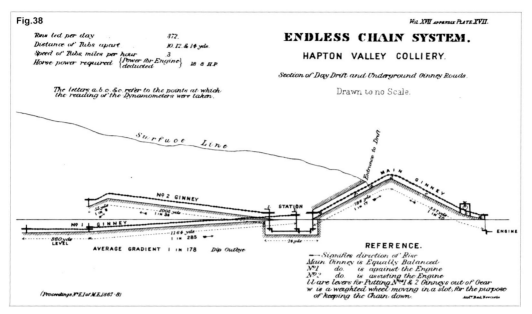

Fig.38 Section of ginney lines serving the Day Drift and underground workings at Hapton Valley Colliery, Burnley, Lancashire, 1868.

boilers 30ft 6in long by 5ft 6in in diameter. The chain, made of links from ⅝in diameter bar, is quoted as 6,414yds long, though this would seem to be the total length of chain needed. As with all endless systems, it needed to be kept in tension, and this was done by passing it round a sliding pulley to which a weight was attached.

The second system (Fig.40) began at the colliery heapstead[2] and ran to a location 1,250yds away called Barclay Mills, where the stationary engine was located. The route was undulating, with the severest gradient being 1 in 9. From Barclay Mills the engine worked a further 750-yard ginney to a loading point on a canal, as well as three short roads, each 18-20 yards long, which respectively took small coal to a washing machine, refuse to a stone heap and brought coke from coke ovens. Here 6 hundredweight tubs were used, with the system needing 83 fulls and 88 empties. The engine was built in 1854 and cost £115-0s-0d and was identical to the first, although the two boilers were only 18ft long and 5ft 6in diameter. The chain length is given as 2,500yds, presumably the length needed for the main section from the colliery.

How long the systems here continued in use is not known (the colliery did not close until 1981). The report in the NEIMME *Transactions* also lists Clifton Hall, Cornwall, Gannow, Marsden, Rowley and Townley Collieries, all near Burnley, where ginney lines were used. Despite their primitive characteristics, many systems in Lancashire survived into the twentieth century and a few until after the Second World War, notably at Bank Hall Colliery.

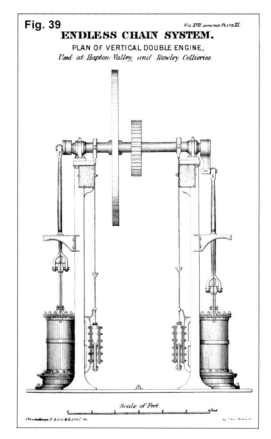

Fig.39 Elevation of vertical double engine used for endless chain haulage at Hapton Valley Colliery, Burnley, 1868.

Narrow gauge endless chain systems were also used in the brick industry to carry clay between the quarries and the brick kilns, though normally using standard rails and flanged wheels. These were a twentieth century development and so are discussed in chapter 9.

Despite the NEIMME investigation into ginney lines in 1867-68 producing a favourable report, it would seem that hardly any endless chain haulages were built in the North-East coalfield, although one was used at Langley Park Colliery in Durham at the beginning of the twentieth century (7-6). Little is

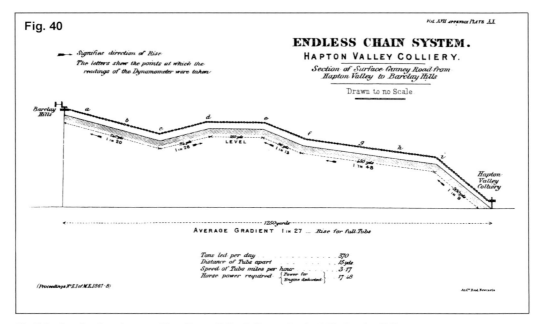

Fig.40 Section of surface ginney road from Hapton Valley Colliery to Barclay Mills, Burnley, 1868.

7-1. Surface endless chain road at Rowley Colliery, Burnley. This ginney line ran for 1,980yds between the colliery and a coal depot. It ran down from the colliery before climbing and crossing the hill in the distance. The steepest section was the first 361yds descending the hill, with a gradient of 1 in 9, seen here. The track gauge was 1ft 10ins and the tubs were attached 25yds apart.

7-2. The terminus of the endless chain system at Rowley Colliery, Burnley. It handled rather more than 400 tons per day at a speed of 3.1 m.p.h. and required 5.16 h.p., excluding the 'power for the engine and screws'. The tubs were made of iron, held 6 hundredweights and had wheels of 10¾in diameter.

known about narrow gauge haulages in the North-East in the nineteenth century, other than that many existed. Narrow gauge haulages were

extensively used underground and were commonly found on the surface also. A form of bridge rail was found, although more commonly flat-bottomed rail was used; in both cases the rail was simply spiked to the wooden sleepers.

The development from the ginney lines used ordinary rails and an overhead rope. This was known as **top endless haulage** or **over-rope haulage**. It employed a stationary engine with its rope wheel or drum at one end, usually the end to which the full tubs were travelling, and a return wheel at the other end. Fig.41 illustrates the general plan for an endless haulage. Note the 'surge wheel', the common term, at least in mining, for the drive wheel. This term arose for the following reason. Power to move the load in this system relies on friction between the sheave, or pulley, and the rope. Since the 1880s both have normally been made from steel, and so the system had to be designed to minimise slip between the two components. The usual way was to wrap the rope around the sheave a number of times, typically two and a half to three

7-3. This ginney run linked Bank Hall Colliery with Bee Hole Colliery, both at Burnley. Coal from Bee Hole Colliery, which was close to Burnley Football Club's Turf Moor ground, was taken to Bank Hall Colliery, crossing the ginney line from Rowley Colliery seen in 7-1. This view shows the line from Bank Hall emerging from the tunnel under the Queen Victoria Road, not far from the colliery, and was taken in May 1927. Bee Hole Colliery closed in 1935.

TWIN CHIMNEYS AT THE WORKS OF
JOS. PLACE & SONS, LTD., HODDLESDEN.
2846.

7-4. *New ginney lines were even opened in the twentieth century. The Hoddlesden colliery and pipe works at Darwen in Lancashire was owned by Joseph Place & Sons Ltd, a firm originally founded in 1863. In 1932 the firm opened a new drift on the moors between Hoddlesden and Edgworth and linked it to the main works here by a ginney line, seen in the centre of the picture. It continued working until the mid-1950s.*

7-5. *The last ginney line to operate was that at Old Meadows Colliery, Bacup. Old Meadows was a drift mine and closed on 14th March 1969. This view shows the tramway late in 1968. The primitive nature of the track is clearly visible. Note that discarded chain has been used for making the fencing on both sides of the line.*

7-6. *This is Langley Park Colliery, north-west of Durham City and owned by The Consett Iron Co Ltd. The colliery was opened in 1875 and re-modelled in the mid-1890s. It was almost certainly at this time that this 2ft 0in gauge top endless haulage was installed to take coal from the colliery for about ¾ mile to the colliery's beehive coke ovens. This is the simplest form of top endless, with the rope resting in a small fork on the end of the tub. The photograph was taken about 1904.*

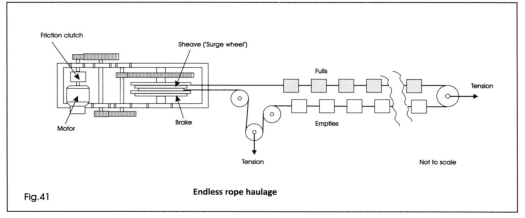

Fig.41 Diagram of endless rope haulage.

and a half turns. Further friction was obtained from installing into the system the tensioning carriage noted elsewhere, or a similar device. Despite this, under certain conditions, especially when starting the haulage, rope stretch and slippage on the drive pulley could cause the system to 'surge'. Whereas a well-designed set-up would not suffer at all from 'surge', in some installations the effect could vary between being noticeable to being alarming. In mining conditions, where the systems were simple, low powered and used only for the transport of materials, 'surge' conditions were virtually normal at start up. This was tolerable during running conditions, as long as it did not cause problems such as derailments.

7-7. This view records a scene underground at one of the collieries at Bedlington in Northumberland, probably about 1930. The vertical bar at the end of the tub was free to move in its slots, allowing the notch at the top to hold the rope secure. Note the very large sheaves on the inside of the bend to accommodate the rope round the curve. The design of the tubs is unusual and the track gauge appears larger than 2ft 0in.

7-8. This photograph shows the next common form of top endless, using a lashing chain. It was taken at Chanters Colliery at Atherton near Manchester, which was sunk in 1854; at the turn of the twentieth century it was owned by Fletcher, Burrows & Co Ltd. Note that the fulls, coming away from the shaft, are on the left and the empties on the right (presumably the men are posed for the photograph). The lashing chain is attached to the top of the tubs, which are made of wood. The track gauge is about 2ft 3in.

As with the ginney lines, tubs were then attached to the rope at intervals. Photographs usually show tubs attached singly, but it is known that, certainly underground, tubs could sometimes be grouped together in sets of up to four.

One simple system is shown in the illustration from Bedlington Colliery in Northumberland, recorded in the 1930s (photo 7-7). The vertical round bar on the end of the tub was free to move in its two slots, allowing the notch at the top to hold the rope secure. Rather more common was a system when one end of a chain about 10ft long and made of links from ⅜in bar was attached to the tub and its other end taken ahead of the tub and wrapped around the hauling rope to make two or three complete coils according to the grip required and then a hook was turned back to be caught round the hanging chain. This tightened up under tension and the tub thus moved with the rope. This had the significant disadvantages of taking time and having to be put on or taken off while the rope was moving. So it is not surprising that engineers considered ways in which a device could be put on the end of the chain and clipped quickly and simply to the rope.

Various clips were invented, but one which became common was the 'hambone clip', so called because of its shape. Here the grip was independent of the weight of the rope, so that if the attachment was

flexible and sufficiently long, as the chain attachment could be, then the clip could be attached to the rope anywhere and the rope did not have to maintain a definite height above the tub. Tubs could now be attached or detached quickly. This remained in use in collieries well into National Coal Board ownership in the second half of the twentieth century. Another top endless clip was the 'pig tail clip', so-called because of its shape.

7-9. On the left is the 'Hambone clip', which became the commonest clip used on top endless haulage. The chain to the tub was attached using the hole in the arm, and had the major advantage that the more the chain was pulled towards the tub, the tighter was the clip's grip on the rope. Interestingly, the same is not true of the right-hand illustration. If the arm was moved in the direction to which it is pointing, it would release its grip on the rope.

7-10. The Eastwell 3ft 0in gauge self-acting top endless haulage in Leicestershire, taken on 29th May 1958 near the top of the incline. Again the tubs are attached to the rope using a lashing chain - its hook can be clearly seen - but the hook at the other end of the chain was attached much lower down to a steel eye. On this system locomotives brought the tubs to the top of the incline, which took them down to a loading point on the British Railways' line between Melton Mowbray and Bottesford Junction.

7-11. The brake house at the top of the Eastwell Incline in April 1960, six months after closure. Note that closure happened with iron ore still waiting to go down; there are full tubs on the left and an empty tub still on the rope on the right. Note the change of angle between the rope and the track at the top of the incline.

7-12. The top endless haulage, using Hambone clips, bringing tubs from the Tilley seam drift in the distance to South Garesfield Colliery in north-west Durham about 1902. The gauge was 2ft 0in. Note the timber chocks to the left and pit props to the right of the waggonway, waiting to be loaded when the tubs are stationary. The man standing in the centre of the picture is the colliery undermanager.

This type of top endless haulage was adopted in other industries besides coal mining. These are far too numerous to mention in detail, but again one may be taken as an example, this time from the ironstone field in the East Midlands – and an endless system not powered by a stationary engine, but operated by gravity.

There was a very large outcrop of iron ore on the edge of the marlstone cliff in the Vale of Belvoir in Leicestershire. The Eastwell Iron Ore Co Ltd was formed to quarry this, and decided that because the cliff was 250ft high, an incline would be needed to bring the ore down to the London & North Western Railway/Great Northern Railway joint line between Melton Mowbray and Bottesford Junction in the bottom of the valley. So a double-track self-acting incline was built with 3ft 0in gauge track, about 1,000yds long, and much steeper at the top than lower down. Tubs were brought by locomotives from the quarries to the top of the incline. Here one end of a short chain was hooked on to the three link coupling on the solebar of the rear end of the tub and the other end clipped on to the rope. The large return wheel was controlled by a brakesman in a wooden building at the top of the incline. He was provided with a crude telephone to communicate with the unloading stage at the bottom, where the tubs were unloaded into standard gauge wagons. The incline began work in 1882.

7-13. Endless rope systems were often found in far-flung parts of the British Empire, installed by British engineers. Here the last section of a bottom endless system on the Mount Rochfort plateau on the South Island, New Zealand, brings coal to the bunkers at the top of the Denniston Incline (see chapter 8), about 1905; but this is a very rare example of a bottom endless system using lashing chains to attach the tubs to the rope. The tubs are also much closer together than was the practice in Britain. Note the tram of pit timber, which has taken longer to attach to the outward rope, hence the gap that it occupies. The visiting ladies suggest that the picture was taken during a Sunday afternoon walk while the haulage was stationary.

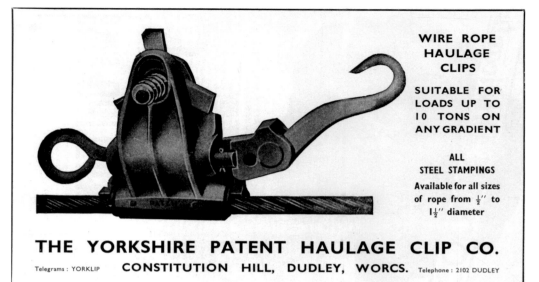

WIRE ROPE
HAULAGE
CLIPS

SUITABLE FOR
LOADS UP TO
10 TONS ON
ANY GRADIENT

ALL
STEEL STAMPINGS
Available for all sizes
of rope from $\frac{1}{2}''$ to
$1\frac{1}{2}''$ diameter

THE YORKSHIRE PATENT HAULAGE CLIP CO.

Telegrams : YORKLIP   CONSTITUTION HILL, DUDLEY, WORCS.   Telephone : 2102 DUDLEY

7-14. An advertisement from the Colliery Year Book for 1949 for what was called a 'Star Clip', the second commonest clip for bottom endless haulage. As with the Smallman clip illustrated next, the hook was put through a steel link on the tub and the jaws at the bottom placed on the rope. Hitting the arms of the 'star' with a steel rod tightened the jaws one way or loosened them when hitting the other way. This needed some skill, as mining trainees sometimes found!

SMALLMAN
HAULAGE CLIPS

Perfect Adjustment · Maximum Grip
Instant Release · Light Weight
Automatic Detachment

21 SIZES TO SUIT EVERY REQUIREMENT
STEEL THROUGHOUT   *Illustrated Catalogue*

—Patentees and Sole Manufacturers:—

JAMES W. SMALLMAN LTD.
NUNEATON, ENGLAND

Central Office: **10 Priory Row, Coventry**   Phone: **64536 Coventry**

7-15. An advertisement for Smallman clips, also commonly found in books for the coal trade in the 1940s and 1950s. A description is given in the text.

Latterly the tubs were made of steel with flared sides. They were an unusual design, measuring 5ft 7in long by 6ft 6in wide by 3ft 0in deep and carrying between 30 and 35 hundredweights of ore. The incline closed on 21st October 1959, the last of the 29 haulages in the East Midlands ironstone field to operate.[3]

Top endless haulage did have disadvantages, not least of having a moving rope at about chest or waist height and also the problem of taking it round a curve, which required either sheaves suspended from the roof or mounted on a frame fixed to stone or brick inside the curve. So **bottom endless haulage**, or **under-rope haulage**, was developed. This operated in the same way, but the rope was kept at ground level between the rails. As with top endless, the rope moved at between 2 and 4 m.p.h. and was about an inch in diameter. Again various types of clip were developed to attach the tubs to the rope, but the types which became the most commonly used were the 'star clip' (7-14) and the Smallman clip (7-15), named after the firm which invented it. In this two steel cheeks are held together by a bolt, a spring keeping them apart at a distance determined by a nut. At the lower part of the clip are two jaws about six inches long, lined with soft iron to grip the rope, while at the upper part of the clip is a recess in which the block, carried at the end of the clamping lever, moves. The parts are so designed that when the clamping lever is forced downwards the block on the other end moves upwards. The

7-16. Photographs of bottom endless systems above ground are rare, but one such system was used at the Irthlingborough ironstone mines in Northamptonshire. These were taken over by Richard Thomas & Co Ltd in 1936 (Richard Thomas & Baldwins Ltd from 1945) and developed on a scale not seen elsewhere in the Midlands ironstone industry. On the one hand there was extensive underground mining, serviced by electric trolley locomotives built to 3ft 0in gauge, while in 1938 the company built a large sinter plant. Sinter is a coke-like material with a higher iron content, produced by heating up a mixture of crushed iron ore, crushed coke and various other additives. Between the mine and the sinter plant were six long sidings. From the mines the electric locomotives brought out their trains of full tubs, normally 25 to a set with each tub carrying three tons, and then collected their empties to return underground. The sidings were equipped with a bottom endless rope system, allowing tubs to be brought as required to the sinter plant for unloading. The system is known to have included a pulley in a pit from which was suspended a concrete weight for tensioning the rope. This photograph was taken on 27th May 1965, just four months before the mines ceased production.

upper edges of the cheeks are forced apart and the lower ones come together, thus clamping the rope between them if the nut is properly adjusted. The clip is provided with a hook to attach it to the two-link coupling on the tub. Thus like the hambone clip for top endless, tubs could be quickly attached and detached from the rope.

There was also bottom endless haulage which was reciprocal, that is, an endless rope with a set permanently attached to it. This was the normal practice when the haulage was used underground for man-riding, which happened quite often, especially before locomotives became more common underground. This type of haulage used higher power motors and hauled faster, sometimes exceeding 15 m.p.h.

The simplest form of powered narrow gauge rope haulage was known as **direct haulage**. The engine was used to haul the load up the gradient and then lowered the empties down using gravity, or with the hauler in gear to control the speed. Very steep gradients were not a problem, but the minimum gradient had to be steep enough to

allow the descending load, with the rope attached, to reach the foot of the incline. Whilst in most cases the hauler was situated at the top of the incline, it was not uncommon to site the hauler at the foot of the bank and haul by means of a return wheel at the top. The landing usually had a kip for the tubs to come up over so that the rope could be detached. Such inclines were of course single line, with sets being run alternately. As photographs show, in some places direct haulage was also used for 'man-riding' - taking the men in tubs to a landing from where they could walk to their work places. Usually a considerable number of tubs were brought together to form a set, usually at least a dozen, but sometimes twice that or more.

Direct haulage was not possible where the gradients were undulating, and endless haulages, hauling spaced out single tubs, had limitations on the capacity they could handle. Consequently the coal industry grew to favour what became known as **main-and-tail haulage**. This was a single-track haulage system operated by a haulage engine with two drums, each with a separate rope. The engine was usually located at the inbye

7-17. This shows two simple direct haulages, hauling full tubs from the floor of a deep limestone quarry. The location is Ford Quarry at South Hylton near Sunderland in County Durham, owned for many years by the Washington Chemical Co Ltd. The quarry had been started in 1894, but as it became deeper in the 1930s the rope haulages were introduced. The method was simple, with the rope simply being put on to a hook on the tub's solebar. Up to four full side-tipping tubs were hauled out at a time. Note that the quarrymen are all digging by hand. The inclines were replaced by a covered conveyor belt in the 1960s. The quarry continued to be worked until 1980.

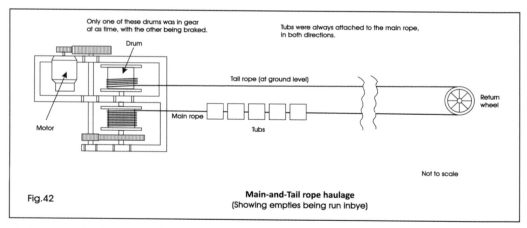

Fig.42 Diagram of main-and-tail haulage.

end of the system. The main rope was attached to the outbye end of the set of tubs, and the tail rope passed around a sheave and attached to the rear end of the set. To draw the full set out, the main rope was wound in, the tail rope being allowed to run free. The main rope ran over horizontal rollers in the middle of the track, with the necessary angles sheaves for corners, while the tail rope was taken over pulleys fixed at one side of the track. To draw the empty set in, the tail rope was wound in,

with the main rope being allowed to run free. Depending on circumstances, the unwound tail rope could be equal to twice the length of the haulage road or could be considerably less.

Main-and-tail haulages only needed one track, or 'road', and so took up less room than endless haulages. They were operated at higher speeds than endless systems, 8 m.p.h. being average. They also ran with very large sets; several dozen tubs in

A. T. WATSON, NEWCASTLE-ON-TYNE.

HAMSTERLEY COLLIERY, DURHAM.

7-18. Hamsterley Colliery in north-west Durham comprised a number of drifts, which were worked by various forms of narrow gauge rope haulage. On the left a set of empties is being lowered by direct haulage. Trains of 20 to 30 half-ton tubs were run. Note that two people are sitting in the train. To the right is a bottom endless rope system, with the full tubs, on the right, travelling from the drift to the main colliery buildings in the distance; because of this, the attachment of the tubs to the rope cannot be seen.

7-19. Lilley Drift in north-west Durham, seen here about 1900, was another location comprising various drifts. A man-riding train can be seen in the foreground, apparently on a direct haulage; but note also the haulages going up the hillside, one to what appears to be a new drift, and the much longer haulage going further away; these would probably be worked by a main-and-tail system. The wires being carried on wooden posts carried the electric bell signals 'rapped' to the haulerman to give him instructions.

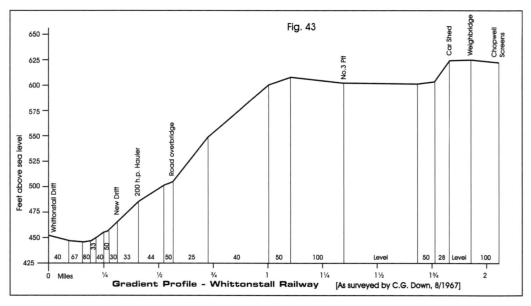

Fig.43 The gradient profile of the Whittonstall Railway (main-and-tail haulage) in Northumberland and Co.Durham, as surveyed in August 1967.

7-20. The 2-mile long 2ft 2in gauge railway between Whittonstall Drift in Northumberland and Chopwell Colliery in north-west Durham was unique. It was built by The Consett Iron Co Ltd in 1908 to be worked by electric locomotives but most of it was converted to main-and-tail haulage in 1913, hauling sets of sixty tubs. After a period of closure it was re-opened by the National Coal Board in 1953 and re-graded over the next two years so that no gradient was steeper than 1 in 25. Here tubs filled with pit props (left) and coal (right) wait at Whittonstall on 19th March 1966. The tubs held 11 hundredweights of coal.

7-21. Looking towards Chopwell, about ½ mile east of Whittonstall, on 19th March 1966. The main rope lies between the rails, the tail rope to the right of the track, supported on the other side of the bridge by sheaves outside the rails.

7-22. The miners had previously travelled between Chopwell and Whittonstall in open tubs, but in November 1957 the NCB purchased three man-riding cars, a master car and two slave cars, from D.Wickham & Co Ltd of Ware in Hertfordshire, makers nos. 7677-79. The master car was fitted with a governor that cut in at 9 m.p.h. to apply hydraulic brakes on the slave cars, thus preventing a runaway if the haulage rope should break. Hydraulic suspension was also fitted, as was manually-operated sanding gear. As the cars were to be used on an exposed, overland line they were fitted with fully-enclosed bodies having four doors on each side, the end two sliding and the middle two hinged, with each car having 24 wooden seats. They are here seen at Chopwell on 16th December 1957. However, they were only used until February 1961, when they were replaced by a bus service.

7-23. This was latterly the hauler house for the system, the former winding house for Chopwell No.2 Pit. It housed a 300 b.h.p. electric hauler built in 1913 and moved here in 1953. Seen here on 19th March 1966, the ropes came out of the building just below the middle windows. The system closed on 25th November 1966.

a set was commonplace underground. They were also sometimes used on the surface, though sadly they were rarely visited or recorded by industrial railway enthusiasts. However, it is possible to include some pictures of one of them, the Whittonstall Railway, which ran for just over two miles between Whittonstall Drift in Northumberland and Chopwell in north-west Durham. Its gradient profile shows some quite severe gradients, and one visitor to Chopwell remembered watching it:

'hardly had an empty set [of sixty tubs] been re-formed at Chopwell than the main rope began to slide past one's feet, denoting the departure of another full set from the drifts. Then followed the slapping of the rope over the manically-revolving rollers, and a quarter of an hour later there was the roar of tiny wheels and a cloud of dust as the set appeared over the rise and rattled to a halt. Within a few moments the rope ends had been transferred to another empty set and off it went in the direction of Whittonstall.'[4]

For many years in the nineteenth century haulage underground, of both coal and materials was undertaken by ponies. There were limits on how much ponies could pull, the gradients they could climb and the hours they could work. Equally, in the large collieries the demands of output began to challenge the quantities that ponies could

handle. So the more powerful owners began to install haulages underground. For many years, when haulages were operated by steam, there were three different ways in which the stationary engines and their boilers could be set up. The first was to have both the engine and the boilers on the surface. This had advantages of convenience, but meant that the ropes had to go down the shaft and then be taken through ninety degrees to go inbye. The second system involved locating the engine underground but retaining the boilers on the surface, a system commonly found if the colliery had a central boiler house. This avoided the ropes going down the shaft, but replaced them with high pressure steam pipes, which took up valuable room and were difficult to maintain. A third method was to install both the engine and the boilers underground. Whilst this might seem to be the best solution, it also raised issues about the disposal of the smoke and exhaust steam, as well as the need for an unpolluted water supply, as the often chemically-contaminated water found underground was completely unsuitable. Sometimes stationary engines worked by compressed air were installed. This could be brought from the surface and distributed more easily underground, and was 'safe'. Although it was inefficient, it was favoured by some colliery engineers for haulage underground.

This all began to change about the turn of the twentieth century, with the development of

7-24. A general view of part of Victoria Garesfield Colliery, probably dating from the early 1920s. Two long batteries of beehive coke ovens can be seen. At the end of both batteries two horizontal return wheels can be seen, but with one wheel offset to the other; what was the purpose of this? The reason for track on top of the ovens is explained in the text.

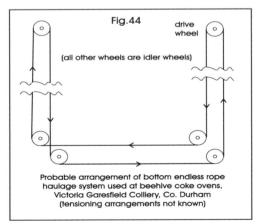

Fig.44

drive wheel

(all other wheels are idler wheels)

Probable arrangement of bottom endless rope
haulage system used at beehive coke ovens,
Victoria Garesfield Colliery, Co. Durham
(tensioning arrangements not known)

7-25. Three 'top runners', the men who worked the tubs out on to the ovens at Victoria Garesfield and then discharged their coal into the oven – and at their feet what is clearly a bottom endless rope haulage system, with the set of tubs behind them clipped to the rope. The dome of the oven, with its charging hole lid, can also be seen. Note how the fishplates holding the rail joints together have been used both to secure a sheave and to bolt a tie bar to hold the track to gauge.

electricity. There were fewer problems with installing electric haulers underground, and as the power of the haulers increased, so did the speed of the haulages. But this in turn increased the dangers. Electricity underground for haulages, pumps and other equipment was one thing, but electric lighting was limited to the shaft bottom and a few other places; for very many years the main source of illumination underground was only the flame in a safety lamp. Because of this, haulage work was easily the main source of fatal accidents underground. This fact was recognised when electric cap lamps were introduced; haulage workers had priority for these until sufficient lamps were available for general use.

Given the general darkness and dangerous conditions underground, and the use of rope haulages sometimes well over a mile long, it was therefore essential to have a simple but effective signalling system to communicate a range of different messages not just from one end of the haulage to the other but also anywhere along it, so that the set could be stopped quickly in an emergency. This was commonly done by using two galvanised iron wires about six inches apart and stretching them along small insulators. Ideally the wires were placed on the opposite side of the roadway from the refuges for the workmen, to avoid them being used accidentally. Signals

VICTORIA GARESFIELD COLLIERY

BROCKWELL SEAM (SPEN DISTRICTS)

MAIN AND TAIL ROPE HAULAGE

	(Rings)
TO STOP	1
" HAUL INBYE	2
" HAUL OUTBYE	3
" SLACK TAIL ROPE	4
" TIGHTEN TAIL ROPE	5
" SLACK MAIN ROPE	6
" TIGHTEN MAIN ROPE	7
" GO TO 1st. WEST LANDING	8
" TO 2nd. WEST LANDING	9
" GO TO NORTH WEST X COT LANDING	10
	11
ROLLEYWAYMAN WANTED	12
ATTEND TO TELEPHONE	13
	14
ENGINE PLANE BLOCKED-ROPES NOT TO MOVE	15
PLANE CLEAR	21

7-26. An enamel plate, now preserved by the North of England Institute of Mining & Mechanical Engineers in Newcastle upon Tyne, showing the different rap codes used on an underground main-and-tail haulage in the Brockwell Seam at Victoria Garesfield Colliery in north-west Durham.

could then be sent from the haulage by using a 'rapper', a metal device gripped by the fingers from underneath, which then rang a bell in the hauler house. This could also be done from anywhere along the circuit by a man pressing the wires together with his fingers or by placing an iron pin across them, thus short circuiting them and making the bell ring. Sounding the bell was known as 'rapping' and different numbers of 'raps' gave specific instructions. As these developed and became more complicated, they had to be approved by the mine manager and were often displayed on enamel plates in important places (photo 7-26). The bell codes for operating the Whittonstall Railway's main-and-tail haulage are also recorded. They were: 'Stop (1 bell/rap), Haul inbye (2 raps), Haul outbye (3 raps), Slack off tail rope (4 raps), Tighten tail rope (5 raps), Slack off main rope (6 raps), Tighten main rope (7 raps), All clear (8 raps), Assistance wanted (10 raps), Rapped back full (11 raps), Attend telephone (12 raps), Switch current off (13 raps). (There was no 9-bell code)'.[5]

Nor were these narrow gauge haulages found only in the coalfields. For example, Huglith barytes mine near Pontesbury in Shropshire used a main-and-tail system underground to haul full tubs for about a mile to the (inclined) shaft for winding to the surface. Then engineers sometimes decided to try using rope haulage as a substitute for other types of power. One interesting discovery is illustrated in No.7-24 and No.7-25. The first picture, from a local resident, shows a general view of Victoria Garesfield Colliery with its batteries of beehive coke ovens in the foreground. These were loaded with crushed coal via charging holes at the top of each oven. This was usually done by hand - by a man pushing a tub out to where it was required. However, some collieries with large numbers of ovens introduced small steam locomotives to do this job. The second picture, from the Regional Resource Centre at the Beamish Museum, shows some of the tubs of coal which were run out on top of the ovens. This was clearly a rare example of bottom endless rope haulage being used for this job, with the pulleys handling the rope to work in both directions. Back to the general picture, and there were clearly return wheels for the ropes at the ends of the batteries, but at first sight more wheels than were needed? Not so, as Fig.44 explains. But using ropes for the job may not have been a completely satisfactory solution to the problem. Planks had to be laid outside the rails for the men, and there was clearly a major risk of a man losing a foot or some other serious injury. The ropes here seem to have been abandoned in the 1930s, although the last 193 beehive ovens here survived until May 1958, the last such ovens to work in Britain. Recent research has revealed a similar system on the beehive

7-27. A picture said to have been taken at a bottle works in Gateshead, Co.Durham, about 1880. It shows a rope haulage, but nothing is known about it.

ovens at Blaydon Burn Colliery, also owned by The Priestman Collieries Ltd, and there is also known to have been rope haulage on the coke ovens at Rockingham Colliery near Barnsley in Yorkshire.

An old photograph (7-27, above) can sometimes bring to light a rope haulage long forgotten. This shows a bottle works at Gateshead about 1880 – and a narrow gauge rail track with a rope, but nothing else is known about this haulage.

****

The area of Britain where there was a far higher concentration of narrow gauge inclines than anywhere else was North Wales, in the slate and granite quarrying industries. Here there were sometimes huge mountains of slate, often to be quarried on 'levels'. Everywhere slate and its waste usually had to travel downhill to the bottoms of the valleys for onward transport, either by railways or tramways to the sea for shipment, or by main line railways. But whereas the vast majority of haulages studied earlier in this chapter were powered, in North Wales the stone was nearly always travelling downhill, and

so the majority of the inclines were self-acting, or 'counterbalanced', as they were called In Wales.

It would be impossible in a book of this size to attempt to study all the inclines in the area. One can only marvel at their number. Blaenau Ffestiniog was the centre of the Welsh slate industry, and Fig.45 gives some idea of the number of inclines in this area alone. Fig.46 takes one of the largest quarries there, Oakeley, to show the inclines it needed – but is also somewhat misleading, as Oakeley was one of the quarries where underground mining was developed extensively. There were more than fifty miles of 2ft 0in gauge track underground here and one of the underground inclines had no fewer than six tracks. Gradients were often very severe, steeper than 1 in 10, with all the difficulties that this entailed. The location of inclines in quarries changed over time, as the needs of quarrying changed and the need for internal transport increased, and then declined as the industry declined.

At the top of these inclines the drum houses were substantial buildings. Two large pillars, built of course of slate, supported a cast iron frame. This

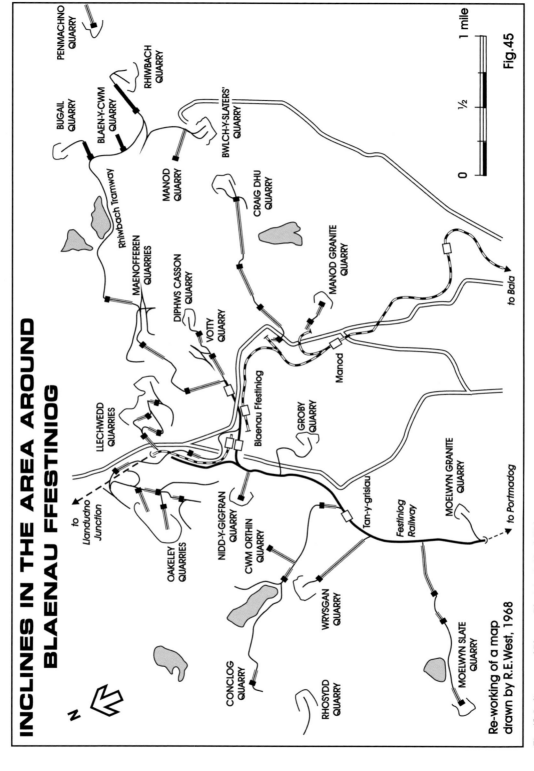

INCLINES IN THE AREA AROUND BLAENAU FFESTINIOG

PENMACHNO QUARRY

BUGAIL QUARRY

BLAEN-Y-CWM QUARRY

RHIWBACH QUARRY

Rhiwbach Tramway

MANOD QUARRY

BWLCH-Y-SLATERS' QUARRY

MAENOFFEREN QUARRIES

CRAIG DHU QUARRY

DIPHWS CASSON QUARRY

VOTTY QUARRY

MANOD GRANITE QUARRY

LLECHWEDD QUARRIES

Blaenau Ffestiniog

GROBY QUARRY

Manod

to Bala

to Llandudno Junction

OAKELEY QUARRIES

NIDD-Y-GIGFRAN QUARRY

CWM ORTHIN QUARRY

Tan-y-grisiau

Festiniog Railway

MOELWYN GRANITE QUARRY

to Portmadog

WRYSGAN QUARRY

CONCLOG QUARRY

RHOSYDD QUARRY

MOELWYN SLATE QUARRY

Re-working of a map drawn by R.E.West, 1968

0   ½   1 mile

Fig.45

Fig. 45. Inclines around Blaenau Ffestiniog in North Wales.

208

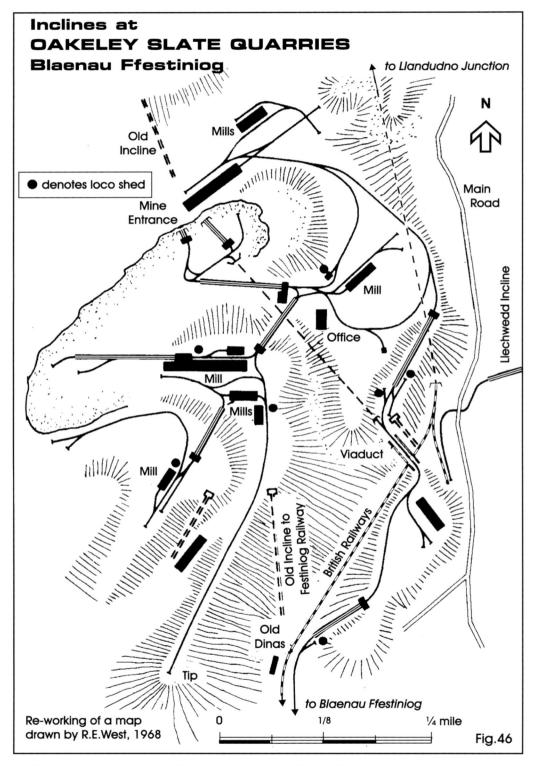

Fig.46 Diagram showing the surface inclines only at Oakeley Quarry, Blaenau Ffestiniog.

7-28. *The view in June 2003 looking across the upper reaches of the Cwm Croesor:*

1. *The Rhosydd drum house at the top of the Rhosydd Incline.*
2. *The top of the incline and the tramway to the right. The gradient of this section was steeper than 1 in 1.*
3. *The bottom of the incline 670ft lower down. At this point the Rhosydd tramway joined the incline from the Croesor Quarry, whose route can be seen to the left. Then followed a level stretch to the left to the head of the Blaen-y-Cwm Incline.*
4. *The Blaen-y-Cwm incline took the tramway down a further 180ft to the comparatively level valley floor.*

Croesor Quarry closed in 1930, but it was decided to keep the pumps there operating in the hope of re-opening. The supply of fuel oil needed for the pumps continued to use the incline, with its upwards progress being balanced by waste rock taken down. The quarry was finally provided with road access in 1944 and the closure of the incline soon followed.

in turn supported a large single wooden drum, with one end of the rope coming off the top and the other coming off the bottom. Alternatively, the drum could be divided in the middle with a rope on each half, with the rope ends coming off the drum in the same way. A hand-operated band brake was fitted to one side of the drum and the building was surmounted by a slate roof, highly desirable given the high rainfall in North Wales. The inclines themselves usually comprised two parallel tracks, thus avoiding the complications of having points. Operating an incline here was known as 'crewling'.

Many of these inclines were very steep, but the steepest was exceptional. About eight miles from Porthmadog, on a remote moor lay what became Rhosydd Quarry. This was begun in the 1840s and initially it had to rely on packhorses and then horses and carts to remove the slate. Its nearest rail connection was four miles away at Tan-y-

grisiau on the Ffestiniog Railway, but this route was not available, so it was decided to make a connection to the 2ft gauge Croesor Tramway, which had its own route down to Porthmadog. This tramway was horse-worked in its upper sections and the quarry owners had to supply their own horses and waggons and pay a fee to use the tramway.

From the quarry the track had to be laid on a narrow shelf cut out of the mountain side, but it was relatively level, until the head of the Cwm Croesor [Croesor valley] was reached, where the first incline was needed, presenting immense difficulties. The vertical drop was 670ft and the horizontal distance was 1,250ft, giving an average gradient of 1 in 1.86. However, at the top the mountainside was practically vertical, with the result that the upper section of the incline was about 1 in 0.97. Partly because of the steepness of this section and partly because of lack of space,

7-29. A pair of self-acting inclines at the Dinorwic Quarries at Llanberis. One set of tracks used the 'ballast' method described in the text, the other was a conventional self-acting incline.

the drumhouse for the incline could not be placed at the top but had to be built some 55ft higher. The brake to control the speed of the wagon was operated using a wheel on a small platform at the top of the incline, connected to the drum by a cable. Given the location, exposed to rain and strong winds, the brakesman was no doubt grateful for the small wind shelter that was provided for him. The track layout at the top comprised a small turntable and a loop line, allowing upward and downward traffic to pass. Only one wagon in each direction at a time was permitted because of the extreme gradient. Whilst the outward traffic was mostly slate, everything needed to service the quarry had to brought in – wood, windows, oil, doors, machinery, pipes, coal, furniture, candles and food.

Inclines were commonly used within slate quarries to connect working levels. Sometimes an incline would cross more than one level, allowing wagons to be moved from a high level to much further down in a single movement. In order to accommodate the intermediate levels, turnouts were sometimes used to allow wagons to leave and to join the incline part way along its length.

7-30. The bottom section of one of the numerous self-acting inclines at Dinorwic, not long before the quarry's closure in 1969.

One arrangement to achieve this was used at the huge Dinorwic Quarries at Llanberis. Although slate working here began in the eighteenth century, it really began to develop after 1830, becoming the second largest slate producer in the world after the Penrhyn Quarries. At its fullest development it comprised two main quarries with twenty galleries in each, with a number of ancillary workings, and covered nearly three square kilometres. It had numerous inclines, some of which used the 'ballast' method to link to intermediate inclines. This used the usual two-track incline, but with one track reserved for fully loaded wagons and the second for partially loaded wagons. The line used by the partially loaded wagons was known as the 'ballast track' and it had a stop placed on it part way down. The distance from the top of the incline to the stop was the same as the distance that the fully loaded wagons needed to travel. Empty wagons were hauled up the incline from the bottom, counterbalanced by ballast wagons descending, the two sets meeting at the stop point. The empties were then detached and replaced with full wagons, and as these descended the ballast wagons were returned to the top of the incline. One of the major inclines at Dinorwic had four parallel tracks, two worked by the ballast method and two as a conventional self-acting incline (see 7-29).

A few quarries replaced the rope with an endless chain, passing around horizontal sheaves at the summit and the foot, which allowed greater flexibility in the way loads could be moved. Besides the Felin Fawr Incline illustrated here (7-31), there

7-31. This was the best-known endless chain self-acting incline in the Welsh slate industry, the Felin Fawr Incline at the Penrhyn Quarries at Bethesda. Felin Fawr was the site of the quarries' extensive workshops, and the incline formed the throat for dispatching slate from the quarries down to the Penrhyn Railway at the bottom, where one of its steam locomotives is waiting for its next train. The wagons were connected to the endless chain by a short chain with a hook at each end, one for hooking to the wagon, the other for hooking to the chain. A chain for the next set lies across the rail, as does a simple steel chock.

7-32. The 'table' used at Moelferna Quarry near Glyndyfrdwy, in what was then Merionethshire. A 2ft 0in gauge system was used in the quarry and in the underground workings, and at one time slate travelled on the 2ft 7in horse and gravity operated Deeside Tramway to reach the Great Western Railway at Glyndyfrdwy Station. The latter was replaced by a road about 1947, but the system seen here on 11th August 1957 continued in use until the closure of the quarry in 1960.

7-33. The table incline at Dinorwic in April 2007, preserved as part of the National Slate Museum at Llanberis. The incline was originally operated by gravity, but is now operated by an electric motor.

were also endless chain inclines at Dinorwic, Goleuwern Quarry in the Mawddach area, which was worked between 1867 and 1920, and Hafodlas Quarry near Betws-y-Coed, which closed in the 1930s.

'Table' inclines were also developed, where one or two larger wagons carrying slate were pushed side by side on to a larger horizontal table. These ran on track built to a wider gauge and allowed an incline to handle four wagons (two fulls and two empties) at the same time. At least two inclines of this type were used underground. One was at Rhosydd Quarry, where a massive underground transporter was counterbalanced by a vehicle, effectively four heavy castings bolted together and running on wheels, which ran underneath it, the rope passing round sheaves at the top of the incline. Another such vehicle was used at the Parys Mountain, the huge copper mine on Anglesey.

With plentiful supplies of water, which were normally free, it is not surprising that from its earliest days the slate industry devised various ways to use it. The first water-wheel to operate an incline is believed to have been installed at Penrhyn about 1810. A 'water engine' and its incline are recorded in the accounts for Cilgwyn Quarry in 1823; Cilgwyn, in the Nantlle valley, is believed to date from the 12th century and to be the oldest quarry in Wales. The next recorded example is on the Festiniog Railway, operational from 1836, where the original plan to drive a tunnel through the col of the Moelwyn Bach was shelved in favour of two inclines, designed by no less than Robert Stephenson. The lower one was a standard self-acting incline, but the upper one, raising the slate wagons to the summit, was worked by a water wheel at its foot. The wheel measured 24ft in diameter by 3ft wide, and a stream called the Nant Ystradau was dammed to supply its water, but how it drove the incline is not known. The two inclines survived until 1842, when the 730-yard Meolwyn Tunnel was driven to make them redundant. This allowed slate to descend all the way from Blaenau Ffestiniog to Porthmadog by gravity.

Water wheels were installed to work inclines at Bryn Hafod-y-Wern Quarry in the Ogwen valley in 1848, although because the quarry was entirely dependent on water power, via a leat at least five miles long, it was forced to close in 1884 when Lord Penrhyn cut off its water supply. They also provided the source of power to enable loaded wagons to be raised upwards, a problem which became increasing acute when slate waste had to be dumped at a higher level than the working gallery. They could also be used to raise slate from

underground to the surface, or between levels underground. Several other water wheels were constructed to drive inclines in the 1860s. The largest was the No.5 Incline at Llechwedd Quarry at Blaenau Ffestiniog. This quarry had been started in 1846 by John W. Greaves and it developed into one of the largest of the Welsh slate quarries and mines, with over 25 miles of underground tunnels, some up to 900ft below ground level. The plans for No.5 Incline, dated June 1867, show three independent tracks, each with its own drum on the one spindle, which could be engaged and disengaged by clutches. Also at Llechwedd a surface water wheel worked an incline underground.

At least two inclines were operated by 'pelton wheels', the impulse water turbine invented by the American Lester Allan Pelton (1829-1908) in the late 1870s. This extracts energy from the impulse of moving water, rather than from its weight, like a traditional water wheel. A pelton wheel was installed at Rhosydd in 1899 and another at Parc Quarry, another of the quarries linked to the Croesor Tramway; it was opened in 1870 and closed in 1920. As these wheels were much more efficient and produced much more power than a traditional water wheel, one wonders what their impact was on a traditional incline. Indeed, little has been published generally about the use of water wheels to drive inclines, and more research is needed to establish the mechanics of how they worked. Water wheels were also used in Cornwall (see chapter 8).

A water balance was a far more common method of operating inclines, again as a solution to raising waste slate for dumping at a higher level than where it was being worked. A steel tank with an open top was mounted on a wooden frame. With the tank at the top of the incline and the wagon of waste slate at the bottom, the tank was filled from a pipe until its weight exceeded that of the wagon at the bottom, so that the tank descended the incline, hauling up the wagon of waste. Once at the bottom, the tank was emptied and then raised back to the top of the incline. Sometimes the load was carried on a wagon transporter. Such inclines were adopted at many quarries in Gwynedd, the last examples being used at Aberllefenni Quarry near Corris. This quarry was the longest continually-operated slate quarry in the world until its closure in 2003, with its earliest recorded working dating from 1500; for many years it dispatched its output via the Corris Railway down to Machynlleth Station. Its water-balanced inclines finally became disused in the 1950s. Water balances were not confined to North Wales; one was used at the Lady's Rake Mine in Teesdale, a lead mine about nine miles south east of Alston, though again little research has yet been done.

7-34. The last slate 'quarry' (most of its workings were underground) to use water balanced inclines was Aberllefenni Quarry near Corris. Despite about fifty years having passed since it was abandoned, the drumhouse, its incline and the tank wagon, seen here in May 2002, are remarkably well preserved.

7-35. A close-up view of the tank wagon, a simple riveted tank mounted on a wooden frame, in March 1999. Note that the rope is still attached.

7-36. This view shows four of the eight large water balance inclines at the Penrhyn Quarries. On the far right a full wagon of slate rubbish is about to be pushed off the transporter while an emptied tub is being pushed on to descend. The water tanks can be clearly seen behind the two balances nearest to the right.

Double-acting water balances were rare, though substantial examples were built at Penrhyn Quarries, where again waste needed to be raised to a higher level than the working area. The two moveable platforms comprising each incline formed transporters, each with a water tank beneath. An empty wagon with a full tank of water would haul up a loaded wagon with an empty tank. Large water tanks were built close by to supply the water to fill empty tanks. The first of these seems to have been built about 1855 and others were subsequently added, until finally eight were in use. One of them has been preserved (see 10-37), but as the quarries remain operational there is no public access.

The first steam engine to power an incline was installed at Cloddfa'r Coed Quarry near Bethesda about 1819, but it was not until 1847 that the next record is found, at Bryn Hafod-y-Wern Quarry (see above). After this, steam engines gained favour, helped by coal being imported into the area. It was in the larger Ffestiniog quarries, where considerable amounts of slate and rubble had to be up-hauled quickly from workings underground, that steam-powered inclines became vitally important. In 1854 a steam engine was installed at Rhiwbryfdir Quarry, later Oakeley Quarry, at Blaenau Ffestiniog, owned by Samuel Holland the younger (1803-1892),

another of the leading quarry proprietors in the industry. This engine operated wooden drums and centralised waste tipping. This lasted until about 1890 when it was either replaced or rebuilt by the engineering company of De Winton & Co[6] at Caernarvon. At the same time the incline was also rebuilt, with six parallel tracks on a gradient of 1 in 2½ with all working independently, each branching off to a different level in the mine, the longest rope being 890ft.

On a smaller scale, this type of incline, with one power source driving more than one incline, became quite common in the Ffestiniog region. The water-wheel incline at Llechwedd Quarries was operated by a horizontal steam engine by 1895, and there was a similar system developed between 1881 and 1895 at Maenofferen Quarries to the north, with a stationary steam engine operating three tracks.

Two remote quarries in the Ffestiniog group were unusual in that they lay below their exit railway and as a result they installed a single track incline powered by a stationary engine at the bottom, with a horizontal return wheel at the top. In 1863 Rhiwbach Quarry installed a horizontal steam engine built by the Haigh Foundry of Wigan in Lancashire, which besides the main incline also operated the slate mill, the shaft and two inclines underground. The neighbouring Blaen-y-Cwm Quarry installed a similar incline between 1872 and 1876, again powered by a stationary engine at its foot which also powered the slate mill.

The next development was the gradual adoption of electricity. Here again the quarries around Blaenau Ffestiniog took the lead. Llechwedd Quarry was the first, beginning its experiments in 1890. Given the high rainfall, there was great potential to develop hydro-electric power. In 1904 Llechwedd opened its own direct current generating station, and in the same year Croesor Quarry opened a 350kw alternate current generating station, one of the major initiatives at the quarry by their Cornish manager, Moses Kellow (1862-1943). Three years earlier the nearby Votty & Bowydd Quarry electrified three steam-powered inclines using six and four-pole Sandycroft motors.

In 1906 Oakeley Quarry invested in five 200 h.p. Bruce Peebles BS90 motors, one of which was installed to operate the six-track steam incline, the rest to other inclines in the quarry. The six track system was to last until the closure of the quarry in 1970. Conversion of the main incline at Maenofferen Quarry took place about 1911, and continued in use until at least 1995. During the First World War Llechwedd's No.5 Incline, mentioned earlier, was converted to operation by a 150 h.p.

General Electric Company motor, winding at four feet a second through a countershaft and gears. Its other main incline went over from water-balance operation to electrical power in the 1920s. The last steam winder to survive was at one of the more remote Ffestiniog quarries, Cwt-y-Bugail Quarry, which began continuous production in 1863. Sometime between its opening and 1870 the owners installed an Aveling & Porter traction engine, taken off its wheels. It survived the closure of the quarry in 1961 and was eventually removed for preservation in 2003.

In the twentieth century, particularly in the smaller workings, smaller inclines came to be powered either by compressed air winches or by internal combustion engines. These were cheap to install, especially if cobbled together by the quarry blacksmith, and cheap to operate.

Some of the bigger slate quarries also installed 'Blondins' – rope inclines without rails. They were a type of aerial ropeway and were used to transport wagons loaded with slate between different locations and to return the empties. They were named after the famous French tight-rope artist Charles Blondin (1824-1897). The first was invented about 1860, but the first quarry in Wales to adopt them was Penrhyn, where they were in use by 1913.

7-37. The first three 'blondins' at the Penrhyn Quarries in 1913, with all three carrying loaded wagons of slate.

7-38. A slate wagon suspended in part of Dinorwic Quarry at Llanberis, now part of the preservation scheme, in March 2005.

Penrhyn Quarry had developed around a single large pit over 400ft deep, worked as a series of terraces. A variety of means were used to transport slate from the terraces to the mills where the rock was processed. The quarry already had an extensive internal narrow gauge railway system in place and many terraces were connected via inclines. The blondins were developed to connect the more remote terraces directly to the slate mills. Two substantial slate piers were constructed, on top of which was a steel tower, with a main rope (sometimes two) slung between them. This in turn allowed a cradle to be wound out along the rope to wherever it was needed to stop and then be lowered down to the terrace. A wagon loaded with rock could be then run on to the cradle, raised and carried to another terrace served, for example, by the narrow gauge locomotives. The ropeways ran horizontally or nearly horizontally until the cradle hit a stop, at which point the wagons were automatically lowered to where they were needed for taking on further. Empty wagons could be returned similarly.

Various designs of 'blondins' were developed, some dispensing with the carrying cradle and simply lifting the wagon using chains from a central hook connected to the four corners. They were spectacular to look at, with wagons often

suspended hundreds of feet above the quarry floor. They continued in use until the 1970s, the last in use being in the Nantlle valley, at Dorothea Quarry, closed in 1970, and at Pen-yr-Orsedd Quarry, where the last 'blondins' ceased work in 1974, five years before the quarry itself closed.

As will be manifestly evident from even this small review of the Welsh slate quarries, the largest quarries were vast, comprising numerous levels. Some were quarries, their workings open to the sky, while others, while still called quarries, had most of their workings underground. As the workings expanded, so too did the difficulties facing the quarrymen travelling to and from their work.

The simplest form of 'do-it-yourself-travel' was the 'ceir gwyllt', illustrated in No.7-39. One of these could be made by a quarry blacksmith for about five shillings. At one end, situated above a small wheel, was the seat, together with a grip for the man's right hand. With his other hand he gripped the balance bar across to the other end of the car, which was fitted with a revolving sleeve. As can be seen from the picture, the ceir was designed to fit between the the left-hand rail of the right-hand track, while the tiny wheel bore on the right-hand rail of the left-hand track, not the rails of the incline itself. It was also light enough

7-39. A 'ceir gwyllt' - in Welsh, 'wild car', in English, a 'velocipede' - being used on 28th October 1897 on one of the three inclines connecting Craig Dhu Quarry near Blaenau Ffestiniog with the Festiniog & Blaenau Railway. The tramway was about 1¼ miles long. Note which rails the ends of the car travelled on.

7-40. A miners' carriage near the top of the first incline at Maenofferen Quarry near Blaenau Ffestiniog, on 19th August 1963. The carriage has a steel frame and tubular framing for the men to hold on to, while the rope is attached to the carriage by three chains for extra safety, although the seating comprises only simple wooden terracing. Note that the incline has three tracks and was only open to the sky for a few yards before entering the tunnel in the background. The track gauge was 2ft 0in.

to be carried on the shoulder between inclines. 'Ceir Gwyllt' means literally 'wild car', as the men must have remembered as they sped downhill! It was common for thirty or more men at a time to travel down an incline together. The car had a rudimentary brake, but 'speeds were high, accidents frequent and fatalities not unknown. Users would carry small children as a treat (?) and occasionally two or even three adults would share one car.'[7] There were three inclines on the tramway from Craig Dhu (see Fig.45), taking the line down 1,400ft, and at the bottom of the third (near a chapel) the men put their cars into wagons, which were subsequently hauled up the inclines ready for the next shift of men to use.

Perhaps reports of serious accidents with the ceir gwyllt persuaded the various quarry owners that some more controlled form of descending transport was needed. This would clearly have to be attached to the rope, whilst still being basic. An example is shown in No.7-40 (p.219). This has a different purpose, in that here the men are descending into the mine to start work, rather than going home at the end of their shift. The incline illustrated went down for about half a mile at 1 in 4, from where a second incline, entirely underground and about the same length, went on into the mine.

The final illustration (No.7-41) shows a carriage in the 1960s, with better comfort for the men, but only allowed to carry eight people. One wonders

7-41. This shows a further improvement to the design of miners' carriages. There are now proper bench seats, on which men can sit comfortably and grip the back of the seat in front, although the 'No Standing' rule is being broken. This is near the foot of the 'C' Incline at Oakeley Quarry on 18th January 1964, showing a Government minister (on the left at the front) on an official visit. Here too the track gauge was 2ft 0in.

how many journeys had to be made to carry everyone working on a shift – and how the men managed for journeys in the opposite direction.

From the beginning of the nineteenth century, as more quarries were opened and output rose, improving the system of transport between the quarry and the sea became increasingly critical. The Penrhyn Tramway, opened in 1801, led the way and transformed the prosperity of the quarry, showing that the tramways in the quarry districts were an indispensable part of the quarrying process. The lines hauled the finished product out, but importantly also hauled in the raw materials - machinery, ironwork, coal, grease and later oil, as well as office equipment, stationary materials and food for horses and humans.

The Penrhyn Tramway or Railroad was 6¾ miles long and included three self-acting/balanced inclines. The great rival to Lord Penrhyn was Thomas Assheton Smith (1752-1828), who developed his quarries at Dinorwic, near Llanberis, and his port to ship his slate, Port Dinorwic[8] on the Menai Strait between Caernarvon and Bangor. In 1824 he opened the Dinorwic Railway, a 7 mile 2ft 0in gauge tramway, between the two. This involved a fall of 1,000ft, with three self-acting inclines, the twin Cwm Inclines, which took the line down about 500ft, and the Garth Incline, with a fall of a further 200ft, with quite steep gradients for the horses used elsewhere. The line was nowhere near as successful as the Penrhyn tramway, and was replaced by a new line built to 4ft 0in gauge, the Padarn Railway, in 1843.

The next line to be opened was the Nantlle Railway, in 1828. This line, 9 miles long, linked various quarries and ran down to Caernarvon. Unlike its predecessors, it was 3ft 6in gauge and had no inclines, but was also operated as a 'rail turnpike', with users providing their own wagons and horses and paying tolls at the various gates. It was extended to Pen-yr-Orsedd Quarry in the 1860s. It was absorbed by the Caernarvonshire Railway in 1865 and later by the London & North Western Railway. It was re-laid to standard gauge between Caernarvon and Penygroes in 1867, and on to Talysarn in 1872; but the remainder continued as a narrow gauge, horse-worked tramway right through until closure under British Railways in December 1963.

The Festiniog Railway, between Blaenau Ffestiniog and Portmadoc, was opened in 1835. It was approximately 13 miles long and built to a nominal 2ft 0in gauge, and after the opening of the Moelwyn Tunnel in 1842 (see above), which by-passed its two inclines, its slate trains could run the whole length of the line by gravity. Its later history is well known.

As mentioned above, the next line to open was the Padarn Railway, the replacement for the Dinorwic Railway between Llanberis and Port Dinorwic. This was built to the unusual gauge of 4ft 0in, but used transporter trucks to carry 1ft 10¾in gauge quarry wagons, four at a time. Initially horses were used, but these were replaced by locomotives in 1848. The line began alongside Llyn Peris at the foot of Dinorwic's C Inclines and then passed through a short tunnel to pick up slate wagons which had come down the A Inclines, the lower sections of which were re-routed to link with it at Gilfach Dhu. It next ran alongside Llyn Padarn and then across country for almost 7 miles with a constant fall of 1 in 200 to Penscoins on the scarp behind Port Dinorwic. Here the slate wagons were off-loaded and then run down the Penscoins Incline, the bottom section of which went through a 43-yard tunnel, taking them down 300ft to the dockside. A miners' passenger service was begun in 1885, by which time the line was more commonly known as the Dinorwic Quarries Railway. Apart from ending the passenger service in November 1947, it remained basically unchanged until closure in October 1961.

Sometime during the 1850s the Deeside Tramway was opened in the Dee valley, between a slate quarry, a mill and the road at Glyndyfrdwy. This was a 2ft 6in gauge line, unusually laid with wooden rails covered with iron sheaths. In the 1870s it was extended at both ends to three miles, linking to Moelferna Quarry and the Great Western Railway station at Glyndyfrdwy. Like the Festiniog Railway, the full slate trains were worked down by gravity and the empties worked back by horses. It ceased to operate about 1947.

Another railway about three miles long was opened in 1859, subsequently called the Corris Railway. This 2ft 3in gauge line in Mid-Wales served various slate quarries north of Corris and then ran down to the station yard at Machynlleth. Locomotives replaced horses in 1878 and five years later a legal passenger service began. The line subsequently had a chequered history, passing into the hands of the Great Western Railway in 1930, which immediately stopped its passenger service but continued a freight service until 1948. Its remaining locomotives and rolling stock were acquired by the nascent Talylynn Railway in 1951, but it has since developed into a heritage railway itself.

It was against the background of these very varied lines that the next line, the Rhiwbach Tramway, opened in 1863. This was financed by the owners of Rhiwbach Quarry, the Festiniog Slate Co, which wanted a 2ft 0in gauge route about 3½ miles long between their quarry, and others nearby, and the Festiniog Railway at Blaenau Ffestiniog. Unusually, the firm employed a professional contractor, Owen Gethin Jones (1816-1883) from Penmachno, near Betws-y-Coed, to construct it, and the quality of his work is still evident today from studying the remains of the route.

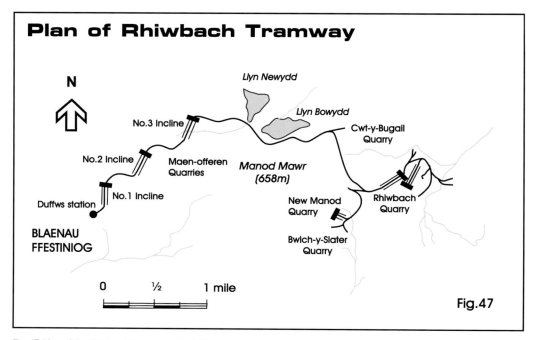

Fig.47 Plan of the Rhiwbach Tramway, North Wales.

7-42. The route of the Rhiwbach Tramway near Blaen-y-Cwm, sweeping round from the top of the incline from Rhiwbach Quarry in the top left corner, March 2009.

7-43. The trackbed of Rhiwbach Incline No.3 in August 2009, with the remains of the drumhouse clearly visible at the summit. This took the line down 250ft. In the foreground are the workings of Maenofferen Quarry.

7-44. The drum house at the summit of Rhiwbach No.2 Incline on 19th August 1975.

Starting at Rhiwbach, the slate mill engine raised wagons 200ft to the start of the tramway; the same engine also worked an incline underground, another on the surface and briefly a vertical shaft as well! Now at 1,600ft above sea level, the line was joined by branches from other quarries – Bwlch-y-Slaters Quarry, 80ft above the line, Manod Quarry (opened in 1866), Blaen-y-Cwm Quarry, which used a stationary engine to reach the line, and Cwt-y-Bugail (old) Quarry, where the slate mill engine brought wagons up to the route. From here the line was engineered for trains to descend by gravity, in the same way as noted elsewhere, although parts of the route today would raise doubts about how successful this was. After crossing the treeless countryside and skirting Llyn Bowydd and Llyn Newydd, the line reached the top of Rhiwbach No.3 self-acting incline. This took the line down 250ft (No.7-43) and a short level section near its foot allowed a link from Maenofferen Quarry, which had begun production before the tramway opened but then sent all its output this way. Maeonofferen became one of the largest slate mines in the world, with very extensive workings underground. Rhiwbach No.2 Incline dropped the line down a further 300ft. It then followed the contour for a short distance, still on a downward gradient, before reaching Rhiwbach No.1 Incline, which took it down the final 300ft to Duffws Station on the Festiniog Railway. So despite it being built in 1863, the line in concept was 40 years earlier, a mix of inclines and gravity/horse working.

Although the tramway was never an official passenger or general goods carrier, it brought up supplies for the Rhiwbach shop, while purchases made by those who walked to Blaenau on Saturdays

7-45. The derelict drum house for the same incline in February 2007.

7-46. Looking up the Rhiwbach No.2 Incline from about half way, amidst the unremitting severity of the slate industry.

came up on Mondays. Blaen-y-Cwm Quarry was the first quarry to close, about 1914. Six years later Maenofferen Quarry built a new incline across to Votty & Bowydd Quarry, enabling it to use the latter's incline down to the Festiniog Railway, only for its owners to buy Rhiwbach Quarry and the tramway in 1928, so that it could continue using the No.2 Incline to dispatch slate. Manod Quarry closed in 1930, but the other quarries continued working until after the Second World War. In fact, Cwt-y-Bugail bought a four-wheeled petrol loco and then a four-wheeled diesel loco, and these were used on the upper section of the tramway, even to the extent of running an unofficial passenger service for the miners. Rhiwbach Quarry closed in 1953 and the track from there to Cwt-y-Bugail was lifted three years later. Cwt-y-Bugail Quarry closed in 1961, with the track being lifted in 1964, while Rhiwbach No.1 Incline became disused. Maenofferen Quarry continued to use No.2 Incline, but in 1975 both the quarry and Votty & Bowydd Quarry were purchased by the owners of Llechwedd Quarry and this brought Maenofferen's use of the tramway to an end, after 112 years.

Other railways were still to come, notably the Talyllyn Railway in 1865 and the Glyn Valley Tramway in 1873, but these lines did not include any inclines.

Although the slate industry was very much the main industry in North Wales for some 150 years, there was also a significant granite quarrying industry. In the nineteenth century granite setts were much needed for roads in towns and cities dependent on horse-drawn traffic, while in the twentieth century granite chips were often used in the production of tarmacadam. Like the slate industry, granite quarries also made extensive use of self-acting inclines. Perhaps the most famous was the collection of quarries overlooking the sea at Penmaenmawr in Caernarvonshire (now Conwy). These were developed in the 1830s by two companies and were greatly stimulated by the coming of the railway in 1848. The two companies amalgamated in 1911 to form The Penmaenmawr & Welsh Granite Co Ltd.

There is not room here to give a full history and description of all the inclines at Penmaenmawr. An excellent account is given in the *Industrial Railway Record*, No.86, 1980, *The Penmaenmawr Quarry Inclines* by Philip G.Hindley, 173-191. Fig.48, drawn to show the complex in the 1950s-60s, shows 44 inclines, but Hindley lists an incredible 62 inclines, although not all were operating at the same time. Unlike the slate industry, which mostly used 2ft 0in gauge track, the gauge here was 3ft 0in. Hindley includes a large diagram with every incline

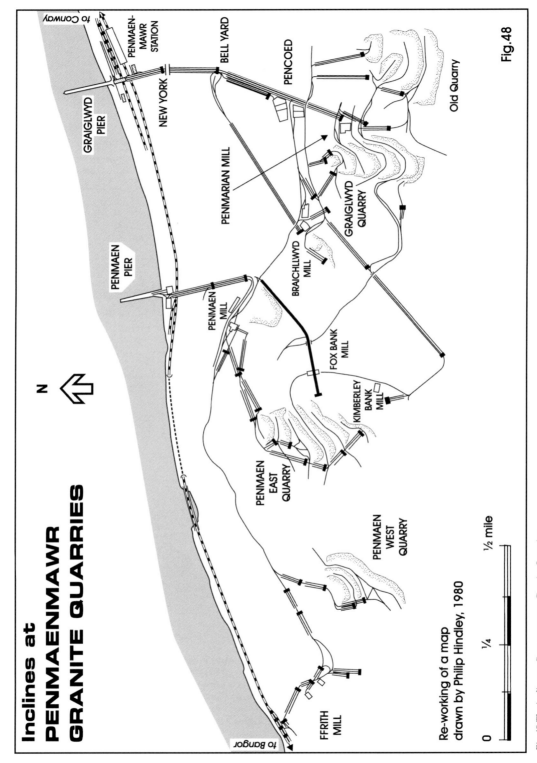

Inclines at
**PENMAENMAWR
GRANITE QUARRIES**

Re-working of a map
drawn by Philip Hindley, 1980

N

to Conway

PENMAEN-
MAWR
STATION

BELL YARD

PENCOED

Old Quarry

GRAIGLWYD
PIER

NEW YORK

PENMARIAN MILL

GRAIGLWYD
QUARRY

PENMAEN
PIER

BRAICHLLWYD
MILL

PENMAEN
MILL

FOX BANK
MILL

KIMBERLEY
BANK
MILL

PENMAEN
EAST
QUARRY

PENMAEN
WEST
QUARRY

FFRITH
MILL

to Bangor

0   ¼   ½ mile

Fig.48

Fig.48 The inclines at Penmaenmawr Granite Quarries.

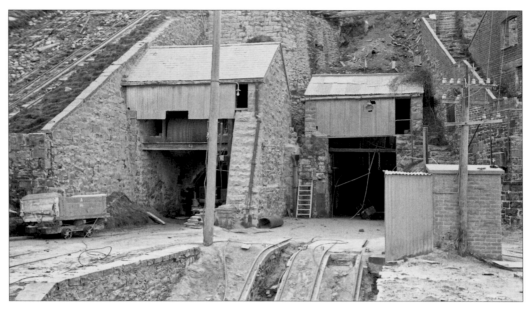

7-47. Drum houses at Penmarian on the Fourth Bank at Graiglwyd Quarry. The incline on the right was the last in use, up to the end of December 1962, but the track here had been covered in dust from the mill by the time this photograph was taken on 3rd April 1965; by 1977 it was completely buried in waste material. The inclines up to the Third and Second Banks can be seen in the upper left hand corner.

7-48. Incline landing at Top Bank, Old Quarry, the highest level of the Eastern (Graiglwyd) workings of Penmaenmawr Quarries, taken on 3rd April 1965, shortly before the drumhouse was demolished. The incline head was in a very exposed position and stone walls were provided on each side to give some shelter. The double track over the summit of the incline (the right hand rail is missing from the nearest track) was singled just before reaching the drumhouse, and then split into separate tracks for full and empty wagons. Note the timber stops in the foreground against which lengths of timber would be placed to prevent runaways and the large diameter pulleys in pits used only at the summit. On the right is the brakeman's shelter with the long brake handle connected to the brake by double rodding on timber posts, a common feature of Graiglwyd Quarry drumhouses. An inclined steel bar was fixed to the front of the drumhouse to deflect the slackened rope clear of the track and beyond that can be seen a horizontal beam across the rear of the drumhouse which marked the lower edge of the missing corrugated sheeting which originally covered the upper half of the rear of the building.

numbered, the numbers developed into a list of several pages giving further information. Most were self-acting inclines, but there were also five 'hoist', or powered inclines, three of them converted from self-acting. Published photographs show drumhouses identical to those used in the slate quarries, usually straddling the track with the wagons passing underneath. As in the slate industry, quarrying was done on a series of levels, with inclines linking them in various ways. The levels and the mills were served by an extensive locomotive-worked system. Both of the original companies had their own shipping pier, the Penmaen Pier to the west and the Graiglwyd Pier to the east, with both piers being served solely by inclines, originally single but eventually doubled in order to handle the huge output. The inclines which survived the Second World War were gradually replaced by conveyors or

by road transport. The last incline to survive lay within the Graiglwyd Quarry and brought crushed stone down from the Penmarian Mill to be tipped into the Pencoed hoppers. This was replaced by a conveyor during the Christmas holiday period of 1962. Some of the drum houses in the remoter parts of the quarries survived for some time after closure. Despite more than 150 years of intensive quarrying, the quarry continues in production (2012).

It is scarcely possible in one chapter to do more than give basic descriptions and illustrations of the main types of narrow gauge haulage and hardly to scratch the surface on the very large numbers of narrow gauge inclines in North Wales. More examples of narrow gauge haulages in the later twentieth century will be included in chapter 9.

7-49. The detail of the brake gear on one of the (disused) West Quarry inclines (the one immediately before the junction with the line from the Ffrith Mill). Note the brake liners bolted to the end frame, and the end of the rope fixed to the wooden drum with staples. The drum was about 6ft in diameter and the rope about 1in diameter.

7-50. This shows the top sections of the Graiglwyd Inclines, looking up from the Bell Yard. The lengths nearer the camera were the Pencoed inclines; this was originally built as a single incline about 1834 and was doubled about 1901. On the far right is the Lower Pencoed Incline, built about 1918. The Pencoed drums were 6ft 8in in diameter and the Lower Pencoed drum 6ft 2in. Beyond them are the Penmarian Inclines. Both pairs of inclines were replaced by conveyors in 1956, though the Lower Pencoed incline was retained and converted to single line, with a winch installed to hoist up equipment. The photograph was taken sometime between the mid 1930s and the mid 1950s.

1   Inbye is a mining term for travelling into the mine from the entrance/shaft; 'outbye' is used similarly for travelling towards the entrance/shaft; a 'landing' was the term used underground for a place where one form of rope haulage exchanged with another, or with tubs worked by ponies.

2   This is the name given to the winding gear, buildings and surface works at a colliery shaft.

3   For more information about the inclines in this area, see *The Iron Railways and Tramways of the Midlands* by Eric S. Tonks, London, 1965.

4   *The Private Railways of County Durham* by Colin E. Mountford, Melton Mowbray, 2004, 98/100.

5   *Industrial Railway Record No.39,* Sheffield, 1971, 147.

6   This firm, which owned the Union Works at Caernarvon, was founded in 1844 and ten years later it was joined by Jeffrys Parry de Winton (1829-1892). It became the main engineering works in the area, serving not only the slate industry but also undertaking marine work. De Winton left the firm in 1890 and it went bankrupt in 1901.

7   *The Slate Railways of Wales*, by Alun John Richards, Llanrwst, 2001, 66-67.

8   Now called Y Felinheli.

Chapter 8 Some unusual incline systems

Many inclines and haulages, both standard and narrow gauge, followed a pattern more or less similar to those which have been described in earlier chapters. There were inevitably some which were different, or which were very sophisticated, or which took incline design to the absolute limits. This chapter looks at a few of them, both in Britain and in other parts of the world.

The Carmears Incline, near Ponts Mill, Par, Cornwall

This is believed to have been one of the very few inclines in Britain worked by a waterwheel. There were others in Cornwall and another is reported in South Wales.

Joseph Thomas Austen (1782-1850), who changed his name to Treffry in 1838, was born in Plymouth and trained as a civil engineer. In 1813 he inherited large estates in south-eastern Cornwall. He soon began to develop the considerable mineral assets, beginning with acquiring major shares in two copper mines, which he combined into what became the Fowey Consols Mine near Ponts Mill. This he developed into one of the largest copper mines in Cornwall, which, at its height, employed around 1,700 men, women and children. Such a large mine needed major sources of power, in the form of water and steam, better shipping facilities, for which he built the artificial port of Par, constructed between 1829 and 1833, and a good transport link between the mine and the sea, for which he built a 2½ mile long canal, also opened in 1833.

With the port opened, he turned his attention to linking these developments to mineral deposits further inland, near Bugle on Goss Moor. To reach these he would have to use the steep and narrow Luxulyan Valley between Ponts Mill and the moor, and construct a standard gauge tramway, which he announced in 1835 would link Par to the harbour of Newquay on the north coast, which he had just acquired. The first stage of this would run from Ponts Mill to Molinnis, near Bugle, a distance of about six miles. This point would become a railhead both for china clay pits and for various tin mines. With the help of his land steward, William Pease, work began in 1835 on a route up the western side of the valley; but after two cuttings through the granite were begun, this route was abandoned, although some remains can still be seen. Whether this was because of the inadequacies of the contractor or for other reasons is not known.

But Treffry was determined and engaged a much more experienced engineer, James Rendel (1799-1856), based in Plymouth, who had already worked with Treffry on Par Harbour. A new route was surveyed up the eastern side of the valley, but this involved some major civil engineering, with a severe climb from the bottom to near the top of the eastern side of the valley and then a large viaduct to cross over to the western side before continuing to Molinnis. The viaduct, to be known as the Treffry Viaduct, was to be 650ft long and 98ft high with ten arches, each with a span of 40ft, the biggest construction project in the south-west peninsula up to that time. Work began in 1837 on the first stage, from Ponts Mill to Colcerrow and Carbeans Quarries, which were to supply the granite for the viaduct. There are no known illustrations of the work in progress, and the only information from this period comes from William Pease's diaries, now in the Cornwall Record Office.

From Ponts Mill the first section of the planned line was to rise 300ft in 2,840ft, a gradient of about 1 in 9 for about half a mile, while from the top the line continued more or less on the level for a further 1¼ miles before branching to reach the quarries. With such a severe gradient, rope haulage was unavoidable and it was decided that the incline would be worked by a water-wheel. How that decision was reached is unknown, but it may well be because numerous large diameter water wheels were already working at Fowey Consuls Mine for winding and crushing duties, so that their engineering technology was already well known. Water would be carried across the viaduct/aqueduct underneath the tramway and then down the leat to the water-wheel, after which it would join the already-existing Carmears leat to provide additional water for the wheels, steam engines and dressing floors at Fowey Consuls.

With this section opened, work on the magnificent combined viaduct and aqueduct began in 1839. From the top of the incline to Molinnis was 3¼ miles, this section being worked by horses. Almost certainly the line was opened throughout at the beginning of 1844, conveying minerals out and coal, fuel and fertilisers in. By 1844 work had also started in earnest at Newquay, coming inland, and two lines were opened in 1849. But Treffry, a man of exceptional energy, imagination and vision, with interests in every Cornish industry, died in 1850 and his estate passed into Chancery. To avoid the transhipment of traffic at the canal

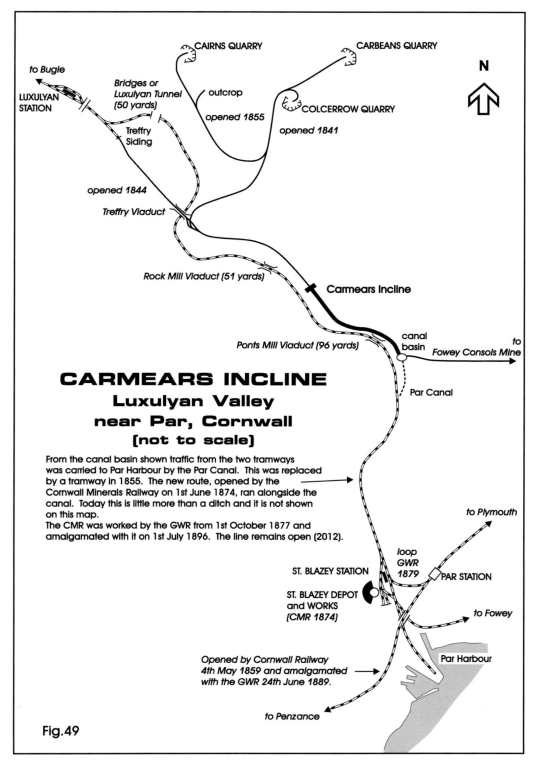

CAIRNS QUARRY

CARBEANS QUARRY

N

to Bugle

LUXULYAN
STATION

*Bridges or
Luxulyan Tunnel
(50 yards)*

outcrop

opened 1855

COLCERROW QUARRY

opened 1841

*Treffry
Siding*

opened 1844

Treffry Viaduct

Rock Mill Viaduct (51 yards)

Carmears Incline

*canal
basin*

*to
Fowey Consols Mine*

Ponts Mill Viaduct (96 yards)

Par Canal

CARMEARS INCLINE
Luxulyan Valley
near Par, Cornwall
(not to scale)

From the canal basin shown traffic from the two tramways
was carried to Par Harbour by the Par Canal. This was replaced
by a tramway in 1855. The new route, opened by the
Cornwall Minerals Railway on 1st June 1874, ran alongside the
canal. Today this is little more than a ditch and it is not shown
on this map.
The CMR was worked by the GWR from 1st October 1877 and
amalgamated with it on 1st July 1896. The line remains open (2012).

to Plymouth

*loop
GWR
1879*

ST. BLAZEY STATION

PAR STATION

ST. BLAZEY DEPOT
and WORKS
(CMR 1874)

to Fowey

Opened by Cornwall Railway
4th May 1859 and amalgamated
with the GWR 24th June 1889.

Par Harbour

to Penzance

Fig.49

Fig.49 The Treffry Tramway, Cornwall.

8-1. Looking up the trackbed of the Carmears Incline from near the bottom on 12th May 2010. Despite closure in 1874, hundreds of the granite setts survive, many with the imprint of the cast iron chairs that were fixed to them.

basin, the tramway was extended to Par in 1855 and the canal abandoned, but the link between the original tramway and the Newquay system was never built. Various depressions in Cornish trade meant there was less money for investment and less need for the link.

The bottom of the incline was situated alongside the canal basin which also served the mine. Today this area has been filled in and levelled to make a car park, but the remainder of the trackbed is now a public bridleway. There are no illustrations of the incline, nor any written description of how it was operated, so that how this was done can now only be deduced from what can still be seen and from knowledge of other inclines and of water-wheel practice.

The track on the incline was laid on granite setts, almost all of which survive, together with a few rail chairs and pins. There are similar blocks, also with two pin holes, in the 'four foot', which accommodated the support for the rope, but it is an open question whether rollers or sheaves were used; on the Portreath Incline in west Cornwall, which was straight (see photo 2-11), sheaves were used on one section and rollers on the remainder. In November 2010 very heavy rain scoured the top surface from the lower section of the trackbed, exposing all the granite setts (photo 8-3); these have now been left exposed after consolidation.

8-2. One of the triangular setts, with its three bolt holes showing where an angled sheave was fixed to retain the rope between the rails. One of the surviving iron chairs can also be seen. 12th May 2010.

8-3. *Very heavy rain on 17th November 2010 scoured the trackbed of the incline, exposing all three previously-covered rows of granite setts, with those for the rails nearest and furthest from the camera and the central set for the sheaves. Subsequent consolidation work left the rows exposed for visitors to see.*

8-4. *The curve in the middle section of the incline on 12th May 2010. Note the cant, a rare feature on an incline.*

About half way up the incline, now in Carmears Woods, is a right-hand curve, which unusually in incline design is canted into the curve; perhaps this was done so that runaway wagons would be derailed away from the steep descent into the valley. On this section the rope blocks continue in the four foot but are roughly triangular but with three pin holes. This must mean that the rope was not allowed to swing across against vertical rollers on the inside of the curve, but was retained on angled sheaves between the rails, similar to the Pwllyrhebog Incline (see photo 8-9)). The route shows no evidence of a passing place, so that descending and ascending wagons must have been run alternately. The gradient here was 1 in 9, the same as the Middleton Incline on the Cromford & High Peak Railway, and as only two wagons at a time were run there, at a speed not exceeding five miles per hour, it is likely that the same rules applied here.

It is the top of the incline which presents the greatest difficulties of interpretation. The wheel pit, which when the tramway was built housed a 30ft diameter overshot wheel, survives, together with the still-running leat, but it is situated at right-angles to and about 20ft below the tramway. The route divides into two tracks at this point, which must mean that one was used for ascending wagons and the other for wagons awaiting descent. Apart from

8-5. The wheelpit from the bottom, on 12th May 2010. Still to be seen are the axle of a 40ft overshot waterwheel, one of its wooden spokes and various pinions on either side of the pit, but these are from the equipment installed in the 1890s to grind chinastone, not from the earlier wheel used to work the incline. Water from the leat, brought over the nearby Treffry Viaduct/Aqueduct, flows as fast as ever.

a stone hut at the top of the incline and a larger stone building set well away from the tramway which does not appear on either of the first two editions of the Ordnance Survey maps, the only other surviving feature in this area is a mound of natural rock, left when the surrounding area was levelled, on top of which is some masonry, in all about 25ft high. Set into the top of the masonry are two holes a foot square, in line with the wheel pit. A view in Cornwall is that there might have been a drum on the wheel shaft, from which came a rope, elevated over the tramway to reach a wheel on the top of the mound, which went through about 270 degrees and then descended to the bank head. To the author this seems not to follow any rope haulage practice known elsewhere, to be a cumbersome engineering solution and to present operating difficulties, and indeed the mound is also not shown on either of the first two Ordnance Survey maps. It would seem more likely that the drive from the wheel was transmitted through flat rodding, driven by a crank on the wheel shaft and taken through 90 degrees at tramway level to run alongside the track to the point where the track from the bank head divides into two. Here there may well have been an elevated drum, similar to that shown on the Froghall Incline in Staffordshire (see photo 1-2), with its single rope coming off the bottom of the drum and fitted with a similar large wooden band brake. If this was what was installed here, then the wheel would be used to rotate the drum to haul the wagon(s) up the incline. When they were near the top of the incline the leat would be closed in order for the wheel to slow and then stop. This would allow the rope to go slack and be detached and the wagons to run down the slightly descending gradient into the road next to the wheel pit. The drum would then be put out of gear and the descending wagons would then be brought forward, probably up to a chock at the bank head. The rope would be attached, the chock removed and the brake applied, this being used to control the speed down to the foot of the incline. Nothing is known about the communication between the two ends of the incline. There is currently no written, visual or physical evidence to support these ideas, though some archaeological excavation in critical places would help to support or disprove these suggestions.

In 1872 some London businessmen came to Cornwall and formed the Cornwall Minerals Railway. This took over the Treffry tramways and planned a new route to link Par with Newquay, including a new and steeply-graded line up the Luxulyan Valley which would pass under the Treffry Viaduct/Aqueduct. It obtained its Act in July 1873, including powers to convert sections of the tramway into railways 'adapted to the use of Locomotive Engines'. The new line was opened for traffic on 1st June 1874, bringing with it the end of traffic over the incline.

It was not quite the end for the wheel pit or the upper tramway route, for in the last decade of the nineteenth century the West of England China Clay Company installed a 40 ft wheel to drive two sets of china stone grinding pans on each side of the wheel pit, and the site was served by a long siding, running from a junction near Luxulyan Station over the viaduct/aqueduct. Production ended in 1908 and the wheel became derelict. In 1942 the wooden buildings, and possibly the wheel, caught fire. The wheel shaft and some of the metal plates on it can still be seen, as can the china stone grinding pits and some of their gearing. As early as the beginning of the twentieth century the Luxulyan Valley and the route of the trackbed had become a popular Sunday walk and today the valley is still a much-appreciated destination for walkers and horse riders. In 1992 the Treffry Estate gave the viaduct to the Cornish Heritage Trust and in July 2006 the valley was included as part of the 'Cornwall & West Devon Mining Landscape World Heritage Site', or 'Cornish Mining', due to its important copper mining associations. As mentioned above, the trackbed up the incline and over the viaduct/aqueduct is now a public bridleway and a safe viewing area has been created near the wheel pit, while the 1874 railway from Par to Newquay also continues in use.

William Pease's diaries record another incline built by Treffry which is also believed to have been worked by a water-wheel. This was at Fowey,

rising 200ft on a gradient of 1 in 3, taking the produce of the limekiln at Caffamill Pill to the land above.

The Pwllyrhebog Incline, near Tonypandy, Glamorgan

Coal mining in the Rhondda Fach area of Glamorgan had begun by 1850 and developed steadily thereafter. This was in turn stimulated by the growth of the largest of the railways of South Wales, the Taff Vale Railway. Its main line between Cardiff and Merthyr was opened throughout in April 1841, and two months later the company began to move into the Rhondda valleys by opening a 4½ mile branch from Pontypridd to Dinas. This was extended up the Rhondda Fawr for a further 6¼ miles to Treherbert and opened only for goods traffic on 7th August 1856. A year later the Taff Vale obtained its Act for the Pwllyrhebog branch, running from a junction about a mile north of Dinas for about a mile up the ravine-like valley of the River Clydach, where further exploration for coal was planned. The name ('yr is Welsh for 'the', 'hebog' for 'hawk' and 'pwll' for 'pool' or 'pit') came not after a nearby settlement but a 1450-feet high mountain, Mynydd Pwllyrhebog, to the south of the Vale of Clydach. Passenger services up to Treherbert were begun on 7th January 1863, and about the same time the branch opened too, just for freight, with Blaenclydach Colliery about to open. At the top of the incline the branch divided, the left hand line serving Blaenclydach Colliery and the right hand serving Blaenclydach Goods

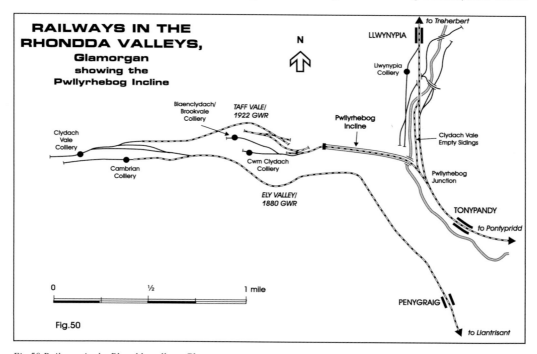

Fig.50 Railways in the Rhondda valleys, Glamorgan.

Depot, via two reverses. At first the Taff Vale ownership stopped at the top of the incline, and presumably the colliery company was responsible for handling traffic over approximately a mile between the colliery and the incline; the Taff Vale purchased this section in 1899.

The opening of the railway stimulated more mining exploration in the valley; Cwm Clydach Colliery opened in 1864, Clydach Vale Colliery in 1874 and Clydach Vale No.2 two years later, all of them linked to the branch. This encouraged the Great Western Railway to enter the valley. The Ely & Clydach Valleys Railway was built as an extension of the GWR line from Llantrisant to Penygraig northwards for 1¾ miles. It was opened on 10th August 1878 and worked by the GWR, which absorbed it in 1880. In 1889 the two branches were linked by the Clydach Vale Colliery Private Railway, which linked the Clydach Vale Colliery to Blaenclydach Goods and so meant the collieries could use either railway to dispatch their coal; the Taff Vale Railway purchased the Private Railway in 1899. Clydach Vale No.3, also known as Cambrian Colliery, opened in 1891. Cwm Clydach Colliery was closed in 1897, but was subsequently re-opened as part of Blaenclydach Colliery, which was re-named Brookvale Colliery after it passed to the ownership of the Rhondda Coal Company. The Clydach Vale Collieries passed to the Powell Duffryn Associated Collieries Ltd in 1935, which closed No.3 Colliery the following year and then purchased Brookvale Colliery in 1940, leaving the three collieries to pass to the National Coal Board in 1947.

As the Pwllyrhebog branch included ½ mile at 1 in 13 and a further ¼ mile at 1 in 29, a rope incline was unavoidable. With the coal travelling downhill, a self-acting incline was the obvious solution; but perhaps fearful of the steep gradient increasing the risk of the brakesman losing control of the wagons or of the damage which might be caused if the rope broke, the Taff Vale company decided to use a steam locomotive on the downhill end of every set. This was almost unique in Britain, though locomotives were similarly used on the Penponds and Tresavean Inclines, both also self-acting, on the Hayle Railway in Cornwall[1] and on the Werneth Incline at Oldham (see chapter 5). According to the Railway Correspondence & Travel Society's *Locomotives of the Great Western Railway, Part 10 – Absorbed Engines*, the hauling gear installed here came from the Dowlais Incline. This incline was worked by a stationary engine as part of a line opened in 1851 and built by the Dowlais Iron Company between its works and the Taff Vale's Merthyr Station; it closed about 1930. It seems strange that equipment from an incline only 12 years old and of a different design should be acquired second hand for this incline. The Pwllyrhebog Incline was double track throughout and utilised two drums in a deep pit at the bank top. Each drum had its own rope but the two drums were fitted on the same shaft, so that as one rope was paid out the other was wound in. The brakes were controlled by a brakesman in a large brick brake cabin near the bank top. This also served as a signal box, as indicated below.

8-6. The view away from the top of the Pwllyrhebog Incline looking towards the collieries on 8th August 1951, just over a month after closure, showing the brick brake cabin/signal box and the corrugated iron loco shed beyond, built in 1919.

At the beginning the locomotives used on the incline were old locomotives on the Surplus Stock list, which was begun in 1864, although the identity of those used here do not survive. As traffic increased, the TVR ordered two four-coupled saddletank locomotives to shunt at the top of the incline. These came from Hudswell, Clarke & Rodgers of Leeds, Works Nos. 160 of 1875 and 165 of 1876. The first, Taff Vale No.106, was small, with only 8in by 15in cylinders and 2ft 6in diameter wheels, and the second, No.107, was not much larger, with 10in by 16in cylinders and 2ft 9in wheels. Their duties were subsequently taken over by larger engines. They were re-numbered 266 and 267 in Surplus Stock in 1891 and survived to pass to the GWR in 1922 as 1343 and 1342, being scrapped in 1926.

Surplus Stock locomotives by definition had a short life expectancy and it clearly became a nuisance to be dismantling the haulage fitments from one loco and fitting them to another. So in 1884 the TVR's Locomotive Superintendent between 1873 and 1911, Mr. Tom Hurry Riches (1846-1911), drew up a special design of 0-6-0T specifically for working on this incline. Three were ordered from Kitson & Co Ltd of Leeds, which was the TVR's main supplier of locomotives in the 1870s and 1880s. They received Works Nos. 2697-99 and were all delivered in December 1884, at a cost of £2,260 each, Taff Vale numbers 141-3. As the only locomotives in Britain designed to spend their lives on a rope incline, and the first in Britain to be built with coned, or tapered, boilers, their principal dimensions deserve to be quoted in full:
Wheels : 5ft 3in, larger than might be expected, but which gave ample clearance over the sheaves on the bottom section of the incline.
Wheelbase: 7ft 3in + 7ft 9in = 15ft 0in.
The boiler barrel was 10ft 3in long and was built in two rings. The front ring, which was parallel, was 5ft 2¾in long by 4ft 2in diameter, while the back ring, horizontal at the bottom, was tapered upwards by 6in to a maximum of 4ft 8in diameter at the throat plate; this ensured ample steam space. With the locomotives destined to face downhill, the inner firebox crown was steeply sloped so that the firebox plates would always be adequately covered with water. There were 187 1¾in tubes, giving a tube heating surface of 808.60 sq. ft; with a firebox heating surface of 67.96 sq. ft, so that the total heating surface was 876.56 sq. ft. The grate area was 15 sq. ft and the boiler pressure 140 lbs. The water capacity was 900 gallons and the coal capacity 1¼ tons, so that the loco fully laden weighed 44 tons 15 cwts, with a maximum axle load of 15 tons. In the 1892 Taff Vale classification of its locomotives, they became the 'H' class. They were reboilered in 1897-8 and again in 1915-6. This time the boilers had three rings, the front ring the same as before, but the middle ring

4ft 5¹³⁄₁₆in, coned 6in to a maximum of 4ft 8in, while the back ring was parallel but only 6⅞in long. Various internal changes increased the total heating surface to 963.5 sq. ft but reduced the grate area to 14.67 sq. ft. At the same time the drag brakes with which the locomotives had been built were removed, presumably because they were felt to be unnecessary.

There appears to be no nineteenth century record of how the locomotives were attached to the ropes, and one can only assume that what was done in later years was very similar. With Nos. 141-3 a strong bar was fitted to the rear buffer beam. This clearly had the same purpose as the 'donkey' described in chapters 3 and 5, namely to keep the rope down in the sheaves between the rails. It would seem that the bottom of the bar was forked, with each fork having a hole through which a D-shackle was fitted. It would seem almost certain that the forks had a releasable section through which the D-shackle was put in position, but how this was secured and released is not clear. Attached to this shackle was a short length of heavy chain, which in turn was secured to a socket at the end of the rope. In addition, a small chain from the bar was bolted to the left hand frame. This was essential to keep the rope

8-7. The rope apparatus as fitted to the rear end of 0-6-0T 194 (Kitson 2698/1884), seen at the foot of the incline on 4th May 1951. Note the vertical steel bar fitted to the underside of the buffer beam, which was essential to keep the rope close to the ground and within the angled sheaves on the curve at the bottom of the incline.

8-8. 0-6-0T 193 (Kitson 2697/1884) descending the 1 in 13 upper section of the incline, probably early in 1949. The loco did not haul or brake, the speed of the sets being controlled by the brakesman in the cabin at the top of the incline.

8-9. The bottom of the incline on 4th May 1951, showing the ninety-degree curve here and the large angled sheaves necessary to retain the rope between the rails, as on the Carmears Incline described earlier. The need for the locomotives' valve gear to clear these large sheaves was the reason why their wheels were 5ft 3in in diameter.

on the angled sheaves on the 90 degree curve near the foot of the incline. When the train had reached the other end of the incline and the rope was slack, the section in the steel ring was released by a lever mechanism on the back of the bunker operated by the fireman, thus allowing the shackle to fall out. However, this description is not known to be supported by any written evidence.

Again, although there is no written record, it would seem likely that when a set of wagons was ready to travel over the incline, it would be drawn by the locomotive over the rope at the top, or propelled over the rope at the bottom, so that the rope could be attached. The Appendix to the No.9 Section of the British Railways (Western Region) Working Timetable for 1950 required that at the top of the incline a guard and a shunter, one on each side, were to pin down whatever wagon brakes were necessary. When a train was ready to leave the top, the foreman at the top rang one bell to 'call attention' to the shunter at the bottom, which was acknowledged by repetition. The foreman would then ring 3 beats for 'Is Line Clear', and close the safety points near the top of the incline. When the train at the bottom was ready, the shunter would acknowledge the three beats and then reverse the lever to operate the starting signal at the top of the incline, which then locked the safety points in position. When the train at the top began to leave the top of the incline the foreman would ring two beats on the bell to indicate 'Train entering section', which the shunter at the bottom would acknowledge. The regulator on the ascending locomotive was opened slightly to get the train on the move, but once moving the counterbalancing took over. It was the responsibility of both of the locomotive drivers and the brakesman to ensure that the speed of the trains did not exceed five miles an hour. When the shunter was satisfied that the descending train was below the safety points, he would return the signal to danger, allowing the foreman to open the points to safeguard the train from runaway wagons. A guard rode on the footplate of each locomotive, carrying a brake stick in case there was a need to alight and pin down further brakes. In the event of an emergency the driver of the train involved was to sound his brake whistle, which would be acknowledged by the driver of the other locomotive and the brakesman (although how he did this is not known), with all three applying their brakes. Once at the bottom the fireman (or the shunter) would operate the release mechanism and the locomotive would draw the train away from the bank foot and then propel it up into Clydach Vale Sidings alongside the main line to Merthyr, thus avoiding the occupation of the main line. It would then bring empties back, propelling them over the rope end to the point for the rope to be re-connected to the loco. The locomotive at

the top of the incline would propel the wagons to the collieries and bring back fulls, and it also had to shunt the Goods Depot.

It is recorded that a loco shed was built for these locomotives in 1884 near Blaenclydach Colliery, although it would seem unlikely that there was not a shed here before this. This was replaced in 1919 by a corrugated iron building near the top of the incline immediately behind the brake cabin. Only basic servicing and preparation duties were done here; for boiler washouts and maintenance the locomotives returned to their parent shed at Treherbert. The Taff Vale Working Timetable for April 1897 listed two locomotives as required on the incline between 7.00am and 6.00pm, with a third handling traffic between the incline top and Clydach Vale Colliery when required between 7.00am and 5.00pm.

If the locomotives working on the incline were very busy, it was possible for there to be traffic waiting to work over the incline when only one locomotive was available. To overcome this problem, by 1913 the Taff Vale had allocated two old tenders here, Nos. 276 and 302, subsequently joined by a third, No.160. The Working Timetable gave the permitted loadings as follows:

**Incline - ascending
(counterbalanced by another loco)**
10 empties or 5 loaded with pitwood
**Incline – ascending
(counterbalanced by two old tenders)**
8 empties or 4 loaded with pitwood
**Incline – descending
(counterbalanced by another loco)**
10 loaded 12-ton wagons or 6 loaded 20-ton wagons
**Incline – descending
(counterbalanced by two old tenders)**
8 loaded 12-ton wagons or 5 loaded 20-ton wagons.

Again, there is no surviving account of how the incline was operated when two tenders were used. One would have thought that operating requirements would want them coupled together, rather than at each end of the wagons, with the rope attached to the rear of the first tender at the downhill end and then running back under the second tender and the wagons.

Almost certainly an increase in traffic brought about the introduction of the tenders, and two years later, in 1915, the TVR decided that it was necessary to have four locomotives dedicated for working the incline; this practice continued under GWR ownership after 1922. The additional locomotive came from stock and was not fitted with the special boilers carried by Nos.141-3, and

8-10. In 1932 the GWR decided to replace the rope drums, making new ones at Swindon Works and then conveying them on well wagons to South Wales. As with many GWR activities, especially the more unusual ones, everything was photographed, and this view shows the old drums being removed from their pit.

so almost certainly worked chimney-first uphill. This was certainly the case with the final Great Western locomotive allocated here, 57XX class 0-6-0PT No. 7722. This loco had the rope apparatus attached to its front buffer beam, and it would seem likely that its predecessors were so fitted also. This position meant that the fireman could not operate the release mechanism, so presumably the shunter had to release the shackle.

The first additional locomotive to be allocated here was No.151, a 'M' class 0-6-2T. Kitsons had started to build these engines immediately after the Pwllyrhebog locomotives, and No.151, Kitson 2708, was added to stock in January 1885. She had the same cylinders as Nos.141-3 and was slightly more powerful and heavy, but she had only 4ft 6in diameter wheels, which were clearly not a problem on the incline. Her arrival meant that it was now possible for the four locomotives to work in pairs, with two weeks on the incline and two weeks back at Treherbert for repairs and maintenance.

In 1922 the Taff Vale Railway was absorbed into the Great Western Railway, which re-numbered 141-3 to 792-4 and 151 to 552. The last was withdrawn in August 1930 and was put on the Sales List, though not sold. She was replaced by another former Taff Vale 0-6-2T, No.107, GWR 486, one of

the 'N' class, which was almost identical with the 'M' class apart from a slightly larger diameter boiler. 107 (numbered briefly 191 when new)/486 was the last of the class to be built – Kitson 3391 of 1891 - and the last to survive. The GWR did little to the original locomotives apart from replacing the spring balance safety valves with Ross 'pop' valves in 1928.

The ropes were almost certainly replaced regularly, as on all inclines. A new one authorised by the GWR Locomotive Committee in December 1928 cost £600. By this time it is hardly surprising that the original drums were worn out. One source suggests that the GWR considered installing a stationary engine here, but eventually it was decided to replace both of the drums and their shaft, and this work was carried out in 1932. It is said that as a result of this repair, the limit on the maximum number of wagons was raised to 16, but this number was noted by a visitor in July 1931. By March 1950 this had been reduced to ten empties or five wagons of pitwood up, with either ten loaded 12-ton wagons or six loaded 20-ton wagons down.

Loco 486 was eventually withdrawn in November 1934. She was also put on the Sales List, but found no takers and was cut up at Swindon in the summer of 1936. Her replacement was No. 2750.

She had been built as an 0-6-0ST at Swindon in June 1899 as a member of the 2721 class, and had been fitted with pannier tanks in June 1915. After six months without replacing 486, 2750 was fitted with the rope attachment gear in May 1935. She in turn was withdrawn in November 1945, and again after a gap of six months, a 5700 class 0-6-0PT, No. 7722, was fitted with the gear in May 1946. She had been built in June 1930, not at Swindon, but at The North British Locomotive Company Ltd's Queen's Park Works at Glasgow as part of a Government scheme to alleviate the effects of the trade depression after 1929. The 5700 class was a modernised version of the 2721 class, with the same sized cylinders and wheels. The incline passed to British Railways on 1st January 1948. A re-numbering scheme in 1948-9 saw Nos.792-4 re-numbered Nos.193-5 in June and September 1948 and February 1949 respectively.

In 1947 Brookvale Colliery was closed, leaving only the two pits of the Cambrian Colliery still sending coal down the incline. With the Ely Valley route also available for this, it was inevitable that the incline could be dispensed with, and it closed on 1st July 1951. Had the photographer R.C.Riley not visited the foot of the incline in May 1951, there would be little surviving visual record of the actual incline and the apparatus used on the locomotives.

Initially locos Nos.193-5 were all put into store at Treherbert. 195 was the first to leave, sold in November 1951 to the National Coal Board for use at its Treorchy loco shed, which served Dare and Park Collieries; she was scrapped on site in April 1957. 193 went next, also sold to the NCB in February 1952 for use at the Caerphilly Tar Plant. Curiously, in February 1957 she was sent for use as a stationary boiler to Roath West Docks in Cardiff, possibly on hire to the Admiralty, who were known to bring corvettes into these docks for boiler maintenance. She returned to Caerphilly at the end of August 1957, but did little work in later years and was cut up on site in January 1960, the last of these three locomotives to survive. 194 also spent short periods on hire to the NCB, but was not withdrawn until November 1953 – after which, curiously, she was also hired to the Caerphilly Tar Plant, apparently to cover 193's transfer in January 1954 for repairs at the NCB's Central Workshops at Tredegar. She ceased work at Caerphilly on 14th April 1954 and was sent to Swindon for scrap on 28th April 1954, the only occasion when one of these locomotives visited the GWR locomotive headquarters. Loco 7722, with its incline gear removed, went back into traffic. It stayed in the Cardiff Valleys Division until 1958, when it was transferred to Old Oak Common in London. It was eventually withdrawn from Stourbridge shed in November 1960.

As for the incline itself, it was reported in 1952 that the water tank and its column at the foot of the incline still remained; but a visitor to the top of the incline in mid-1954 reported that all the facilities there had been removed.

8-11. 0-6-0T 195 (Kitson 2699/1884) standing outside the loco shed on 14th October 1949. Normally only two locomotives were kept here, with both in use, the other two being at the parent shed at Treherbert. As can be seen, the locomotives had to be coaled by hand from an adjacent wagon.

The Khojak Tunnel Inclines, India

Although Britain saw some railway companies trying to build railways to prevent their rivals getting control of an area, it did not in general experience the concept of railways being built for political and military reasons. Yet in the expansion and development of the British Empire during the nineteenth and twentieth centuries the construction of railways for these reasons was a major aim.

Influential political opinion in London in the 1870s held the view that the competing empires of Britain and Russia were bound to clash in Central Asia at some point, with Russia's eventual goal being the invasion and seizure of Britain's prize possession, India. This attack seemed likely to be made from Afghanistan and so Britain's aim should be to forestall Russia by gaining political influence there and then building a railway, both to tap Afghani trade and to be able to move troops quickly. To achieve this the Kandahar State Railways was formed, with the aim of linking Sukkar in the province of Sindh to the south-east east, through Quetta, a strategic location in India's north-west frontier area and on to Kandahar in Afghanistan. War broke out between Britain and Afghanistan in 1878 and lasted for two years, ending in a British victory which secured British influence but without the presence of British troops. Work on the railway had begun in 1879, but in 1888 the section to Kandahar was shelved and the project re-named the Chaman Extension Railway, Chaman being on the border between India (now Pakistan) and Afghanistan. But to reach Chaman the line was faced with the mountain range of Khwaja Amran, which reached over 7,200ft. This was regarded as insurmountable, so instead it was decided to drive a tunnel nearly 2½ miles long, double track throughout and built to the Indian gauge of 5ft 6in. In the severe conditions such a task would have been a major undertaking on its own; but the Indian government also decided to construct a temporary railway over the mountain range, both to transport men and materials to the tunnel works and to carry military personnel and equipment to Chaman.

The temporary railway included four rope inclines, which had to have a lifespan of three years and be inexpensive to construct, to be capable of carrying the largest locomotives and have a minimum capacity of 400 tons per day. With the eastern entrance of the tunnel at 6,375ft, the temporary line was taken up to about 6,800ft before the first of the inclines, 465yds at 1 in 3, raised the line up to the summit at 7,189ft. This first incline was unusual, because below the meetings, instead of there being just one track to the bottom there were two, but only six inches apart. Why this was needed is unknown. Then followed a section of 1,100yds before the first of three inclines on the western side, No.2, 510yds at 1 in 2.5, and then No.3, 1,327yds at 1 in 8 and No.4, 1,573yds at 1 in 12.5. Between Nos. 2 and 3 and 3 and 4 there were short sections worked by a locomotive. Nos. 3 and 4 Inclines were

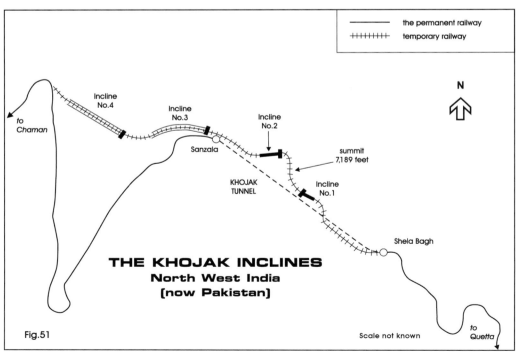

Fig.51. The Khojak Inclines, north-west India.

8-12. Research has revealed that this view shows Khojak No.1 Incline, 465yds at 1 in 3. The meetings can be seen between the two travelling platforms. On arrival at the bottom the descending platform went into a pit – the track in the foreground does not go straight on to the incline – so that the vehicle could be run forward and be collected by a locomotive.

lower than the western end of the tunnel, and as Fig. 51 shows, the permanent line had to take an extended circuitous route to reach the same level.

The first two inclines comprised two counterbalanced platforms running on a single track with a passing loop. Each platform had a horizontal floor fitted with rails and was large enough to accommodate a locomotive. The maximum load was limited to 30 tons. At the bottom of each incline was a pit into which the platform was lowered for the vehicle to be hauled off (8-13), whilst at the top there was a ramp, as illustrated in photo 8-14. Both inclines were operated by stationary locomotive boilers fitted with gears and sheaves, but apparently without being enclosed in a building. The other two

inclines seem to have been self-acting, but with two parallel tracks; No.3 had a maximum of 40 tons capacity, No.4 of 50 tons capacity.

The tunnel itself, 70 miles from Quetta, was another example of the vision and determination of British Victorian railway engineers. Quetta itself was 5,600ft above sea level, and the western end of the tunnel, where a small settlement called Shela Bagh was built, was 5,394ft. The tunnel was to be the fourth longest in the world, and be dead straight throughout, but with a rising gradient from each end. It was lined with bricks, with nearly 20 million having to be made. It was to be built by direct labour, but while labourers were brought from all over India, it was from England that the skilled

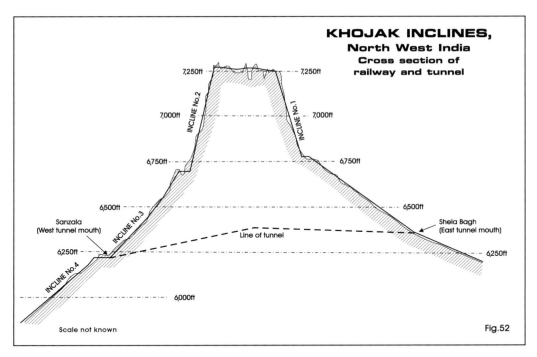

Fig.52. The cross-section of the Khojak Inclines, north west India.

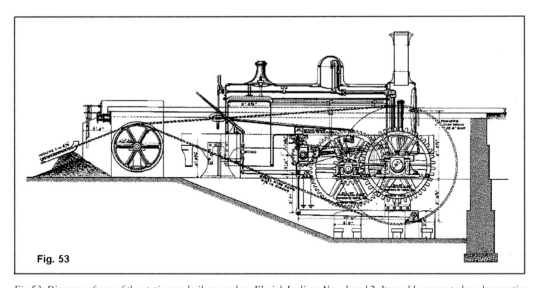

Fig.53. Diagram of one of the stationary boilers used on Khojak Inclines Nos. 1 and 2. It would appear to be a locomotive boiler fitted with winding equipment.

miners came and all the engineering material that was needed. The eastern end was to be fortified against attack and a small settlement, Sanzala, was built here. The terrain was harsh, treeless and lacked water, so that 80 tonnes of water had to be brought in every day for the workers.

Many hundreds died of pneumonia or typhoid during the construction. Work began on the tunnel on 14th April 1888 and the first train ran through it on 5th September 1891, with the temporary railway and its inclines then being dismantled.

8-13. One of the travelling platforms used on Nos. 1 and 2 Inclines. Note the different-sized wheels of the trolley, its angled buffers and the chock behind the uphill rear wheel. Note too the steel straps and chocks used to keep the vehicle being carried in position – and all done at over 7,000ft above sea level.

8-14. This view shows No.2 Incline, slightly longer but steeper, and like No.1, worked by a stationary engine at the summit. In the traditional British way of doing things, the Viceroy of India sent out a photographer, a man called Bremmer, to this inhospitable location to record the work; his name is visible on each photograph.

The Denniston Incline, South Island, New Zealand

As in Britain, the economic driving force behind the development of railways in the South Island of New Zealand was the developing coal industry. Coal was first discovered on the west coast in 1859, and topographical and mineral surveys in 1873 by William Cooper and Robert Denniston estimated that there were more than 70 million tons of high quality, bituminous coal on the Mount Rochfort plateau, on the north-west of the island, although the uninhabited plateau was isolated from the plain by very steep, wooded cliffs about 1,700ft high. A harbour had been developed at Westport and gradually a railway was built north-eastwards along the coast, reaching Conn's Creek in 1877. In the following year the Westport Colliery Company was formed. This took over the railway from Waimangaroa to Conn's Creek and then faced the problem of how to connect it with the Mount Rochfort plateau. Once again an incline was unavoidable, and with the coal needing to travel downhill, the self-acting principle would be needed, but in extremely severe conditions.

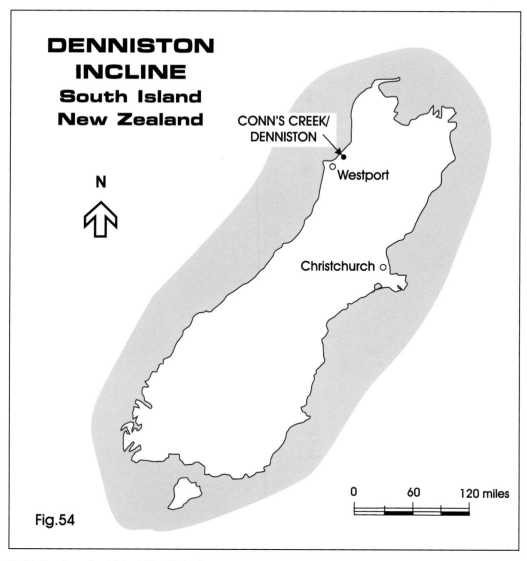

DENNISTON INCLINE
South Island
New Zealand

CONN'S CREEK/
DENNISTON

N

Westport

Christchurch

0   60   120 miles

Fig.54

Fig.54. Denniston, South Island, New Zealand.

Because it was decided that because the preferred route involved a change of direction, the standard gauge incline would be divided into two sections. The upper section was 726yds, the vertical fall being 830ft, with the steepest gradient 1 in 1.69, while the lower incline was 1,100yds with a vertical fall of 864ft, its steepest gradient being 1 in 1.25. At the exchange between the inclines, known as the Middle Brake, the gradient was 1 in 120. At the bottom a bridge 10ft wide took the line across Conn's Creek 42ft above the water. The track layout on both sections comprised three rails at the top, four in the middle and two down to the bottom. With such steep gradients, a reliable braking system was essential. There were two drums on a central shaft in each brake house, with a cylinder controlling each drum and with water being used to control the speed of the pistons, being drawn off and replaced by fresh water at each stroke because the intense pressure made the water boil. By controlling the water supply to the cylinders the brakesman controlled the speed of the drums. There was also a strap brake mounted between the two drums which could be wound up tight in an emergency and bring a load to a stop. Good braking control was essential, as under normal operating conditions the wagons travelled at 80 kilometers (50 miles) per hour, with about fourteen wagons an hour being handled.

8-15. The top of the upper incline at Denniston, probably taken before 1897, as the wagon shown is not a 'Q' class wagon, and these were introduced in 1897. The centre road is for descending fulls, with empties coming up the outer lines, with their kips and 'bulls', the hinged bars for catching the wagon axles and preventing runaways. The brake house reveals its divided drum, with the storage 'bins' for coal from the mines on the plateau on the right. Note the hand winch in the foreground.

The engineers for the construction of what was always regarded colloquially as one incline were the Scots brothers Henry William (1841-1909) and Robert Austen Young (1842-1922), who had emigrated to New Zealand in 1864. Construction began late in 1878 and the incline was opened on 24th October 1879. Certainly from 1897, and probably from the beginning, the practice was to run only one full and one empty wagon at a time. From 1897 these were the 'Q' class steel wagons, which held about 7 tons. The design was unusual by British practice, because the box could be lifted off the frames on hooks, so that on arrival at the docks it could be swung out over the ship's hold, where it was discharged before being put back on to the frames.

At the top of the incline a settlement named after Denniston was established. Conditions on the barren, tree-less plateau were wet and hostile. The incline was the only means of access, so that all the goods for normal living had to pass up it, and it also had to carry men, women and children. Some of the latter were so terrified by their upward journey that they refused to go down again for many years. Equally, the ground on the

8-16. Children from Denniston on a field trip alongside the upper incline in 1945 – but note the 'Q' class wagon behind them and the steepness of the gradient!

8-17. The 'Middle Brake' area about 1900, with its brake house, again showing the divided drum with its ropes for the lower section of the incline. In the distance on the upper section two wagons are passing at the meetings, and again look at the gradient! Presumably the rope on the descending full wagon was released at the bottom of the gradient for it to run round by gravity into the dish which is visible, while once again the empties came up on either side alternately.

plateau was so hard that graves could not be dug and so the incline was used to convey coffins down to better ground at Conn's Creek. In 1883-84 runaways caused two people to be killed on the incline, and so a winding footpath was opened up, although many years passed before a tolerable road was constructed.

Coal was brought from drift mines on tramways operated by endless rope haulage (see 7-13). At the summit of the incline were a number of large hoppers, or 'bins', into which the tubs were tipped, for subsequent loading into a 'Q' class wagon. New mines were opened to replace those that were exhausted. In 1952 the last tramway was replaced by an aerial ropeway.

In the 1960s the demand for coal declined, while after over sixty years' service the wagons were wearing out and it was felt to be too expensive to build replacements. So on 16th August 1967, after handling millions of tons of coal, the incline was closed, together with the branch line to Westport, with the reduced output being handled by road transport. Very fortunately, the New Zealand Government was aware of its historical importance and before closure had a film made, entitled *After Ninety Years*, which is still available on DVD from Archives New Zealand. Curiously, it would have closed anyway in the following year, as on 24th May 1968 the Inangahua earthquake destroyed the upper part of the incline and buried it under a huge rockfall.

New Zealanders had regarded the incline as the 'eighth wonder of the world', and in 1990 the Institution of Professional Engineers New Zealand marked its importance as part of New Zealand's engineering heritage by placing a plaque at the bank head. This has since been followed by a proper conservation and presentation of the remains around the top of the incline and the provision of an information centre.

8-18. The bottom section of the lower incline, about 1910. Waiting to assemble a train for Westport is New Zealand Railways 'C' class No.7, a 0-4-2ST built originally as a 0-4-0ST by Dübs & Co of Glasgow in 1875, one of Works Nos. 802-04.

Another spectacular incline in New Zealand, this time on the North Island, was the **Billy Goat Incline**. About half way down the east coast is the Coromandel Peninsula. It is sparsely populated even along the narrow coastal strip, where the main town is Thames. The interior is steep and hilly and is largely covered in subtropical rain forest. One of the coniferous trees found in the forest is the kauri tree, and from the 1870s it was increasingly felled for timber. Inland from Thames is the Kauaeranga Valley. One of the leading logging firms here was the Kauri Timber Company, which in 1921 built the Billy Goat Incline. This utilised a mountain ridge and was 1,256yds long, but descending 942ft in that distance. This time a steam hauler was installed, but fitted with water brakes and with band brakes in reserve, as at Denniston. The picture (8-19) appears to show free bogies positioned under the ends of the logs. From the foot of the incline the kauri logs went on a rail tram journey of 13¼ miles before being placed on a raft to float for 50 miles to Auckland. The incline closed in 1926 with the end of logging, and the route is now a path within a national park, with much of the forest restored.

8-19. The upper section of the Billy Goat Incline on the North Island of New Zealand in the early 1920s, surely rope haulage at its most brutal. It would seem that the logs were placed on free bogies, so that the distance between them could be adjusted according to the length of the log.

The Serra Velha and Serra Nova Inclines, near Sao Paulo, Brazil

There was a plateau here too, but here it produced coffee beans – the state of Sao Paulo produces about four-fifths of the world's supply. The nearest port on the Atlantic seaboard was Santos, but although the plateau came close to the sea, there was a huge precipice down to the narrow coastal strip. By the mid-1850s the Brazilians had realised they needed a railway between Sao Paulo and Santos, a distance of 49 miles, but they were at a complete loss as to how to overcome the precipice, called Serra do Mar; for over 2,500ft it fell almost precipitously into the sea and was completely covered in thick tropical forest with a high rainfall. They obtained a concession from the Brazilian government for a 71-mile railway between Santos, Sao Paulo and Jundiahy, but imposed conditions that demanded a first-class

locomotive-worked line, built on schedule and with a financial limit of £2 million. So they sent to England for help, to James Brunlees (1816-1892), a Scottish-born engineer then completing the Ulverston & Lancaster Railway.

Brunlees sent to Brazil Daniel Fox (1830-1918), a Yorkshireman and former pupil. Fox had worked on railways in North Wales, but the Serra do Mar was an extremely challenging task for a young man only 26 years old. Having decided that a circuitous route was out of the question because of the cost, he found the only possible solution was to install rope haulage, a system which became known as the **Serra Velha.** Four inclines, 1,947, 2,129, 2,292 and 2,339 yards, took the railway up 2,500ft in five miles. Each incline was operated by a pair of non-condensing steam engines of 150 nominal horse-power with 26in by

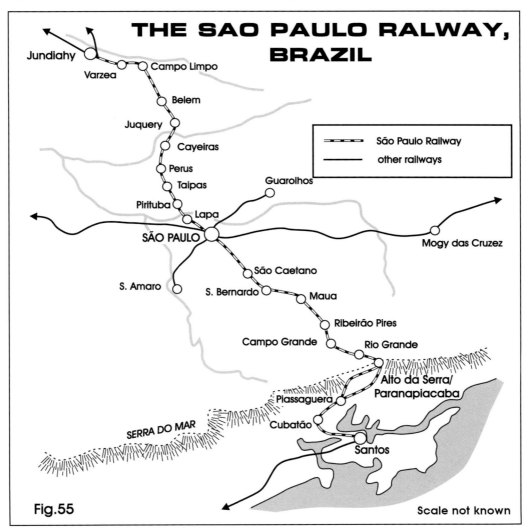

Fig.55

Scale not known

Fig.55. The Sao Paulo Railway, Brazil.

60in cylinders, built by William Fairbairn & Co of Manchester. Between each incline was a section of 83yds, arranged so that the wagons could be moved by gravity. Fox described the railway in a paper entitled *The Sao Paulo Railway*, read to the Institute of Civil Engineers on 8th March 1870 and recorded in the Institute's *Minutes of Proceedings*, together with lithographed plates and the discussion which followed his presentation. Fox described the inclines as worked on the 'tail end system, well known in the north of England'. In fact, it was a variation of the self-acting system, balancing the ascending and descending sets and worked by the stationary engines, but also with each set having a brake vehicle at the uphill end of each set. These vehicles were built by the Ashbury Company of Manchester, and were fitted with what were called 'clip brakes', devices which could be wound down to grip the rails in case of emergency. These vehicles were permanently attached to the rope as 'runners'. They were built originally as open vehicles, as Plate 7 in the paper illustrates, but were subsequently roofed, to give an appearance similar to a brake van (see 10-30 for a preserved example). Upward and downward sets of three vehicles with the 'brake van' were run simultaneously, passing at a meetings. Each incline could be passed in about 15 minutes, so

that the climb, between Piassaguera and what was initially called Alto da Serra, was achieved in just over an hour. Construction from Santos began in 1860 and on the inclines in 1861, and despite horrendous problems, the whole railway to Jundiahy was opened on 16th February 1867, ten months early and within budget. Fox adopted the 'Irish gauge' of 5ft 3ins.

In 1870 the line carried 71,531 tons of freight and 70,930 passengers, but by 1890 these figures had risen to 534,389 tons and 346,804 passengers and traffic had reached the saturation capacity of the line. So it was decided to build a new line, a fascinating example of the developments in engineering and in rope haulage technology being applied to the same problem. Interestingly, Daniel Fox was again the consulting engineer, jointly with Alexander McKerrow (1837-1920), who had married James Brunlees' daughter. Although the same basic route was followed, the new line, known as the **Serra Nova**, was rather higher up the mountain. The scale of the engineering on this new line was monumental, another example of magnificent British achievement. It was decided that the new line should be longer to give a new ruling gradient of 1 in 12½ and that there should be five inclines, each about 1½ miles long and with a vertical rise of 525ft.

8-20. The Serra Nova under construction in 1898, at the No.4 Patamar. The third of the four Lancashire boilers is being lowered as part of the installation of the No.4 Engine here. The Grota Funda viaduct can be seen beyond.

8-21. View along the right-hand side (the driver can be seen on the elevated platform) of one of the 1,000 h.p. stationary engines, probably No.5 at Paranapiacaba and probably taken in 1920. The drive wheel with its flywheel is in front of the platform, with the second wheel and its flywheel in the foreground. Because the engine is underground, the rope has to rise to go through the roof to ground level.

8-22. The rear view of probably the same stationary engine, showing the left-hand cylinder, also taken in 1920. The 'box' behind it is its condenser, later removed. The driver's position on the elevated platform can clearly be seen.

Each incline would have a three-rail section at the top, becoming four rails for the meetings and three rails again to the bottom. For the new line a system of endless rope haulage was adopted, with ascending and descending trains being handled simultaneously. All of this meant that the new line was much more heavily engineered, with thirteen tunnels totalling 1,476yds and sixteen viaducts totalling 1,508yds. The inclines were each operated by 1,000 h.p. steam stationary condensing engines, each with two horizontal cylinders 32in in diameter with a 60in stroke. The engines were all built by Joseph Foster & Sons Ltd of Preston, each having four Lancashire boilers measuring 27ft long by 7ft 6in in diameter, built by Yates & Thom Ltd of Blackburn (founded in 1826), two Lancashire firms famous for their steam engines. Unusually, all of the engines were named, with the full name cast into the crosshead guide and a monogram of the initials cast on to the valve chest of the right hand cylinder. The names were of leading Brazilian politicians of the period, from 1st to 5th being PRUDENTE de MORAIS, PAULA SOUZA, ANTONIO OLINTO, ALFREDO MAIA and Dr. CAMPOS SALLES.[2]

8-23. A descending train approaches No.4 Patamar in August 1949, with the engine house and all the usual features. Note the semaphore signal.

8-24. Coming further down, this shows the bank head and its associated engine house at the No.2 Patamar on the Serra Nova system. Note the decorated top to the boiler house chimney.

Each engine house was served by four Lancashire boilers measuring 27ft long by 7ft 6in in diameter, with at least one always laid off for maintenance. All of the boilers were fitted with automatic coal feeders, probably from the beginning. The boilers for the first two engines were located below ground, but not beneath the track. This was not possible for the next two engines, and here the boilers were housed in brick vaults beneath the track. At Alto da Serra (re-named Paranapiacaba in 1907) the boiler house was at ground level. However, all five engines were housed beneath the track, in vaults about 26ft high by 81ft long, allowing the rope to enter the engine house vault from ground level and then after being routed through the engine, to rise up again to go back out at ground level.

The condensing steam engines drove two motion shafts, each carrying a 25ft flywheel with twelve grooves and a 14ft friction pulley known as a differential rope drum. The four rope grooves on the drum wheel were each formed on a loose ring slipped over the turned rim. This design avoided the excessive strains on the rope which would be caused by inequality in the diameter of the rope grooves due to uneven wear. The primary motion shaft was driven directly by the engine and was a component of the crankshaft. Twelve cotton ropes on the primary shaft flywheel transmitted power to the secondary shaft flywheel which in turn transmitted power to its drum wheel. The haulage rope entered the engine house from the up line and passed back and forth over the differential rope drums, each wrap in its separate groove, then left to the rear of the engine where it passed around a 14ft return wheel and returned to the main line. Multiple wrapping of the haulage rope on the drum provided the necessary friction to drive the endless system. At the downhill end of each incline there was a pit where a six-ton weight kept the adjustable return wheel under constant tension and thus also the rope.

The new line also had its equivalent of the old line's 'brake vans'. These were called 'locomotive brakes' - four-coupled tank engines enclosed within a brake van shell and looking not unlike a steam railcar of the period. But whereas the original vehicles gripped the rails, these gripped the rope. A 7½in steam cylinder mounted transversely and centrally lowered the apparatus

8-25. The bottom of the rope haulage at Piassaguera, with the marshalling yard for traffic to and from Santos beyond. The descending rope goes underground on the left and emerges as the ascending rope on the right. Passengers stand on the platform next to the signal box awaiting a train.

8-26. One of the first twelve 'loco brakes' under construction in Kerr, Stuart's works at Stoke-on-Trent in 1899-1901. The additional cylinders for the rope-gripping apparatus and the 'sledge brakes' can be clearly seen.

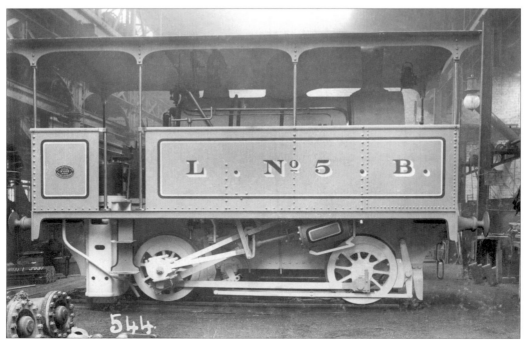

8-27. Loco Brake No.5, Kerr Stuart Works No.665 of 1899, completed in the works.

to pick up the rope, then dies were brought together to grip it tightly before the apparatus was raised, lifting the rope out of the sheaves. This was done over a pit at the bank head, known as a 'patamar'. The loco brake was attached to the downhill end of the train, with the chimney facing downhill, presumably so that steam and smoke would not obscure the driver's view when propelling. It was also fitted with two further 12½in cylinders to operate 'sledge brakes', large wooden blocks which could be slammed down on the rails in an emergency. However, its most important job was to shunt the train between one incline and the next, thus speeding up the flow of the traffic.

The first twelve of these 0-4-0Ts were built by Kerr, Stuart & Co Ltd of Stoke-on-Trent, Works Nos. 661 to 672. They had steeply-inclined 12in by 16in outside cylinders with outside valve gear and 3ft 0in diameter wheels and were dispatched between July 1899 and May 1900. Robert Stephenson & Co Ltd supplied the next four, Works Nos. 3065-68. These had the diameter of the cylinders increased to 13 inches and were almost the last locomotives built at the firm's Newcastle Works, being ex works in October 1901.

Stephensons built another two locomotives at Darlington in 1903, Works Nos. 3112 and 3113, dispatched in July 1903. They also received the final order for two more, ex-works in November 1930, Works Nos. 4034 and 4035. For these the cylinders were increased again to 13½in by 16in and the weight was increased from 31 tons to 34½ tons, very probably because of an increase in the size and weight of the vehicles on the Railway. As can be seen by comparing the original locomotives as built in 8-27 and their subsequent appearance in 8-28, the first sixteen vehicles subsequently had an enclosed verandah added on to the front end, complete with a bench, for railway staff and occasional visitors to travel in.

The official Railway dimensions for the last pair gave the boiler as having 79 2in tubes, giving a tube heating surface of 208 sq.ft; with a firebox heating surface of 38 sq.ft, the total heating surface was 246 sq.ft. The boiler pressure was 150 lbs. The water capacity was 324.5 gallons, and the weight loaded was 39.75 tons, distributed at 17.75 and 22 tons, with a wheelbase of 8.5ft. The locomotives were 23ft 6in long, 9ft 8in wide and 11ft 7in high.

8-28. Loco brake No.13, RS 3065/1901 at Piassaguera in July 1950. At the far end can be seen the enclosed verandah which was subsequently added to at least the first sixteen locomotives; the original buffer beam can be seen behind the steps. At the rear end the 'sledge brakes' are clearly seen. These locos were driven from the right-hand rear corner. This loco had just been converted to oil burning, with the oil tank on the roof, and the extended bunker at the back has been replaced by a plain sheet.

The average weight of trains on these new inclines was 120 tons, comprising six loaded wagons averaging 89 tons and a locomotive brake weighing 31 tons (originally). The vehicles on one side were again counterbalanced by those on the other side. There were of course imbalances, but statistics showed that the differences were not significant and were usually on the down side.

On arriving at a patamar, both uphill and downhill locomotive brakes dropped their ropes and then shunted their trains forward to the next incline, where they picked up its rope standing over a pit, so that the apparatus and the rope could be examined. When both loco brakes had done this, the signalman closed the downhill catch point in front of this train and cleared the inclines' starting signals. These were originally low level lower semaphore signals, latterly replaced by two-aspect colour light signals. He then cleared a semaphore signal on the end wall of the engine room from the driver and rang a bell, at which point the haulerman opened his throttles. Latterly the semaphore signal near the pit was replaced by a two-aspect colour light signal. When this was cleared, it closed a contact in a series circuit running through all five signal boxes. When the contacts on all five inclines were closed, lights (replacing the signal inside the engine room) were illuminated at each of the winding engines' control platforms and a bell rang. The winding enginemen then started their engines simultaneously, so that all ten trains moved in unison.

The haulerman sat on an elevated platform above the main steam pipes. On either side of him were several short levers, including throttles and brakes for both cylinders, a rope footage indicator and a time clock. He also had a speaking tube linking him to the signal box. The operating sequence was based on an eight-minute cycle - 6½ minutes for traversing an incline and 1½ minutes for dropping the rope, moving to the next rope and gripping it. Once cleared to drive, the haulerman accelerated the engine and then, watching his indicators, adjusted his speed, passing the mid-point at 3¼ minutes and then decelerating to stop the rope precisely at 6½ minutes. This was done 60 times per shift, for 24 hours a day, every day, and each train took 40 minutes to travel over the inclines. At maximum speed the engines worked at 25 r.p.m. and the trains travelled at just under 12 m.p.h.

From the opening of the line in 1901, both freight and passenger traffic over the inclines increased steadily:

	Freight in tons	Passengers
1901	1,965,920	1,059,761
1910	2,103,882	1,858,722
1920	3,517,302	4,586,141
1930	3,724,296	10,767,853
1940	5,875,777	16,847,497

The 'English Railway' was nationalised in September 1946 and the line was re-named Estrada de Ferro Santos-Jundiai. The coal-fired boilers were replaced by Amesteam oil-fired boilers manufactured by the Ames Iron Works Inc of Oswego in New York State, USA, early in the 1950s. The loco brakes were also converted to oil burning, with a tank added to the back of the bunker. By now enormous quantities of coffee, fruit, meat, timber and cereals were carried down to Santos, while coal, machinery, cotton, motor cars, jute, salt and sugar were hauled up. Traffic was further increased in the 1940s when iron ore traffic was diverted to the line to travel down to a new steel plant at Piassaguera at the foot of the inclines, although half of the 70-ton payload in each wagon had to be offloaded to a second wagon north of Paranapiacaba because of weight restrictions on the inclines' viaducts. Despite this, the traffic saturation point of six million tons per year on the inclines was being reached. At the same time suburban passenger traffic was increasing substantially, although even electric multiple units had to take a steam loco brake on the inclines as they had no apparatus for gripping the rope. Figures continued to increase:

1950	6,007,897	58,694,719
1956	6,363,310	recorded as same as 1950

The original Serra Velha inclines had remained open alongside the new route for out-of-gauge loads and occasional traffic. In 1970 they were closed after 103 years' service and underwent major reconstruction. In another up-dated solution to the original problem, the line was re-engineered on an almost uniform gradient with just a handful of level sections. The Abt rack system was installed and the line electrified, with locomotives supplied by Hitachi of Japan, helped by Schweizerische Lokomotiv-und-Maschinenfabrik of Winterthur in Switzerland, famous for its rack locomotives. It was opened on 22nd March 1974, but almost immediately there was a major fatal accident and the route was closed for several years while various issues were resolved, including the reduction of the planned tonnage per train. The electric locomotives were used in pairs, hauling 500 tons per train, nearly five times more than the rope inclines and steam locomotives could haul. Despite this, the volume of traffic initially continued to require the use of both systems. But with the decline of freight traffic and a severe reduction in the passenger service, the inclines were reduced to one shift in the winter of 1980-1, and commercial use effectively ceased the following year. Passenger services over the electrified line ceased in January 1984. However, the iron ore traffic continued to expand and new locomotives for the rack system were ordered in 2010 to replace the life-expired Japanese electrics.[3]

8-29. The underside of one of the loco brakes in the loco shed at Paranapiacaba, showing the rope-gripping apparatus.

8.30. Patamar No.2, with 11, KS 667/1900, descending with a mixed train of a workman's coach and a wagon, with the signal box on the left and a water crane on the right. Note the signal at ground level at the pit, which needed to be released before the train could move. Ahead another train is waiting to ascend No.3 Incline.

Paranapiacaba was served by an electric suburban service from Luz station in Sao Paulo, and this made it possible to develop a preservation scheme here. This is described in chapter 10. The operation of the 5th incline was ended in 1990, partly because the rope was condemned and partly because the preservation scheme lost money. Although the track was lifted on the first four inclines from the bottom, the stationary engines were left intact, together with the whole of the 5th incline, its stationary engine and its oil-fired boilers. A plan in 2004 to replace the Serra Nova route with a conveyor belt to carry the iron ore was not proceeded with and so this famous route and its equipment is being reclaimed by the tropical jungle it passed through.

The Katoomba Incline,
New South Wales, Australia
This is the steepest incline ever built, and one with a fascinating history. In the Jamison valley of the Blue Mountains of the Sydney basin various coal seams were discovered, the top one being the Katoomba seam, which varied between 1m and 1.8m thick. In another, lower seam, there was also oil shale of a particular type called Torbanite. This shiny, light, bituminous rock was valuable for its ability to be retorted and produce a high luminosity gas, and for its wide range of oil and grease by-products. Various companies explored and then developed this coalfield, one of these being the Katoomba Coal & Township Land Co Ltd, registered on 28th June 1878. The company's principal shareholder was John B. North (1831-1917), who had been born in Taunton and emigrated in 1852. By early in 1879 the firm had opened up the Katoomba seam, but at the base of a 200m sheer cliff. A large block of coal from the seam was displayed at the Sydney Exhibition of 1879, as a result of which the company was given a contract to supply coal to the New South Wales Government Railways. North now had to develop a system for transporting coal from the mine to the Great Western Railway, 2½km to the north and almost 300m above the mine entrance.

At the top of the cliff there were several fissures. One of these measured about 6m wide and 40m high at the downslope end but narrowed to 300mm wide at the top, where it was roofed over by large stones. It was decided to construct an incline utilising this fissure. The engineer employed by the company to design the system was Norman Selfe (1839-1911). Also an emigrant Englishman, his work included marine, mechanical and civil engineering. He had installed a similar incline at Hartley, some 30 miles away, in 1868, where the gradient varied between 1 in 1 and 1 in 4 in a fall of rather more than 200m. No drawings of Selfe's Katoomba design survive, but it involved tunnelling down the natural fissure, widening out the 300mm section and breaking out into the wider area below, the whole

incline being 405m long. The top of the incline, where the tubs (in Australia known as 'skips') were attached and detached from the rope, was flat, but the remainder of the incline varied between 1 in 1 and 1 in 1.24. At the bottom it terminated on a convenient flat area at an elevation of about 715m, about 35m below the level of the Katoomba seam. A second, short, self-acting incline linked the mouth of the mine to the main incline, where the tubs from underground were emptied down a chute to load into tubs/skips. A large flat area at the top of the escarpment accommodated a twin drum winch powered by a 30 h.p. steam engine served by two boilers, in turn served by a 19.8m brick chimney. Water for the boilers was piped from a dam built on a creek 210.3m away.

The incline was a double track system of 60cm gauge, with a set of five full tubs/skips being hauled up on one track while five empties were being lowered on the other. The ropes were some 455m long with a diameter of 20mm, and each tub held about half a ton of coal. As the slack was taken up at the start of a haul the rope rose, so to prevent the back tub being lifted off the rails, beams of timber were fixed about six feet above the ground across the twin tracks. The incline began operation in 1882.

From the top of the incline the coal was originally taken to the railhead in carts hauled by bullocks, but these were soon replaced by a double track 60cm gauge tramway. This route included some severe changes of gradient and used a top endless rope (in Australia known as 'overrope') haulage system. The round trip for a tub/skip, from the bank head down the main incline, back up and then to the railhead and back, is reported to have taken 1½ hours in normal circumstances.

In 1890 North leased his operation to the Australian Kerosene Oil & Mineral Co. The new operators installed an extensive new transport system to serve various workings in the Jamison Valley. At Katoomba this involved constructing a new tramway on the level from the mine entrance across to the main incline, reducing the main incline to 305m and allowing the remainder and the self-acting incline to be abandoned. The tramway continued through the old workings, out into the open, continuing for another kilometre before a horse drawn branch led off to the Ruined Castle Shale Oil mine. From here the line tunnelled 300 metres through a sandstone ridge and continued for a further two kilometres to a second oil shale mine. By 1895 the shale seams were becoming thin and uneconomic to work and with the added effects of an economic depression, the manpower fell to a handful of men and two years later the mine and the incline closed. By 1903 all of the incline equipment had been removed and the route had become damaged by heavy rains; all that remained was the stationary engine chimney.

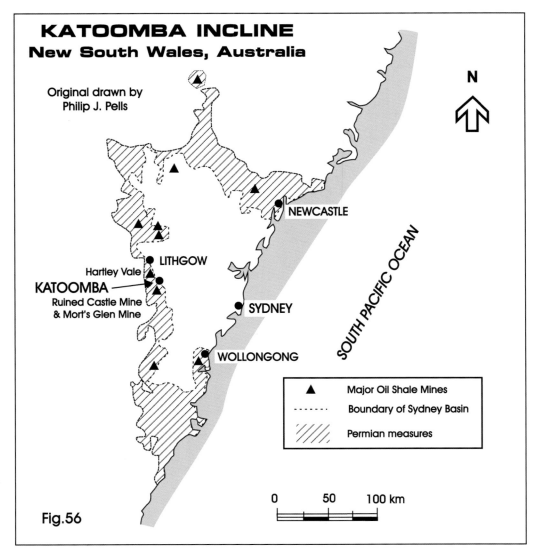

KATOOMBA INCLINE
New South Wales, Australia

Original drawn by
Philip J. Pells

N

NEWCASTLE

SOUTH PACIFIC OCEAN

LITHGOW
Hartley Vale
KATOOMBA
Ruined Castle Mine
& Mort's Glen Mine

SYDNEY

WOLLONGONG

▲   Major Oil Shale Mines

- - - - -   Boundary of Sydney Basin

/////   Permian measures

0   50   100 km

Fig.56

Fig.56. The Sydney Basin, New South Wales, Australia.

Then in 1925 a group of Katoomba businessmen formed a syndicate to extract the small coal left by the previous operators. A small steam winder was purchased from the Australian Navy and a second-hand Cornish boiler installed. The incline was rebuilt as a single track with a gauge of 47 inches. Because it was deemed too expensive to elevate the track supports to reduce the angle as Selfe had done, about 64 metres was rebuilt to 52 degrees, or 1 in 0.78, the steepest incline ever constructed. The incline from the 1890s was also extended by about 10m to accommodate a tippler, which tipped the skips from the mine into a large, crude wooden wagon. This was built mainly to handle coal, but passengers and other goods,

such as fodder for the pit ponies, and sometimes the pit ponies themselves, were also carried, and to lessen the angle of the base, the front wheels were bigger than the back wheels. A 80 h.p. electric hauler replaced the steam winch in April 1935. The mine and the incline continued to operate for another ten years, when the loss of a contract forced its closure.

During 1930-31 there was the threat of a major collapse of a cliff above the old workings, bringing many travellers to the region hoping to see it. The majority of it fell overnight in May 1931, creating a spectacular sheer cliff. Tourist passengers (clearly not daunted by the 1.3 in 1 gradient!) had been

8-31. This spectacular picture of the Katoomba Incline was taken about 1885. On the left is the mine entrance with its self-acting incline. At its foot the skips/tubs went through 50° to be run on to the tippling chute. At the foot of the main incline five tubs wait to be filled, while five fulls wait to be hauled up through the 1 in 1 cleft and tunnel to the top of the escarpment. Note the two wooden bars across the track to prevent the rope rising too high, one near the bank foot and one where the tracks enter between the cliff faces.

8-32. The skip constructed for the rebuilt incline in 1925 which transported coal and people. On the side is chalked 'Don't forget to feed and water the pony'.

8-33. The 150 kW hauler built in 1994 by the Australian Winch & Haulage Co Pty Ltd of Sydney, with its two drums, one with twin ropes for the cars and the other for the aerial counterweight, photographed on 1st April 2010.

8-34. The modern Scenic Railway's set of 2009, comprising three 28-seat cars. Note the twin ropes. The train is near the position of the upper timber bar across the track in the first picture.

carried in the coal skip on the incline for many years on weekends and Public Holidays. In 1933 the original coal skip was supplemented by a 12-seater car to cater for this demand, soon to be extended to accommodate fifteen people. When electric haulage was introduced, capacity was increased to 24 passengers. After the closure of the mine in 1945 its lease was taken over by Harry Hammon (1911-2000), who saw the opportunity to develop a profitable business based on attractions and facilities for tourists, with the incline carrying passengers seven days a week. Since then various improvements have been made to the rope haulage, one of the most notable being the introduction of twin 6-stranded 20mm ropes, with an aerial counterweight and the increase in passenger capacity to 28. This was done whilst the original 80 h.p. hauler was still being used, but in 1994 this was replaced with a new 150kW (204 h.p.) hauler, together with three 28-seat cars, while 7-stranded 28mm ropes were adopted in 1999, so that rope life is now 122,000 cycles compared with 40,000 previously. To accommodate the longer train the incline was extended by 20m to 320m.

The modern incline is acknowledged in the *Guinness Book of Records* as the steepest rope incline in the world. The trip on it was joined in 1958 by an aerial ride in the 'Skyway', a 370m aerial ropeway, and then in 2000 a second access into the valley, the 'Cableway', was added. A new corporate name, 'Scenic World', was adopted in 1996. Since the late 1950s the railway has operated every day between 9am and 5pm, having originally been 10am to 5pm.

There is no road access into the Jamison Valley, so all visitors arrive at the top of the incline, where today is the largest souvenir shop in Australia, a 200-seater revolving restaurant and other refreshment facilities, together with a 100-seat theatre. After the ride down the incline, there is 1.8 km of boardwalk through the rainforest, with audio-visual displays in the former mine entrances. Visitors return to the top of the cliff either by the Railway or by walking 800m to the Cableway. There are many kilometres of bush walks from both the top and bottom stations through the adjoining World Heritage listed Blue Mountains National Park.

The whole area has been transformed since its mining days, and since 1975 the incline/Railway has carried over 20 million passengers, averaging 800,000 per year, an incredible change from the ½-ton tubs with which it began in 1882.[4]

---

1   *History of the Great Western Railway,* Vol. II, by E.T.MacDermot, London, 1927, 300.

2   Prudente de Morais was President of Brazil from 1894 to 1898, the country's first civilian president and the first elected by popular vote; Alfredo Maia was Minister of Transportation between 1900 and 1902 and Dr. Campos Salles the President between 1898 and 1902 and so in office when the line was opened.

3   This order, for seven locomotives at a cost of 60 million Swiss francs, was placed by MRS Logistica with Stadler Rail Group of Switzerland. They are the largest and most powerful electric rack locomotives ever built. Each locomotive produces 5,000 kW/approx. 6,800 h.p. from a 3 kV DC supply. It weighs 121 tonnes and is 18.72m over couplers. Used in tandem, a pair of locomotives can travel at 30 km/h uphill, 25 km/h downhill and 60 km/h on normal track, hauling 850 tonnes. The first locomotive was completed in June 2012.

4   For a fascinating and more detailed history of the mine, the incline and the area see *The Burning Mists of Time : A Technological and Social History of Mining at Katoomba* by Philip J. Pells and Philip J. Hammon, Philsquare Publishing, PO Box 1042, Katoomba 2780, New South Wales, Australia, 2009.

Chapter 9 Haulages in the 20th and 21st centuries

Since the 1840s there had been a vast expansion of the use of railways, both in this country and around the world, and haulages, whether operated by chain or by rope, had been part of that expansion. In Britain they were no longer part of passenger-carrying main line railways, but from the North-East to Cornwall they were used on mineral lines wherever they were the solution to the terrain the engineers needed to travel over. Many dated back to the early days of railways, but others were built after 1860. Most of the powered standard gauge inclines now employed second-generation horizontal stationary engines, but some engines from the 1820s and 1830s survived. All inclines, whether self-acting or powered, now used wire ropes, and the accidents of early days were now much more the result of human error rather than the failure of equipment. All of these were inclines above ground; underground there were

many hundreds of narrow gauge haulages of the various types described in chapter 7. There were also a significant number of similar narrow gauge haulages on the surface, in a variety of industries. Amongst these there were still some chain-hauled plateways.

Whilst it was necessary to include some twentieth century photographs in previous chapters, it is hoped that those in this chapter will provide examples of the wide range of inclines and haulages which were operated in the 20th century, and indeed on into this century. They are presented more or less chronologically, and extended captions will be developed where necessary to expand the historical or operational information. Towards the end of the chapter three further examples of haulages abroad have been included.

9-1. Looking west at Birtley on the Pelaw Main Railway, at either the bank foot of the Birtley Church Incline, or at the foot of what became the Blackhouse Fell Incline after the two inclines were merged about 1904. The road across the middle foreground is the Durham Turnpike, later the A1 and now the A6127; the level crossing here was replaced by a bridge in 1903. Note the landsale coal depot on the right, which of course had to be shunted on the rope by the hauler driver nearly a mile away, a very skilled task. A specially-short length of rope, known as a 'fly rope', was used for this, probably the rope on the right; the main incline rope lies on the left. On this rope the engine at the start of a sequence used to haul up 18, with the back twelve being slipped when they reached a certain point (known as the 'mark'), leaving the engine to haul up the front six. Next time the twelve were hauled, again slipping the back six, and then finally the remaining six were hauled up.

Pelaw Main Railway, County Durham

The Pelaw Main Railway was one of the largest colliery railways in the north of Durham. For many years until 1926 it was owned by The Birtley Iron Company, which had foundries alongside the line at Birtley. The Railway comprised two 'arms', which joined at Whitehill, near Heworth, before going north to shipping staiths on the River Tyne at Bill Quay, about five miles from the mouth of the river. The northern arm dated back to the construction of the Team Waggonway in 1669, being subsequently rebuilt as a railway with a mixture of locomotive working and rope inclines. It passed to The Birtley Iron Co in 1882. The southern arm developed from the Ouston Waggonway (see chapter 4), and was likewise a mix of locomotive working and rope inclines.[1] For the overall plan of the Railway by the turn of the twentieth century, see Fig.57.

In 1955 the National Coal Board built a short curve between the Pelaw Main Railway and the Bowes Railway (see later) at Eighton Banks, so that when the southern arm of the former closed, coal from the northern arm could be brought round to the Bowes Railway, either for washing and/or coking at Monkton or for shipment at Jarrow. This eventually happened on 31st January 1959, although Pelaw Main Staiths continued to ship until May 1964, with all coal being brought by road.

9-2. The remains of the Birtley Church engine house on 16th May 1964. This engine had ceased work by 1909, and probably became redundant in 1904. Built in 1809, the railway originally passed to the left over a level crossing. When this was replaced by a deviation including the bridge, the boiler house had to be demolished. This work was probably done when the Birtley Church and Blackhouse Fell Inclines were combined into one. This left the Birtley Church Engine redundant and enabled its boiler house to be demolished to accommodate the deviation. The hauler was re-installed in the Eighton Banks engine house, while the building was first used as a Fire Station and later as a store for building materials for the company's housing department!

9-3. The remains of the Blackhouse Fell Engine, also on 16th May 1964. This building almost certainly dated from the 1890s, when a new engine was erected offset and behind its predecessor (see 2-4). Note the unusual angled corner on the left-hand side, to accommodate a track close to it. By 1930 a 500 brake horse power electric hauler had been installed here and the former boiler house, which was situated on the grassy area to the right, had been demolished. By 1964 it was being used as a chicken house, but note that the caged sheaves survived.

9-4. The remains of the Eighton Banks engine house, probably built just after the First World War. It too had received an electric hauler by 1930, this time of 250 b.h.p, (see Fig.37) and its boiler house had also been demolished. It was remarkably intact on 16th May 1964, but not long afterwards it was set on fire by vandals and had to be demolished. In the background is the Blackham's Hill engine house on the Bowes Railway, for which see later in the chapter.

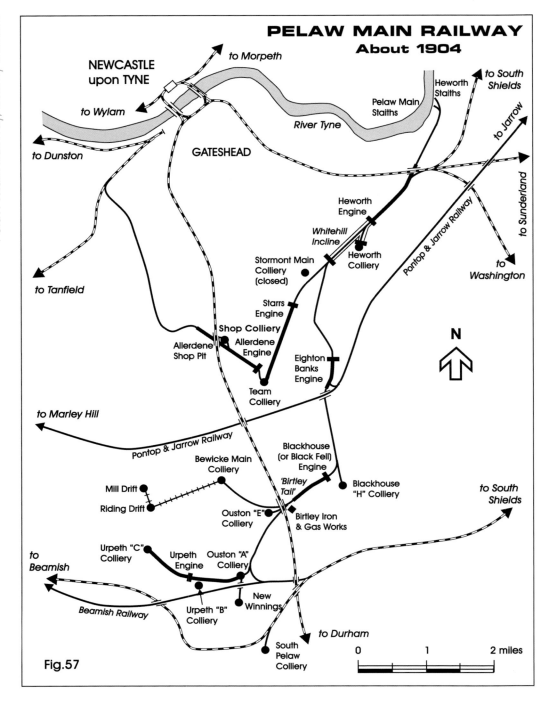

PELAW MAIN RAILWAY
About 1904

NEWCASTLE
upon TYNE

to Morpeth

to Wylam

to Dunston

GATESHEAD

River Tyne

to South Shields

Heworth Staiths

Pelaw Main Staiths

to Jarrow

to Sunderland

Heworth Engine

Whitehill Incline

Heworth Colliery

Pontop & Jarrow Railway

to Washington

Stormont Main Colliery (closed)

to Tanfield

Starrs Engine

Shop Colliery

Allerdene Shop Pit

Allerdene Engine

Eighton Banks Engine

N

to Marley Hill

Team Colliery

Pontop & Jarrow Railway

Blackhouse (or Black Fell) Engine

Bewicke Main Colliery

'Birtley Tail'

Blackhouse "H" Colliery

to South Shields

Mill Drift

Riding Drift

Ouston "E" Colliery

Birtley Iron & Gas Works

to Beamish

Urpeth "C" Colliery

Urpeth Engine

Ouston "A" Colliery

Beamish Railway

Urpeth "B" Colliery

New Winnings

to Durham

South Pelaw Colliery

0   1   2 miles

Fig.57

9-5. This shows the Pelaw Main side of Heworth Bank Foot, the bottom of the Whitehill Incline (see 1-17/1-18), about 1904. Immediately to the east (right) was the bank foot of a self-acting incline from Heworth Colliery (under separate ownership). The Heworth Engine here (behind the photographer) worked the section from here to a yard close to the river, with the Heworth fulls on the far end of the set as their staith lay further downstream. 28 wagons were worked in each direction, 18 Pelaw Main and 10 Heworth. Note the gas lighting, and the system it superceded - the up-turned 'fire basket' lying on the ground, near to the 'gallows' up which it was hoisted.

9-6. This shows the self-acting incline down to the later Pelaw Main Staiths, both probably built in the late 1920s to replace earlier systems (see 1-16). Two wagons at a time were run down for emptying. Three ships are at the staiths or waiting off; the ROYSTON was built in January 1924 and was sunk by enemy aircraft in May 1941. The staiths, with the incline, continued in operation until May 1964, although by then all coal arrived by road, to be transferred into railway wagons for transfer to the staiths.

9-7. The works of the Steetley Lime & Basic Co Ltd at Worksop in Nottinghamshire in 1910. By calcining dolomitic limestone at a high temperature, doloma was produced, an essential component in the Gilchrist-Thomas steel-making process invented in 1879. With the quarried limestone needing to be brought up to the kilns at the works, this is a powered incline operated by a stationary engine and running fulls and empties simultaneously, possibly a bottom endless haulage. However, handling waggons one at a time would have restricted production, and how long this haulage lasted is not known. The quarry closed in 1960 and the works closed in 2001.

The Oxford Clay Formation is a huge sedimentary rock formation underlying much of England, from Dorset to Yorkshire. A very large area of lower Oxford Clay in Bedfordshire and Cambridgeshire saw the development of numerous brickworks there. One of these began production in 1897 at Wootton Pillinge in Bedfordshire, but it subsequently developed massively under what became The London Brick Co Ltd. A model village was constructed, and in 1937 the complex was re-named Stewartby. The top endless chain haulage was replaced by conveyors in the 1950s. The brickworks went on to become the largest in the world, employing 2,000 people and manufacturing 500 million bricks annually. The London Brick Co Ltd was taken over by Hanson in 1984, and the works closed in February 2008.

9-8. Like several brickworks, Stewartby installed a top endless chain haulage, to the unusual gauge of 2ft 11in, to bring clay from the claypit to the brickworks. At a curve in the haulage sometimes overhead sheaves were needed or a completely new haulage took over. Either way, the tubs needed to be released from the chain, and this picture shows how easy that was. As the chain was raised the tub was freed and ran forward, either by momentum or on a favourable gradient; as the chain descended, it slipped into the fork on the tub again to haul it forwards. The tubs are of all-welded steel construction; note the small oval buffers.

9-9. A lovely general view showing in the bottom left corner two electric haulers positioned at about 120 degrees to each other, one to work the haulage up to the brickworks, where the large horizontal return wheel was situated, the other to work the next stage on to the quarry, together with the frame where the chains crossed but were kept in their correct positions by sheaves. All three Stewartby photographs were taken in the 1930s.

9-10. Looking on towards the claypit and showing the arrangements for accommodating the chains on a bend, where two frames with overhead sheaves were needed. Note the 'unchained' track on the inside of the curve, which was locomotive-worked and used for maintenance and the transport of materials, including machinery, between the brickworks and the claypit.

A few miles south-west of Stewartby lay the small villages of Lidlington and Ridgmont, close now to junction 13 of the M1 and to Milton Keynes. Here there was another large area of Oxford Clay, and in the 1930's two large brickworks were opened near these villages. Clay was brought from a claypit near Brogborough approximately a mile away. Subsequently the ownership passed to the Marston Valley Brick Co Ltd, to be acquired in turn by The London Brick Co at the end of the 1960s. But the market for the so-called 'Fletton bricks', made from the lower Oxford clay, was declining steadily as other materials replaced bricks, and the works was closed in May 1981.

9-11. Despite being only a few miles from Stewartby, Marston Valley used a completely different haulage system. This was a bottom endless rope system of 2ft 6in gauge. The tubs, manufactured by W.G. Allen & Sons (Tipton) Ltd in Staffordshire, were again of all-welded steel, but of a very different design in detail from those at Stewartby, and with their numbers neatly stencilled. They were fitted with an autogrip apparatus, which automatically gripped the rope on contact. This view, showing part of the system, was taken in April 1976. The last haulage, to the Ridgmont Works, was replaced by conveyors on 6th November 1978; the works itself closed in May 1981.

9-12. The overhead sheaves on the top endless chain haulage at Elstow Brickworks, which lay about three miles north-east of Stewartby. The gauge was between 2ft 3in and 2ft 6in. Note that here the tubs are side-tippers, rather than having fixed bodies for going through a rotary tippler. Work began here in 1897 under B.J.Forder & Co Ltd, which in 1926 merged with The London Brick Co Ltd to form The London Brick Co and Forders Ltd. The works closed early in 1948.

9-13. Six miles east of Peterborough in Cambridgeshire is what was originally called Whittlesea, now Whittlesey. Brickmaking began here in the 1890s, with the Whittlesea Central Brick Co Ltd being founded in 1898. The company's No.1 Works was another that used top endless chain haulage, this time on 2ft 0in gauge track. In this picture, taken on 25th March 1960, the clay is travelling uphill from the claypit. The building at the bottom of the incline was the interchange point to which locomotives brought tubs from the claypit. The haulage was replaced by conveyors about 1962. The King's Dyke Works, also in Whittlesey, is now the country's only manufacturer of Fletton bricks.

9-14. A quite different purpose for rope haulage! The water storage reservoir at Thornton Moor, about five miles west of Bradford near the village of Denholme, was built in the 1840s by what became the Bradford Corporation Water Department. It was replenished from conduits across the moor, and to purify the water it was fed through four sand filter beds comprising 3ft of sand, 1ft of pea gravel and 3ft 9in of graded stones. The sand was removed when necessary for washing in a specially-built plant, and a 2ft gauge railway was laid to serve this. On 20th July 1970 loco L2, an unidentified 4wDM built by Ruston & Hornsby Ltd of Lincoln in the 1930s, is attached to a rope to haul a tub of sand out of one of the filter beds. For a fuller description see INDUSTRIAL RAILWAY RECORD No.50, BRADFORD WATERWORKS NARROW GAUGE by Sydney A.Leleux, 99-100.

After the middle of the twentieth century, the British Railways' mineral lines and the National Coal Board's private railways in Durham, both of them including numerous inclines, began to close as the collieries that served them became exhausted or uneconomic. One of these was the **Sacriston Railway**, owned by the NCB. This had started in August 1831 as a short railway from Waldridge Colliery linked to the Ouston Waggonway, but when the Stanhope & Tyne Railroad opened in September 1834 it was linked to it to allow its coal to be shipped at South Shields. The line was subsequently extended southwards to serve collieries at Sacriston, this section being opened on 29th August 1839. The extent of the system in 1920 is shown in Fig.58. The Railway was closed in February 1955.

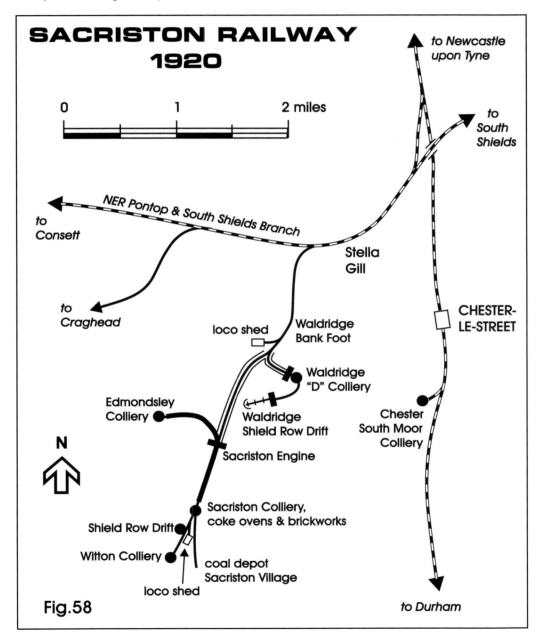

SACRISTON RAILWAY 1920

0   1   2 miles

to Newcastle upon Tyne

to South Shields

NER Pontop & South Shields Branch

to Consett

Stella Gill

to Craghead

loco shed

Waldridge Bank Foot

CHESTER-LE-STREET

Waldridge "D" Colliery

Edmondsley Colliery

Waldridge Shield Row Drift

Chester South Moor Colliery

N

Sacriston Engine

Sacriston Colliery, coke ovens & brickworks

Shield Row Drift

Witton Colliery

coal depot Sacriston Village

loco shed

Fig.58

to Durham

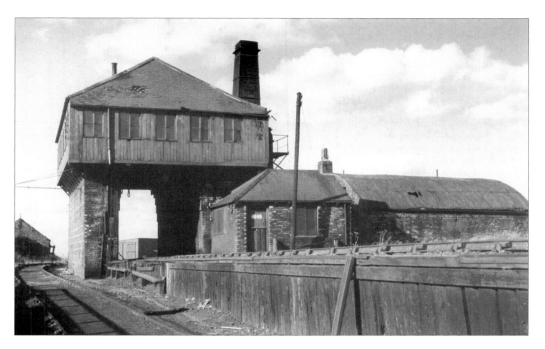

9-15. The southern side of the Sacriston Engine on 28th August 1955, six months after closure. This Engine replaced an earlier hauler in 1902 and was almost certainly the last steam hauler in Durham to straddle the track. It was built by The Grange Iron Co Ltd of Belmont near Durham City. It was also unusual in hauling up full wagons from collieries both to the south and north.

9-16. The Sacriston Engine was fitted with a unique auxiliary steam cylinder, seen here on 31st August 1955. It was used to operate the return wheel of the Waldridge self-acting incline running down northwards from the stationary engine when wagons became stuck on the incline. (This Waldridge incline should not be confused with the incline of the same name illustrated in 9-19 and 9-20).

The history of the **Tanfield Branch** in north-west Durham went back more than a century before the Sacriston line. It was built between 1725 and 1727 between the Tanfield area and the River Tyne at Dunston, a distance of about eight miles, and was of course a wooden waggonway. The original route included the now-famous Causey Arch, the first dry-stone viaduct ever built. In 1837 it was acquired by the Brandling Junction Railway, which began re-laying it southwards. Built completely under way-leaves, it was a mix of three self-acting inclines, three inclines worked by stationary engines and sections worked by horses. To reach the main Brandling Junction line between Gateshead and Monkwearmouth (Sunderland), traffic had to pass over a short section of the Newcastle & Carlisle Railway to reach the Redheugh Incline (see 6-15). Although the stationary engines were not ready and horses had to be used on their sections, the line opened for traffic on 26th November 1839.

Coming southwards from Dunston, the first horse-worked section took the line to the foot of the Lobley Hill self-acting incline (1-21), 1,100yds at between 1 in 16 and 1 in 18. Then followed a relatively level section to the bottom of the Fugar Incline, also known as Fugar Bar, Baker's Bank or the Sunniside Incline. This was about 1,850yds and its gradient varied between 1 in 12 to 1 in 46. From Fugar bank top wagons were hauled up a gradient of 1 in 50 to a summit at Bowes Bridge, where there was the first of the stationary engines. Here there was a link to Marley Hill Colliery and what became the Pontop & Jarrow/Bowes Railway. This engine also hauled wagons up on its southern side, known as the Causey East Incline, which had a gradient of 1 in 57 and was about 3,300yds.

Another section of horse-working took the line down to the Causey Engine,[2] which worked the Causey West Incline on its southern side, about 440yds at 1 in 38. A final section of horse-working took the line to the foot of the Tanfield Moor self-acting incline, about 1,000yds long, part of which was as steep as 1 in 9.

On 16th June 1842 a passenger service was begun on the branch, and of course over the inclines. This ran between Tanfield Lea, at the foot of the Tanfield Moor Incline, and Gateshead, with stations at Tanfield Lea, Bowes Bridge, Fugar Bar and Redheugh, and an unofficial stopping place by the Whickham turnpike road at Lobley Hill. It only operated on Saturdays, and the journey took an hour. At first a passenger carriage was provided, but eventually the passengers were reduced to using coal wagons. On 1st September 1844 the Brandling Junction Railway was acquired by George Hudson (1800-1871), who then transferred it to the Newcastle & Darlington Junction Railway; the passenger service ceased soon afterwards. In 1854 the N&DJR was merged into the North Eastern Railway, which was in turn merged into the London & North Eastern Railway in 1922.

Little changed until July 1881, when locomotive working replaced the stationary engines and the horses. The Bowes Bridge engine house was converted into Bowes Bridge loco shed. After this nothing happened until the closure of the Tanfield Moor Colliery site and its incline on 4th December 1947. The branch and its inclines passed to British Railways on 1st January 1948. The closure of Tanfield Lea Colliery on 25th August 1962 saw the closure of the line from Tanfield Lea to Watergate Colliery, which was linked to the section between the Fugar and Lobley Hill Inclines; the final section followed on 20th August 1964.

9-17. The meetings on the Fugar Incline on the Tanfield branch, looking uphill, on 17th December 1960. The next ascending set will travel up the right-hand track, with the passing descending set setting the points for the next ascending.

9-18. Although the Tanfield branch self-acting inclines were built to transport coal downhill, coal also had to be brought uphill each Saturday for the loco shed at Bowes Bridge. Here the shed's current residents, N10 class 0-6-2Ts 69109 and 69097, propel two 21-ton wagons up a 1 in 21/1in 16 section of the Fugar Incline on 17th December 1960.

The sections of the **Stanhope & Tyne/ Pontop & South Shields Branch** (see Fig. 20) still open in 1945 slowly diminished. The Stanley and Eden Hill Inclines (5-36, 5-37, 5-38) were closed in 1946, leaving the western end of that section to start at the Pelton Level. This left just the Waldridge Incline, 1,518yds at gradients between 1 in 20½ and 1 in 24½, still working to carry coal down to the sidings at Stella Gill, north of Chester-le-Street. On the 'Stanhope & Tyne' section at Stanhope, the Crawleyside and Weatherhill Engines ceased work on 28th April 1951, although the line remained open to just east of Weatherhill to serve a sand quarry at Parkhead until 29th April 1968.

The Pelton Level was served by the Sacriston Railway, closed in February 1955 – see above, although in the same year the Beamish Railway traffic was diverted to Handen Hold Colliery, served by the Level, after a new coal washery was opened. The Level was also linked to the branch from the Craghead collieries, which included its own self-acting incline, the last in Co.Durham to use set-riders. Reacting to an increase by British Railways in their 'demurrage' charges (charges while BR wagons were standing at collieries), the NCB diverted the Craghead traffic to the Handen Hold Washery to road transport, from 1st July 1966. The last Beamish colliery, Beamish Mary, had closed on 26th March 1966, to be followed by Handen Hold Colliery on 1st March 1968. When Craghead Colliery closed on 11th April 1969 the Handen Hold coal washery closed with it, thus bringing to an end traffic over the Waldridge Incline.

9-19. *The bank head of the Waldridge Incline, Pontop & Shields Branch (not to be confused with the self-acting incline of the same name on the Sacriston Railway nearby) about July 1950. The empties travelled up the kips on the outside. Note that the rows of terraced houses came right up to the railway's boundary wall.*

9-20. *A set of eight fulls leaves the middle road at Waldridge Bank Head. Note the set-rider sitting casually on the rear wagon, and how neat and tidy the railway is.*

Closures were not just happening in Durham. The Pwllyrhebog Incline in South Wales (chapter 8) had closed on 1st July 1951, and the closure of the Whaley Bridge Incline on the **Cromford & High Peak Railway** followed on 9th April 1952. This used its endless chain haulage operated by a horse gin to the end, certainly the last example of this in Britain.

The other two remaining inclines on the Railway, the Middleton and Sheep Pasture Inclines continued in use, kept busy by the considerable volume of limestone traffic, which fortunately the inclines' capacity of two wagons per 'run' (set) was able to handle. But both stationary engines were nearing the end of their working lives. The Sheep Pasture Engine was the converted six-coupled goods engine installed in 1884, while the Middleton Engine, whilst recognisable from the original engine of 1829-30, had had parts renewed over the years and its two Cornish boilers were approaching one hundred years old. The Middleton Incline received a new rope on 4th September 1957, but when some three years later the second of the Cornish boilers had to be taken out of use, British Railways sent as a replacement the boiler from a former LNWR Ramsbottom DX 0-6-0 goods engine, mounted on the frame of an old tender, which was installed at the rear of the loco shed here. This supplied steam at 150lbs p.s.i. to a 2½in reduction valve to bring the pressure

down to the 5lbs required. This could only be a temporary measure. In March 1961 the Middleton Incline handled 229 'runs'; the downhill wagons comprised 224 fulls and 73 empties, while the uphill runs comprised 83 fulls and 114 empties. Plans were put in hand to replace the Engine, presumably with an electric hauler. Fortunately, before this could happen, the Hopton Wood Quarry closed on 16th June 1962 and the Middleton Engine and its incline were used for the last time on 31st May 1963,[3] with the rope then being cut outside the engine house. This allowed the Engine and its building to be preserved, and indeed the Engine was demonstrated for visitors on a number of occasions. It was subsequently acquired by Derbyshire County Council and carefully preserved (see chapter 10).

Traffic on the Sheep Pasture Incline still totalled 60,785 tons in 1961. It was estimated that the local limestone quarries had reserves for a hundred years and that rail traffic could increase to 100,000 tons per year. This placed a major question over the future of the old 0-6-0 engine and its winding gear, and also how that tonnage would be handled, as it was anticipated that by 1970 the 13-ton steel wagons would be replaced by 16-ton wagons. So a 100 h.p. electric hauler was installed by a consortium headed by John Boyd & Co (Engineers) Ltd of Annan at a cost of £31,700, and brought into use in September 1964.

9-21. Sheep Pasture Bottom and Cromford Wharf on 18th August 1959. A single empty wagon is beginning its ascent, with its companions behind it divided into pairs for their turn, while a J94 0-6-0ST shunts in the background.

Looking back now nearly fifty years later, it has to be said that the exercise does not reflect well on British Railways' officials of the time. Two of the designs of wagon preferred for limestone traffic could not pass each other on the incline. The new 'winch' was supposed to be capable of handling 100 tons, or four loaded 16-ton wagons, but it was soon found that the winch could only haul one 16-ton wagon up at a time; the rope kept slipping on the drum; the brake linings had to be renewed after only six months in use. Moreover, incredibly, the engine was not designed to be reversed, as was revealed in a double accident on the incline on 15th June 1965.

To improve the comfort of the planeman in charge of the catch pit, his cabin was provided with a fire; but that meant he needed a supply of coal. To provide him with this, it had become the unofficial practice to stop a descending set including a wagon of coal alongside the cabin for him to unload a supply. To do this the planeman had to use a bell to tell the engineman where to stop the haulage. On this particular day, mid-morning, an empty water tank, an empty tender and a wagon part loaded with coal were lowered down, balanced by two empty wagons attached to the rope at the bottom. The planeman was late operating the bell to the engineman and the descending set was not brought to a stand until the leading wheels on the first wagon were derailed at the catch pit. It would have been a simple job to pull them out again if the engine could have been reversed; now it became a major exercise with experienced railwaymen thinking on their feet. The three wagons at the catch pit were detached from the rope; an empty wagon was attached to the rope at the bottom, and to

balance this, and the two empties already on the incline, two loaded wagons were attached at the top. The empty wagon was then brought to a position where the three wagons could be attached to it, and this set of four was drawn back up the incline clear of the catch pit points. So far, so good. The three wagons were then re-attached to the downward rope to be run to the bottom. But the planeman then gave a second stop signal to the engineman so that the equipment and materials could be loaded into the empty wagon for removal. The haulage did not stop and the run/set continued for the 290yds to the bottom of the incline, where the chains holding the wagons to the rope were torn away as the rope ran into the return wheel guide shoes. The rope and the rope tensioning gear were damaged. In the resultant enquiry the railwaymen disagreed as to the cause of the second accident. The wagons were eventually retrieved – only for them too to slide down the incline for 290yds.

Moreover, while the old engine was being replaced, traffic from Middleton Quarry was worked by road down to Wirksworth where it was loaded into 25-ton wagons, which could not be used on the Sheep Pasture Incline at all because of the narrow distance between the tracks. This unexpected revelation proved so much more economical that it was decided to work all the traffic by road to Wirksworth and out by the former Midland Railway branch to Duffield. The last wagons were worked down the Sheep Pasture Incline on 1st April 1967, which was perhaps the outcome that British Railways had wanted to happen. Virtually all of the remaining locomotive-worked sections of the Railway were also closed during 1967.

9-25. Here a 16-ton British Railways full wagon is descending and an empty is coming up; the third wagon on the right was the remains of an accident when a diesel loco was unable to control its train at the top of the incline.

9-26. The incline on 19th March 1966. It was 160yds long, with an overall gradient of 1 in 4. Unusually, it was laid with flat-bottomed rail. Rail joints were often welded and the rails either spiked direct to the sleepers or welded to the soleplates which were then spiked to the sleepers. The colliery closed in September 1973, although 9-23 above would suggest that rail traffic had ceased before then.

Bowes Railway, County Durham

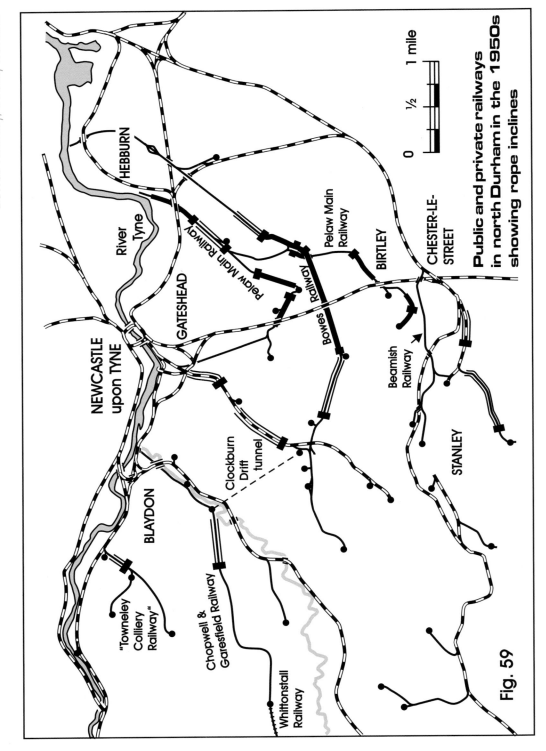

Public and private railways in north Durham in the 1950s showing rope inclines

Fig. 59

0   ½   1 mile

NEWCASTLE upon TYNE

HEBBURN

River Tyne

GATESHEAD

Pelaw Main Railway

Bowes Railway

Pelaw Main Railway

BIRTLEY

CHESTER-LE-STREET

Beamish Railway

STANLEY

Clockburn Drift tunnel

BLAYDON

"Towneley Colliery Railway"

Chopwell & Garesfield Railway

Whittonstall Railway

By far the biggest private railway in County Durham in the 1950s was the **Bowes Railway**. The first part of this system to be built was the Springwell Colliery Railway, opened in June 1826 (see chapter 5). A stationary engine at Blackham's Hill, at Eighton Banks, south of Gateshead, hauled waggons up from Mount Moor Colliery and then lowered them to Springwell Colliery, east of Gateshead. From here a self-acting incline took them down for 1¼ miles to Springwell Bank Foot near Wardley, where locomotives took over for the 4¾ mile run to staiths on the River Tyne at Jarrow. The design was originally credited to George Stephenson, but is much more likely to have been the work of Joseph Locke. The line was owned by 'The Grand Allies', the local name for Lord Ravensworth & Partners, one of the leading firms in the North-East coal trade.

In 1842 this line was extended across the Team Valley to serve Kibblesworth Colliery, owned not by the Allies but George Southern. This involved two more inclines. From Kibblesworth, half way up the western side of the valley, the coal had to travel downhill for 1¼ miles; but because the gradient was 1 in 16 near the top and 1 in 90 on the bottom section, it was decided to use a stationary engine, partly as a brake on the upper section and partly to utilise the speed of the flywheel to move the set over the bottom section. The incline was only single line, so that sets, latterly of 12, had to be run alternately. The original steam hauler and the electric engine which replaced it in 1947 are described in chapter 6. The colliery had originally been linked to the incline's bank head, but in 1914 a drift mine was opened alongside the incline about half way down, so that the hauler had to work traffic in and out of here too. This closed in 1932, but four years later a new shaft was sunk not far from the original one, and the site of the drift was used for the new colliery screens, with coal from the two shafts being brought down to the screens by two 2ft 0in gauge bottom endless systems. Within the screens area wagons were shunted by the 'Drift's' own electric hauler, but traffic to and from the main line was provided with its own dish and kip. The main line hauler worked empties in here over the kip and then the rope was attached to the full set to be sent out on to the main line.

From the bottom of the Team Valley there was a second incline up to Mount Moor, near Eighton Banks. At the bottom the gradient was 1 in 30, but it soon stiffened to 1 in 15 for most of its 1¼ miles and so a stationary engine was necessary. Again, the steam and then the electric hauler here are discussed in chapter 6. Originally this incline too was single line. The extension from Mount Moor to Kibblesworth was opened on 30th May 1842.

Meanwhile, near the Tanfield branch at Bowes Bridge, Marley Hill Colliery was re-opened on 28th June 1841 by the Marley Hill Coal Company, headed by John Bowes (1811-1885), the illegitimate son of the deceased 10th Earl of Strathmore. The line from Bowes Bridge to the colliery was subsequently extended south-westwards to Crookbank and Burnopfield Collieries. The biggest engineering work on the line was Hobson Bank, a steep, winding one-mile bank for which again a stationary engine proved necessary. This line was completed early in 1845.

The partners in the Marley Hill Coal Co included Nicholas Wood (1795-1865), who had both played an important part in locomotive history and was prominent in the coal trade; amongst other positions, he was Agent to Lord Ravensworth & Partners, of which Bowes was a partner. In 1844 they were joined by Charles Mark Palmer (1822-1907), who two years later became managing partner. Palmer re-named the firm John Bowes, Esq, & Partners in 1847 and immediately pressed for the Marley Hill and Springwell railways to be linked up, to free the firm from the power and monopoly of George Hudson and to gain access to the staiths at Jarrow. However, he found that to do it he had to acquire all the other interests. The Crookbank and Burnopfield Collieries, with their waggonway, were under Palmer's control by 1849 and by 1851 he had acquired Lord Ravensworth & Partners, together with the Springwell railway and its extension to Kibblesworth with its colliery.

The 2¼-mile 'missing link', between Marley Hill and Kibblesworth, was eventually begun in July 1853. This involved another self-acting incline, from the top of the western side of the Team Valley, at Birkheads, down to Kibblesworth, about 1,300yds at between 1 in 18 and 1 in 20. As part of a major investment, the Black Fell Incline was rebuilt to allow fulls and empties to be run simultaneously and the engine modified accordingly. At Blackham's Hill a more powerful stationary engine was installed and the working of its two inclines altered to make it possible for sets to be run on both sides simultaneously. Mount Moor Colliery was re-opened. Palmer intended the railway to handle a hugely increased tonnage, and new shipping staiths were built at Jarrow. At the western end of the line Andrews House Colliery near Marley Hill was acquired and re-opened and in 1860-61 Crookbank Colliery was replaced with a new colliery at Byermoor, while a new colliery was sunk at Dipton, with the railway being extended from Burnopfield to serve it. The new section between Marley Hill and Kibblesworth was opened in September 1854 and the extension to Dipton seven months later. The line was now fifteen miles long, and to mark its importance Palmer named it the **Pontop & Jarrow Railway** (although in fact the railway never reached Pontop).[4]

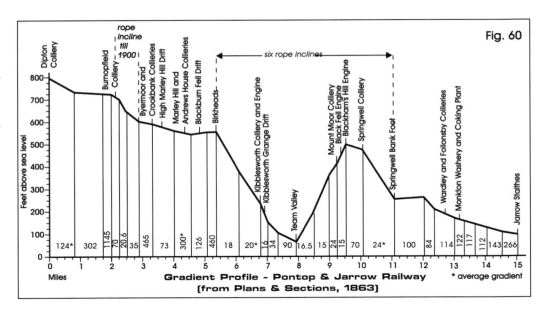

Gradient Profile - Pontop & Jarrow Railway
[from Plans & Sections, 1863]

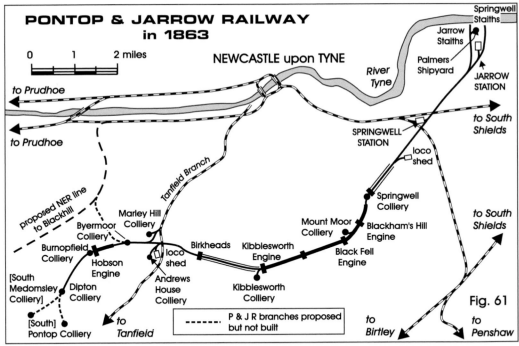

Fig. 61

Although several branches were built, the main line remained unaltered for many years, except that about 1900 the stationary engine at Hobson Bank near Burnopfield was removed and the bank slightly re-modelled to allow locomotive working over it, subject to special restrictions. In the depression of the 1930s new directors were introduced, and in 1932 the line was re-named the **Bowes Railway.** The only major change before the nationalisation of the coal industry in 1947 was the closure of Dipton Colliery and the railway to it in 1940.

So when the National Coal Board was set up from 1st January 1947, the Bowes Railway's main line ran for 13¼ miles between Burnopfield & Jarrow (see Fig.62). The far western section, three miles between Burnopfield and Birkheads, served Burnopfield, Byermoor and Marley Hill Collieries, together with Blackburn Fell Drift and from 1948 High Marley Hill Drift. Traffic here was handled by locomotives from Marley Hill Shed. Then came six miles with six inclines, Birkheads and Kibblesworth down to the bottom of the western side of the Team Valley, Black Fell and Blackham's Hill West up to the top of the eastern side of the valley, and then Blackham's Hill East and Springwell down to Springwell Bank Foot.[5] Locomotives from the shed here handled traffic on the final section to Jarrow, serving Follonsby and Wardley Collieries, via short branches, and Wardley Coal Washery and Monkton Coking Plant. There were links with British Railways at Marley Hill, at Wardley on the Follonsby branch and at Jarrow.

John Bowes & Partners Ltd were already replacing the 105 year old Kibblesworth Engine with a 350 b.h.p. hauler in a large new engine house straddling the line, which began work on 9th August 1947. Three years later, with work starting on 30th July, the steam haulers at Black Fell and Blackham's Hill were replaced by 500 and 300 b.h.p. electric haulers, but retaining the existing brick engine houses.

In 1955 the NCB decided to link the Pelaw Main and Bowes Railways at Eighton Banks, south of Gateshead, between just above Eighton Banks bank head and half way down the Blackham's Hill East Incline, where the gradient was 1 in 70. The plan was that as soon as the East Incline empties had landed on the kip at the bank head, the Pelaw Main loco would propel its train of 12 fulls on to the incline and down into Springwell Yard and then bring out 12 empties before the East Incline was ready to run fulls again. In practice the whole sequence, both Blackham's Hill inclines and the Pelaw Main train, could be completed every 30 minutes.

In January 1959 the NCB closed Ouston 'E' Colliery, the last colliery still sending coal along the southern arm of the Pelaw Main system, which allowed this section to be closed and for coal from the Ravensworth collieries to be diverted into Springwell Yard. The Pelaw Main branch, as it now became, used a locomotive between Ravensworth Park Drift and Allerdene Bank Foot, a distance of ¾ mile. Along this section a 1½ mile branch left to go northwards down the Team Valley to a coal depot and the British Railways' Tanfield branch at Norwood, near Dunston. From Allerdene bank foot, also known as the Shop Pit, a single line powered incline took wagons up to Ravensworth Ann Colliery. En route it passed Ravensworth Shop Colliery, which was another colliery which relied entirely on rope haulage, being shunted partly by the Allerdene Engine and partly by using gravity. Ravensworth Ann was shunted by a locomotive as well as being the interchange point between two inclines.

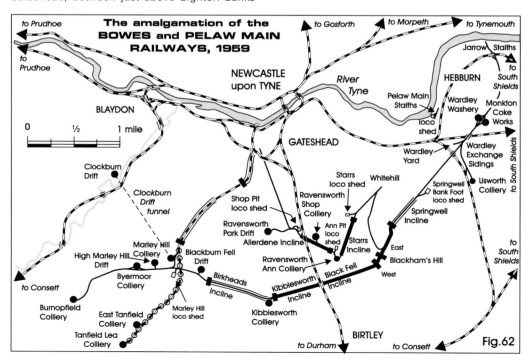

From here a second powered incline, also about a mile long and called the Starrs Incline, took the wagons up to the Starrs Engine at Wrekenton, south of Gateshead. Then locomotives from the shed here worked traffic up to the former Whitehill Bank head, where the train reversed to propel back along the line to Eighton Banks and on to Springwell Yard.[6] The whole branch was about eight miles long.

In 1962 the NCB undertook a study to assess whether coal from the western end of the Bowes Railway could be carried by road transport. But at this time the inclines were handling 1.2 million tons of coal per year, and their operation proved cheaper than the costs by road. But on this section High Marley Hill Drift closed in June 1963, to be followed by Byermoor Colliery in February 1968 and Burnopfield Colliery in August 1968. This led to the closure of the Railway between Blackburn Fell Drift and Kibblesworth, including the Birkheads Incline, in March 1969. Blackburn Fell Drift was converted to road transport in March 1970 and Marley Hill loco shed closed in November 1970.

On the Pelaw Main branch Ravensworth Ann Colliery closed in February 1962, and in March 1968 Ravensworth Ann Colliery was re-organised, with coal ceasing to be wound at the shaft and instead being drawn at Ravensworth Park Drift, which was re-named Ravensworth Ann Colliery. In April 1973 this was merged with Kibblesworth Colliery, so that traffic over the Pelaw Main inclines ended on 18th April 1973.

This left only Kibblesworth Colliery to send coal along the five remaining inclines for dispatch onwards from Springwell Bank Foot, so that when Kibblesworth closed on 4th October 1974 all of these inclines closed, ending well over a century of history. Fortunately, the newly-created Tyne & Wear County Council was persuaded to commission a film of the line in the summer of 1974. This was made by Amber Films of Newcastle upon Tyne and was called 'The Bowes Line', although unfortunately it was made without a commentary. The film then caused Tyne & Wear to wonder whether a part of the railway should be preserved, perhaps in working order, and so the council acquired the section from Black Fell to Springwell Bank Head, together with samples of the whole range of the rolling stock. In 1977 the Springwell Engineering & Wagon Shops were added to the scheme (see chapter 10).

9-27. The top of the Birkheads Incline early in the morning of 15th December 1968. The kips on the outer roads flank the next full set waiting to come down. This will descend on the left hand pair of rails, with the rope on the right attached to the empties to come up.

Bowes Railway, County Durham

9-28. The bottom two-thirds of the Kibblesworth Incline on 4th March 1965. The railway passes under the East Coast Main Line, which crosses the view at centre height. On the right is the so-called Kibblesworth 'Drift' – the screens of the colliery, where the railway wagons were loaded, with their 80 h.p. electric hauler housed in the green corrugated iron building on the right.

9-29. *When a full set left the 'Drift' and joined the main line, the rope had to be pulled across on to the main line rollers, no mean task with the rope some 1¼ miles long moving at over 20 m.p.h. Using his brake stick as a lever in the wooden socket provided, the ropeman reached across with his steel hook, pulling it first on to the steel strap and then on to the roller. His cabin can be seen beyond him. This was taken on 8th May 1969. Re-positioning the moving rope when the set started to run was not uncommon on inclines; it also had to be done at the bank head of the Blackham's Hill East Incline.*

9-30. Looking down the Blackham's Hill West Incline, 750yds at 1 in 15, on 24th July 1974. Half way down was the Mount Level Crossing, and beyond the bank foot the Black Fell Engine House can be seen. At the bank head the almost-buried track going off to the left used to serve a small landsale coal depot, while on the right a facing siding used to come off to service the Lancashire boilers. All this shunting, using 'fly ropes', had to be done by the engine in addition to working the two main inclines here.

9-31. When the full set from Black Fell arrived at Blackham's Hill, seen here on 29th August 1974, two bankhead men were needed. The back man took the small chain off the handrail of the wagon, and when the West Incline rope went slack, he pulled out the pin to enable the slip coupling to dis-assemble and fall from the wagon. When that happened, the front man hooked the rope and pulled it on to the decking out of the way of the wagon wheels. Then both men used their brake sticks to bring the wagons to a stand. At about the same point, underneath the track, the East Incline rope from the engine house went round its return wheel and emerged in the gulley where the roller can be seen at the foot of the vertical post. The men did this four times an hour on working days, starting work at 7.00am.

9-32. Sets at Blackham's Hill, both with ropes attached, on 23rd July 1974. On the far side the set of twelve empties from Springwell has been divided into two sixes and the rope attached to the rear of the first six, ready to descend to Black Fell, while on the left the slip coupling has been attached to the twelve fulls to go to Springwell. Note the brake stick leaning against the footstep; this was used to pin the brakes down as the wagons arrived here from Black Fell.

9-33. The curve in Springwell Yard at the bottom of the Blackham's Hill East Incline on 4th October 1974, the last day of commercial operation. Note the large conical rollers, the two steel bars for the rope to slide across and the horizontal roller to keep the rope off the ground. In the background are the Bowes Railway's Wagon Shops.

9-34. Springwell Bank Head on 20th September 1974. Looking straight ahead is the fenced wheel pit; the left hand side of the rope can be seen going underground to reach it. On the right is the two-storey brake cabin. Steel and wooden hoppers in various liveries can be seen going round into the dish for the haul up to Blackham's Hill.

9-35. Springwell Bank Foot on 29th July 1974. There were two kips here, side by side, each holding eighteen empty wagons. This was an hour's supply, as the incline handled six sets of six wagons each hour. This meant the locomotive had to bring 36 empties an hour. Each 18 would be uncoupled into sets of six, which would roll forward on the downhill gradient as the set on the rope left for the incline. Note the cabin, unusually made of wood, for the man here, and the lever, by then disused, for working the catch points.

9-36. Now on the Pelaw Main branch, this shows the bank head of the Allerdene Incline on 17th April 1973. As can be seen, it was very cramped, with the kip being for the fulls and the nearer side with its massive chock for the empties. Behind the photographer there was a sharp 90 degree curve. The engine house was set back on a hill, so that caged sheaves were needed to keep the rope at ground level.

9-37. Coming away from Ravensworth Ann Colliery, closed here, there was a 270 degree curve at the bottom of the Starrs Incline, and a set of fulls comes round this curve on 24th October 1969. Although the interchange between the two inclines lay alongside the colliery yard, the colliery itself was shunted by a locomotive. Its shed was the former engine house building used until 1937, when the ungated level crossing on the A1 road below Allerdene Bank Head was replaced by a bridge and a new engine and engine house were installed.

9-38. One of the large horizontal sheaves with its associated equipment used on the Ravensworth Ann curve on 24th October 1969.

9-39. Starrs Bank Head at Wrekenton, south of Gateshead, on 18th July 1972. On the far left is the long brick loco shed, built by the NCB to replace the wooden shed which had straddled the fulls road in the foreground (wagons went through it during working hours). The loco has brought twelve empties and has removed the twelve fulls that had collected on the nearer road. The empties have been divided into two sets of six, and the front six have been run forward on to the chocks and the rope attached to the rear end. To the right is the Starrs Engine, housing a 500 b.h.p. electric hauler. Note the new brickwork in the engine house, the result of the men being unable to detach the rope in time, thus pulling the full set into the building.

9-40. The 1ft 6in gauge haulages of John Knowles & Co (Wooden Box) Ltd at Woodville in south Derbyshire, with the 'jig' (self-acting incline) serving No.2 Pit on the left and the main-and-tail system serving No.5 Pit on the right. The photograph was taken in 1966, just before closure in April 1966.

9-41. Incredibly, one top endless chain plateway survived past 1980. In 1869 Henry Birkby set up a brickworks at Storr Hill, Wyke, near Bradford. A century later, by now the last traditional brickworks in Bradford, it was still using this nineteenth century system to bring clay to the works. The clay was brought by road to the loading hopper seen here. An incoming empty tub was released from the chain and manoeuvred over to the loading point, operated by a simple hatch. About fifty tubs were used on the system. The plateway itself, of 1ft 6in gauge, was constructed of various sizes of angled steel, nailed to the sleepers.

9-42. From the loading point to the works was about 250yds, slightly downhill at first but then ascending quite a steep gradient. At the works another return wheel was driven by an electric hauler under the floor of the unloading shed. On being released from the chain, the tub was run forward to an end-over tipping platform for the clay to be discharged into the mill. The business was owned for many years by H.Birkby & Sons Ltd, latterly Birkbys Ltd. It was closed in 1981.

9-43. As already noted, many of the brickworks around Peterborough also used chain or rope haulages, and again one of these haulages lasted into the 1980s. Situated on both sides of the East Coast Main line through the Fletton area of Peterborough were numerous brickworks. Two of these were the LB1 Works, opened in 1889, and the Hicks No.1 Works, opened in 1897-8. Latterly these were owned by the London Brick Co Ltd. Originally they used tramways to bring the clay from the pits to the works. In the second half of the twentieth century clay was brought by conveyor to Hicks No.1 Works, which retained some for its own use and transferred the remainder to a 2ft 6in gauge bottom 'ground haulage' to be taken to the LB1 Works.

9-44. The haulage is believed to have been modernised to the form seen here in the 1930s-1940s. It was about a mile long and had to cross the East Coast Main Line on a bridge, involving two sharp right-angled bends, as seen on the previous photograph. Note the large vertical roller on the inside of the bend, to restrain the rope in the event of it coming out of the sheaves on the curve. The clip to the rope, yet another different design, is seen here. The two works and their haulage closed on 29th January 1982.

9-45. In the early 1950s the NCB was looking for previously-unworked areas of coal that it could develop. In Northumberland one such area lay at Brenkley, about seven miles NNW of Newcastle and a mile west of Seaton Burn Colliery. A new drift was driven into the coal, worked by direct haulage on 2ft 6in gauge track. Here a loaded set of mine cars emerges from underground on 20th October 1975.

9-46. So that the miners did not have to walk down the drift at the beginning of a shift, or back up at the end of it, man-riding cars were introduced for the journey, using the direct haulage. The train is seen here near the drift entrance in June 1983. Note the small slides outside the left-hand rail on the adjacent track, and the grooves cut into them by the rope. The electric hauler was about 20yds behind the photographer.

9-47. To work traffic between the drift and the screens at Seaton Burn Colliery a main-and-tail haulage was installed, worked by an electric hauler at the screens. Here an empty set for the Drift rattles past about half way along the haulage on 20th October 1975, hauled by the 'tail' rope and dragging the 'main' rope. Note the colour light signal.

9-48. The end of the line at Seaton Burn screens, with a set of fulls having just arrived on the kip. The tail rope will be uncoupled and then attached to the empties waiting on the left. Haulage of coal on the main-and-tail system was replaced by road transport in March 1981, but it continued in use for the transport of materials, together with the direct haulage down the drift. This was the last narrow gauge surface rope haulage system in North-East England. The drift ceased production on 25th October 1985 and closed altogether, with the haulage, on 20th December 1985.

The last standard gauge inclines to operate in Durham were to be found on the railway between South Hetton and Seaham Harbour. Seaham Harbour, opened in July 1831, was built by the 3rd Marquis of Londonderry to handle the shipment of coal from his collieries, but he was keen to persuade other colliery owners to use it. The chief of these was The South Hetton Coal Co, whose South Hetton Colliery lay about four miles south-west of Seaham. The colliery and its railway to Seaham Harbour were opened on 5th August 1833.

The first mile from South Hetton was fairly level and may originally have been worked either by horses or the colliery's early locomotives. The next section, about ¾ mile, was originally worked by the Cold Hesleden stationary engine, bringing the waggons to the summit of the line at Hesleden. From here two consecutive self-acting inclines took the line down to Seaham. Official details of these seem never to have been published, but the first was called the Stony Cut Incline and was about 1¼ miles long, taking the line down to what later became Dawdon. Then followed the Swine Lodge Incline, which was about 1,000yds long and took the waggons down close to the entrance of the harbour. A contemporary illustration of one of the inclines can be seen in the Frontispiece.

Branches were built from South Hetton, but these lie outside the scope of this book. In 1843 Murton Colliery was added to the line. The Cold Hesleden Engine survived until about the mid 1890s, when it was replaced by locomotive working. Otherwise there was no significant change until 1958-59, when the NCB opened the new Hawthorn Combined Mine and its adjacent Coal Washery and Coking Plant, situated between South Hetton and Murton. The Combined Mine drew coal from Murton Colliery and the two Hetton collieries, Elemore and Eppleton and was capable of winding 8,000 tons of coal per day. Although most of the coal and coke would be dispatched via British Railways, coal also continued to go down the inclines to Seaham Harbour. But colliery and washery waste began to be taken down to Seaham too, for dumping at sea. In 1965 the shipping of waste exceeded the shipping of coal at Seaham, until eventually the inclines were used solely for waste traffic. This ceased abruptly on 5th March 1984 with the start of the year-long miners' strike. It had not been the NCB's intention to cease using the inclines, but their embankments had been made of waste coal back in the 1830s and during the strike these were heavily excavated by the miners and their families for the coal. So the NCB had to abandon the inclines and instead re-lay a branch to a nearby quarry to tip the waste there. The inclines were dismantled during the autumn of 1985.

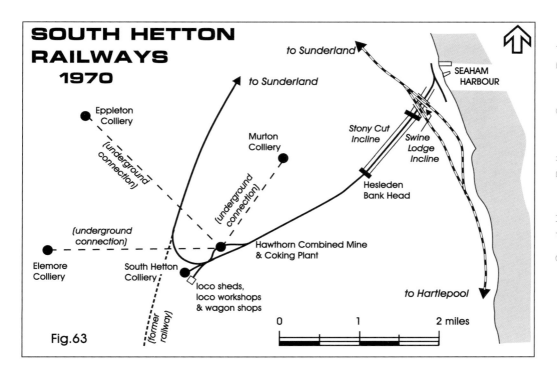

9-49. *The slip coupling used on the inclines between Hesledon and Seaham Harbour. It is a very different design from those illustrated in 3-11 and 3-12.*

9-50. A set of fulls waiting to leave the Stony Cut bank head on 15th August 1983. With the exception of the last but one wagon at the far end, they are all 16-ton steel wagons rebuilt with wooden boxes and larger cornerplates at Seaham Wagon Works. Note the long chain between the slip coupling and the rope, and the rollers outside the track to accommodate the rope once the set had left the bank head.

9-51. A set of empties coming up one of the kips at Stony Cut bank head at Hesledon on 29th May 1974. The kips on both inclines here were quite shallow, in contrast to those on the Bowes Railway. All the wagons except the first are 21-tonners, which were very rarely used on inclines, often because they were too big to pass through overbridges.

9-52. *The bank foot of the Stony Cut incline and the bank head of the Swine Lodge Incline at Dawdon on 29th May 1974. Here the kip, for the ascending empties, was the middle of the three roads, with tracks for the fulls on either side. There used to be a second bank foot here to the right of the one seen, which was the interchange point round to the Londonderry Railway, later the LNER and British Railways.*

9-53. *A set of empties ascending the 3-rail section near the top of the Swine Lodge Incline at Dawdon, again on 29th May 1974. The rope on the right is attached to the descending fulls, now nearing the bottom of the incline.*

Another National Coal Board standard gauge haulage to close in 1984 was its last powered incline, at Nottingham between Gedling Colliery and its landsale coal yard at Mapperley Plains. The colliery, on the north-eastern outskirts of the city, was opened in March 1903, but it was ¾ mile from – and significantly, in a valley several hundred feet below – an important road into the city, latterly the B684. The colliery company's answer was to provide a landsale yard alongside the road at Mapperley Plains and construct a railway from the colliery. The exact date of opening is uncertain, and it may well date from the opening of the colliery; it was certainly in existence by 1914. The line was rather less than half a mile long, straight and on a gradient about 1 in 13, and so a stationary engine had to be provided at the yard. Very probably at the beginning this was a steam engine; latterly it was an electric hauler. The incline was single line, working fulls and empties alternately.

This domestic coal depot was rebuilt by the NCB and was one of the largest of its type, so large that a shunting locomotive was required here during its daily operation. Five full wagons a time were hauled up from the colliery. The locomotive then shunted single wagons into a tippler, from where the coal was taken up by conveyor to fill four large hoppers, from which lorries were filled, some of them quite big vehicles. Other wagons were emptied with a grab. Empty wagons were subsequently shunted into sets ready to go back to the colliery. Normally sets of five were run, but sets of four or six were also known. The yard was always busy, especially in the mornings.

A special fleet of wooden 7-plank wagons was kept for this traffic, denoted by being painted black with yellow cornerplates; similar wagons were found at other Nottinghamshire collieries. The steam locomotive that originally shunted the yard was brought up on the rope at the start of the week and then lowered at the end of the week; but latterly, with the yard being un-manned at night and vandalism becoming a problem, it was not safe for the diesel locomotive that subsequently worked here to be left overnight, and so it had to be hauled up each morning and lowered down each afternoon.

With the decline in the consumption of household coal, the landsale yard and its incline closed in August 1984, the colliery following six years later.[7]

9-54. A set of five empty wagons waiting to descend of the incline between Mapperley Plains landsale yard and Gedling Colliery at Nottingham on 4th July 1980. Note the lengths of rail between the two tracks for the greased rope to slide across and be kept off the ground.

9-55. This hut was where the bank head man communicated with the bank foot and the engine house, using a gong which was operated by a lever and wire, seen here in front of the hut on 4th July 1980. The codes, as displayed in black lettering on a yellow board inside the hut, were simple: 1. Stop when in motion; 1. To raise; 2. To lower; 4. To raise steady; 5. To lower steady (there was no 3).

9-56. *A set of fulls coming up the incline on 4th July 1980. Note the absence of a chain between the rope and its coupling on the wagons.*

9-57. *The yard's shunting locomotive on 4th July 1980 was 4wDM RH 375714/1955, and its work over for the day, it had to be lowered down the incline to the colliery for safety overnight.*

The last commercial use of standard gauge steam locomotives by British Railways ended in 1968. When most people are asked when the last commercial use of standard gauge rope haulage ended, they are amazed when told that at least two haulages survived until 1986. Admittedly, they were not on British Railways, but that scarcely detracts from their surprise.

Knowledge of the haulage shown on 9-58 and 9-59 was unknown until they came to light early in 2012. They show the direct haulage used at the landsale depot at South Hetton in County Durham, which lay alongside the Pespool Branch from South

Hetton to Tunstall Quarry, where colliery and washery waste was tipped after the closure of the inclines to Seaham Harbour.

The haulage appears to be little more than 50yds long and was used to haul two wagons at a time up into the depot. After discharging, they ran out by gravity, taking the rope with them. The dates when this haulage was installed and when it ceased to operate are unknown, but given that the photographs were taken only four months before the closure of the Corkickle Incline (see next), it may have outlived its Cumbrian neighbour.

9-58. Two full 21-ton steel hoppers are hauled up to the depot on 25th June 1986. The rope has no chain between the rope coupling and the rope because the rope was not taken off the set during use, raising the full wagons and then lowering them when empty.

9-59. The same pair nears the landsale depot. The electric hauler, of which details are unknown, was presumably at the far end of the building. The wagons, Nos.571 and 391 of the Hawthorn fleet, have both been rebuilt from eight doors to four and fitted with new boxes.

The final standard gauge incline was the 'Corkickle Brake', sometimes known as the Kells or Marchon or Monkwray Brake, near Whitehaven in Cumbria. It had an interesting history. It was built in 1881 by the Earl of Lonsdale's Whitehaven Colliery Co to carry coal from the company's Croft Pit near the top of the incline down to a junction with what was then the Furness Railway just south of Corkickle Station. The incline was 525yds long, most of it with gradients between 1 in 5.2 and 1 in 6.6. Because of these, it was worked by a steam stationary engine, taking steam from two of three boilers. Later it concentrated on coke traffic from the ovens at Ladysmith Colliery, together with by-products destined for the steelworks at Workington and Barrow. The maximum number of wagons in a set was limited to four. Then the depression of the early 1930s saw Ladysmith Colliery and Coke Works closed in January 1932 and the incline became derelict, passing in this condition to the National Coal Board in 1947.

Meanwhile in 1940 a firm called Marchon Products Ltd had moved from London to Whitehaven, initially to manufacture firelighters. Soon the company was making chemicals as raw materials for detergents, and in 1943 it moved to the site of the former Ladysmith coke ovens. Ten years later the firm was a major manufacturer of 'cosmetic' detergents, 'fatty' alcohols, 400,000 tons of sulphuric acid and other chemicals and an equivalent tonnage of cement. Its increasing rail traffic had to travel over the NCB's rail system to go down the Howgill Brake to Whitehaven Harbour, where locomotives handled the exchange traffic with the sidings at Bransty. The solution to this congestion was for the NCB to hand over the derelict Corkickle Brake, which Marchon Products would rebuild and operate.

The new Brake was opened for traffic during May 1955, the last new major standard gauge incline to be built in Britain. The incline was laid out on the 3-rail/4-rail/2-rail system, although on the northern side of the 2-rail section a link was installed to serve the adjacent works of The Whitehaven Brick & Tile Co Ltd. At the summit of the incline a new engine house was built, straddling the track and housing a 500 b.h.p. Crompton Parkinson Ltd electric hauler, with two ropes, so that ascending and descending sets could be handled simultaneously. Approaching the bank head from the works, the single line became two, allowing wagons to be stabled here and the hauling locomotive to run round or return to the works for another load. Between the loop and the bank head there was a gated single line level crossing. When traffic levels were reduced, wagons were run down to the bank head one at a time by gravity, or by using a small 65 h.p. electric hauler to bring the wagons within reach of the main haulage ropes. A similar sized hauler was installed at the bank foot of the main incline, either to bring tank wagons from the nearby sidings, where they were left by British Railways, up to the rope end, or traffic for the brick works, which had its own 2ft 6in rope haulage to connect with a shale pit on the opposite side of the incline, the narrow gauge line passing underneath the main incline.

The maximum load on the Brake was 72 tons downhill and 60 tons uphill, and it was capable of being run with a difference of 25 tons in the loading. This allowed uneven loads to pass at the meetings, even four wagons against one. Sand drags were provided on the incline, fitted with electro-pneumatic points. If wagons exceeded a speed of 9 m.p.h. on the descent, the points would operate automatically and the wagons were diverted into one of the sand drags. The Brake was capable of handling over 200 wagons in 16 hours (two shifts), if the need arose, representing about 2,000 tons of traffic per day into and out of the Marchon Works.

The modernised Brake suffered from a serious design weakness, in that the engineman's control cabin was located in a position where he was unable to see down the full length of the incline and had to rely entirely on his indicators and bell signals from the men outside. So in 1972 a new engineman's control cabin was built on the roof of the engine house, at last giving the engineman a clear view. The new cabin was fitted with a track circuit diagram, although unusually it was not provided with a seat!

Besides the out-going cement and sulphuric acid, the works brought in anhydrite and phosphate rock, although the latter had a sand-like consistency rather than being lumps of rock. Thus, unusually amongst rope inclines, most of the traffic was carried in tank wagons. However, after 1980 traffic on the incline began to reduce considerably, partly because of the development of road transport and partly because British Rail's newer tank wagons were either of a longer wheelbase, which had difficulty passing over the hump at the top of the incline, or were a bogie design, which were not allowed on the incline; instead road tankers were used to take material down to Preston Street Goods Yard to load bogie tank wagons there.

With traffic dwindling, it was decided to close the Brake to traffic on 31st October 1986. It was used for the last time on 4th November 1986 to lower the two works' diesel locomotives, 0-4-0DH Rolls Royce 10206/1965 and 0-6-0DH Hunslet 7017/1971, down the incline. So ended standard gauge chain and rope haulage in Britain, after more than 180 years.[8]

9-60. *The Corkickle Engine House from the rear, with the 1972 engineman's control cabin on its roof on 16th May 1981. 4wDH Rolls Royce 10206/1965 has moved forward, over the level crossing, to collect empties.*

9-61. *The engineman in his cabin on 16th May 1981. Visible are his two control levers, the communication button box and the illuminated track circuit diagram.*

Corkickle Incline, Whitehaven, Cumbria

9-62. *The engineman's view down the whole length of the 525-yard incline, with empties for the works at the bank head and a further curving line of white empties in the distance at the bottom, on 16th May 1981. Note the catch points and sand drags, mentioned in the text.*

9-63. *A set of Allbright & Wilson's own full tank wagons leaves the bank head, while the second rope hauls up a set of empties, on 16th May 1981. These wagons carried phosphoric acid from Marchon probably to Associated Chemical Co Ltd at Barton-on-Humber.*

9-64. An empty wagon arrives at the bank head on 31st March 1981. This wagon, a BR Preswin, carried tripolyphosphate, an ingredient for washing powder, from Marchon to works either at Warrington or Port Sunlight. Note that there is no chain between the rope socket and the coupling link to the wagon.

9-65. A general view of the bottom of the incline in 1985. On the higher level are wagons brought in by British Rail waiting to go up the incline. Note that the lower level was designed so that wagons detached from the rope would run on by gravity to await collection by British Rail, leaving room for others to follow them.

But even towards the end of the twentieth century, narrow gauge haulages continued in use, usually because they were seen as the best solution for the owner's transport problem.

9-66. *A simple direct haulage on 2ft 0in gauge track at Great Row Colliery at Peacock Hay near Kidsgrove in Staffordshire, on 8th October 1975. The coal was tipped close to the drift entrance. The Great Row Colliery Co Ltd was registered on 7th December 1970 and dissolved on 29th September 2009.*

9-67. *A main-and-tail 2ft 0in gauge haulage at Strathfield Colliery near Stretton in Derbyshire on 7th April 1979. The owners here were H. & C. Hartshorne, who opened their first drift and screens in 1960. The haulage served No.2 Drift, about 300yds away, bringing coal to the screens. A 50 h.p. electric hauler was used. Note how the main rope is kept above the ground by raised sheaves. No.3 Drift was opened in 1978, with No.2 closing in 1980. The site was cleared in 1988.*

The lead mining industry in Upper Weardale and Northumberland effectively ceased in the 1920s. Fluorspar is commonly found with lead, but for many years there was no commercial use for it. Then in the 1960s technological improvements in the steel industry incorporated the use of fluorspar in the blast furnace to facilitate the separation of impurities. This demand led to the re-examination of old lead mines for sources of good quality fluorspar. Subsequently it was also used in the smelting of aluminium, as well as an additive in the production of petrol, some foams and refrigerants. As old lead mines were re-opened, both battery locomotives and rope haulage were used to bring tubs of fluorspar to the surface.

Cambokeels Mine near Eastgate in Weardale was driven originally in 1847 as a drainage drift for nearby lead mining. After various periods of closure and different owners it was re-opened to mine fluorspar in 1948. After further closure it was opened again in 1969 and two years later passed to Swiss Aluminium Mining (U.K.) Ltd. In 1975 a new large diameter drift was driven just to the east of the old one, to reach veins of fluorspar much deeper than were accessible from the original drift. It was 1,500 metres long on a gradient of 1 in 4, and worked by direct rope haulage. The mine was taken over in August 1982 by Weardale Minerals Ltd, who closed it in September 1988. It was re-opened about August 1989, but was reduced to care-and-maintenance from August 1990. It passed to Weardale Fluorspar Ltd in June 1991 and became derelict from about 1993.

9-68. The Cambo Keels drift of 1975, with 2ft 0in gauge track, was operated by direct haulage using an electric hauler on the surface on the end of the tipping gantry. Battery locomotives used the drift to travel and then work underground, though their shed was on the surface. Here a set of full side-tipping steel tubs emerges from the drift in August 1979. The notices on either side of the entrance banned people from the incline whilst the haulage was in motion and strictly forbade man-riding in the tubs.

Some historic inclines in other parts of the world were described in Chapter 8. But interesting inclines and haulages still continue to be used, fortunately still sought out by intrepid British travellers who seek to record them.

A number of forestry systems in Romania used self-acting inclines, one of them being the Siclau Incline in the eastern Carpathian Mountains of western Romania, near the border with Hungary. One source states that it dates from 1886, another that it was built in the 1920s by an Austrian firm for the Hungarian company Erdely Erdoipar. The track gauge is 1,445mm and it climbs 327 metres in a distance of 1,236 metres, giving a gradient of about 1 in 4. Although a self-acting incline, it operates with tables carrying railway vehicles, similar to those used in some North Wales quarries. The track layout is on the 3-rail/4-rail/2-rail system.

Trains of logs hauled by steam locomotives were brought to a saw mill at Comandau, not far from the top of the incline. Here the logs were cut into planks and loaded on to railway vehicles. These, one at a time, were then worked on to the table at the summit using horses. Meanwhile, at the bottom of the incline empty wagons were hauled by steam locomotives from the siding at Covasna to Siclau, where again horses were used to pull loaded wagons off the incline and put empties on.

However, a table carrying a wagon with wood, even stacked as high as here, did not have the weight to haul up an empty table from the bottom with the weight of the rope to which it was attached. So weights were added to the loaded table sufficient to overcome the resistance. The tables were then worked as far as the passing place in the middle, where a control cabin stopped them. The weights were then transferred to the empty wagon, which even with them was now less than the descending table, so that the loaded table could continue to the bottom and the empty table to the top. A complete journey took about 20 minutes.

The incline became recognised as the last of its kind in Europe, and when it closed in 1999, together with the saw mill and the railway, it was declared 'a protected national monument' and moves were made to take its future into preservation. The Siclau Association has made some progress, including re-opening the saw mill, but up-to-date information is unclear.

9-69. One of the loaded tables on the Siclau Incline in Romania passes from the central passing loop on to the 2-rail lowest section. Health & Safety regulations are not as strict here as they are in Britain.......

The incline opposite was part of Tipong Colliery, in Upper Assam in north-east India. It is located at the far eastern end of Upper Assam, so remote that few people ever visit it. Equally, the main attraction for those that made the long journey was the aged steam locomotives still in use. The colliery comprises drift mines and opencast working and continues in production because of the very high quality of the coal.

This incline lay at the extremity of the system. Visitors were not allowed up to the summit, but it was believed to be an opencast mine. The rope-worked section was about half a mile long, on a severe gradient. Older photographs show what is thought to have been a return wheel at the bottom, which would suggest some form of endless haulage. Latterly this was not there, and with the normal weather being rain and mist, little could normally be seen. The incline was believed to be self-acting, but on this rather better day there does not seem to be a meetings, which might suggest that it was operated by direct haulage, using a stationary engine at the top to run fulls and empties alternately (9-71). These pictures were both taken on 24th March 2004.

It is believed that the incline has since been obliterated by the development of a large opencast working.

9-70. The rope is taken off the just-arrived pair of fulls, to be put on the empties behind. The remains of old drift mines can be seen in the background.

9-71. Two empties leave the bottom to ascend the incline. There would seem to be no sheaves or rollers, just steel posts to keep the rope 'en route'.

In Japan, around 70km to the west of central Tokyo, at the end of the Ōme line operated by the East Japan Railway Company, lies the small town of Okutama. The town, situated in an area of high, tree covered hills, is popular with tourists visiting nearby lakes and limestone caves, and is located at the point where the Nippara River, in its deep gorge, flows into the Tama River. Immediately to the north of the railway station is the Hikawa processing plant of Okutama Kogyo Co Ltd (Okutama Industry Co Ltd), Hikawa being the old name for Okutama. The plant's output is limestone, dug from an opencast mine approximately 10km up the Nippara River and destined for the industry of Kawasaki. Until the late 1990s limestone was despatched from Okutama by the main line railway, but all traffic now travels by road.

The limestone is extracted using a 'bench cut' system and is moved by heavy off-road equipment to a shaft, down which it is tipped before being conveyed below ground to the underground northern end of a 4.9km long 762mm gauge double track bottom endless rope haulage system to the Hikawa plant. The line, known as the Hikawa line, opened in 1953 and replaced an earlier aerial ropeway. For the vast majority of its length, the 'cable line', as it is known locally, runs in tunnels under the valley sides of the Nippara River. The line does not run deep underground, and so at the three points where a valley crosses the route of the line, it emerges from a tunnel into the open to cross the valley by a viaduct. The middle one of these is spectacular, spanning the Nippara River gorge on a high-level, single-span arched girder bridge. Around half way along the line, a short section of perhaps 20 metres also runs in the open air where the line crosses a small gully on a slight bend between two lengthy and straight tunnel sections.

The rolling stock used is a fleet of steel mine-cars of a U-shaped design, numbered in the range 1 to 250, of which around 220 seem to be in use at any one time. Individual mine cars operate at an average headway of around 17 seconds, but with gaps between individual wagon pairs varying between 10 seconds and 40 seconds; right hand running is the rule. The line appears to operate for a day shift only, with a break of around an hour at 12:00 midday, and there are additional stoppages from time to time for reasons unknown. When the haulage is operating continuously, mine-cars complete a round trip in around one hour and five minutes, suggesting a running speed of around 10km/hr, or slightly higher depending on how long mine-cars spend 'off the rope' at each end. The capacity of the mine cars is not known, perhaps 5 tonnes, which would give the line an hourly capacity of around 1,000 tonnes of limestone.

The company does not allow visits, even to local enthusiasts, and so no details appear to be published of the underground loading and unloading facilities, which are invisible to the outside world. It can be assumed that the wagons are detached from the endless rope at each end of the line, and it can be seen from the photographs that the mine cars appear to have an automatic system by which they grip the rope. It seems likely that the small wheel on a lever on one side of each mine-car rides up on a raised rail to open the 'jaws' that grip the rope to release it; when re-attaching to the rope, the wheel presumably then drops down to allow the 'jaws' to close and grip the rope.

The endless haulage at Okutama, still in operation in late 2011, is understood to be the last of its type still operating in the open air in Japan. One can only speculate as to the reasons for its survival: the road along the valley is narrow and twisting, and unsuited to heavy goods vehicles, whilst its replacement by a conveyor would be both complex and expensive, and would be likely to lead to an extended break in production.

9-72. Mine car No.39, showing the small wheel just ahead of one of the rear wheels. It is assumed that this runs up a small ramp alongside the track, thus releasing the gripping mechanism from the rope. 2nd November 2011.

9-73. At this location a small skeletal bridge carried the track over a gully, and during the system's lunch-time stoppage, one mine car stopped directly above the gully. By standing in the gully on tip-toe and holding the camera up 'blind' in the gaps between the sleepers (and trying five times!), this view on 2nd November 2011 successfully shows the gripping apparatus underneath the car.

9-74. Mine cars 55 and 83 on the short section between two of the tunnels and on the small bridge mentioned in 9-73, on 2nd November 2011.

9-75. The single-span arched girder bridge which carries the system over the Nippara river gorge on 2nd November 2011.

Coal mining in the Forest of Dean in Gloucestershire has been carried on for centuries, notably by 'free miners'. One of these, Gerald Haynes, located some coal towards the bottom of the Bixslade valley on the western edge of the Forest, and in 1980 he opened the Hayner's Bailey drift mine, the second-last colliery in Britain to be worked by one man. In 1995 he installed a direct haulage powered by a new electric hauler manufactured by Peckett & Anderson Ltd of Glasgow. In the following year he reconstructed the entrance and flattened the incline there.

In 2000 Mr.Haynes retired and the mine was taken over by Mervyn Bradley and Ray Ashley. In the autumn of 2000 they re-named the mine the Monument Mine, after a monument nearby to those who died in an accident at the former Union Colliery, now closed.

The gauge is 1ft 6in, and the hauler is located at the end of the tipping gantry, shown in 9-76. The simple direct haulage pulls out full tubs from the 200-yard drift up to the tipping point, where the tubs are emptied. Tubs of dirt waste are also brought to the surface and are placed on the turntable seen on 9-77. Here the rope is uncoupled and the tub turned through 90 degrees, then to be pushed for quite a distance through the forest to be tipped on the waste heap.

Most of the mine's output is household coal, which is bagged before delivery. The mine produces between 400 and 500 tons of coal per year.

Monument Mine, Forest of Dean, Gloucestershire

9-76. A general view of Monument Mine in the Forest of Dean on 23rd August 2001.

9-77. The electric hauler and the turntable mentioned in the text on 23rd August 2001.

Another direct haulage can be found in the Scottish borders, north of the A701 road from Biggar to Penicuik, where on exposed, rain-sodden moors, some 900ft above sea level, peat is harvested. One of these is Springfield Moss in Midlothian, where cutting began in 1981. It is now owned by William Sinclair Horticulture Ltd of Lincoln. This site is one of three locally owned by the firm to produce milled peat and also includes workshops which serve all three workings. Normally road vehicles are used to bring the peat from the moor, but a 2ft 0in gauge railway has been retained out from the Springfield Workshops to do this work for 2-3 months during the winter when the weather is at its worst.

9-78. Direct rope haulage in the peat harvesting industry: the simple system at the Springfield Workshops and Moss in Midlothian, showing the tipping dock and the electric hauler with its rope, together with the red disc used to control traffic movements, 24th August 2011.

When the system is working, a locomotive propels a rake of five wagons to near the tipping dock. Here they are attached to a wire rope and an electric winch then hauls them to the tipping dock, a distance of about 75yds. When these are emptied, a loop line allows them to drop back down to the locomotive. Even here there is 'something different'. A hut near the tipping dock is provided for the workers, and to this is attached a large red disc, which allows the person in charge to control rail movements. While tipping is in progress, a second set of five wagons is being filled out on the moss.

This chapter describes and illustrates rope and chain haulages across more than a hundred years and into the twenty first century, using a wide variety of methods and of gauges. Yet they are as much a part of railway history as famous steam locomotives and well-known stations, and thus equally deserve to be recorded and remembered.

Springfield Workshops, Midlothian, Scotland

1   For a full history of the Railway, see *The Private Railways of County Durham, chapter 11, The Pelaw Main Railway,* by Colin E.Mountford, Melton Mowbray, 2004. For a history of the Team Waggonway, see *A Fighting Trade – Rail transport in Tyne coal, 1600-1800, Vol.1- History, Vol.2, Data,* by G.Bennett, E.Clavering and A.Rounding, published by the Plateway Press, 1990.

2   For the advertisement inviting the supply of the Bowes Bridge and Causey Engines, see chapter 6.

3   Marshall, in *The Cromford & High Peak Railway* (1996, reprinted 2010), 81; 3rd June and 12th August 1963 are also found.

4   See *The Bowes Railway,* 2nd ed. 1976 by Colin E.Mountford, London, 1976 and *The Bowes Railway,* chapter 3 of *The Private Railways of County Durham by* Colin E. Mountford, Melton Mowbray, 2004.

5   For other illustrations of these inclines, see as follows:
Birkheads: 1-19, Fig.7;
Kibblesworth: 3-14, 3-20, 6-21, 6-22, 6-36, 6-37;
Black Fell: front cover, 2-18, 6-30, 6-31, 6-38, 6-39, 6-40, Fig.8;
Blackham's Hill: 6-41, 6-42, 6-43;
Springwell: 1-20.

6   For an additional picture from the Starrs Incline, see 3-22.

7   For a longer description, see *Railway Bylines,* October 2001, 522.

8   For a more detailed description, see *Industrial Railway Record,* No.111, *The Corkickle Brake,* December 1987.

Chapter 10 Preservation

Whilst some preservation from the early days of haulages did take place, this happened by chance. Some former stationary engine houses survived because their owners needed them for new uses. For example, the Birtley Church Engine House on the Pelaw Main Railway in Durham, built in stone about 1809, ceased to be used as an engine house about 1904. Because it had access from an adjacent road, it then became the Fire Station for its owners, The Pelaw Main Collieries Ltd. After this it was used as a storehouse for materials for the company's Buildings Department, but when this moved elsewhere, the building soon became a shell and was eventually demolished.

It is believed that the oldest railway engine house to survive is the original Brusselton building, which was part of the Stockton & Darlington Railway when it opened in 1825. It was not used for long, as it was replaced by a new engine inside a new building in 1831. It survived because it was converted into a domestic house. It is one of a clutch of former SDR buildings at Brusselton.

The routes of the two inclines there can be seen easily too, together with many of the stone blocks that were used to support the rails, because they lie in rural land. Unfortunately, an explanatory board fixed to the building does not explain its history or that of the Engine clearly, and uses as illustrations 5-10, which is dominated by the 1831 engine house, now demolished, and part of 2-17, which again describes the later engine, not the one which the surviving building housed. One could wish that local councils took more care in preparing such display panels. It is believed that the building for the former Etherley Engine on the SDR also became incorporated into a house.

The next oldest engine house still to survive is at Middleton on the route of the Cromford & High Peak Railway in Derbyshire, and not just the building but also the engine inside it.[1] Although major components were replaced during its lifetime, it remains in essence the twin-cylindered beam engine of 1829 in its original engine house. When its section of the C&HPR closed in 1963 the

10-1. The remaining building from the Brusselton Engine of 1825 on the Stockton & Darlington Railway in County Durham, on 27th March 2011. Although it housed a vertical twin-cylindered beam engine, it was laid out as a steam packet engine with the beams nearly at floor level, so that the usual two-storey building was not needed.

10-2. The preserved Middleton Engine House from the north on 30th August 2010, alongside the trackbed of the Cromford & High Park Railway in Derbyshire. The two Cornish boilers, not used since about the late 1950s, remain in place. The engine still operates an endless rope, which emerges from the front of the building underground to pass round a sheave before returning into the engine house, so that visitors can watch the rope circuit when the engine is demonstrated.

historical importance of the engine and its building was recognised, although it was not until 1971 that it and the trackbed were acquired jointly by Derbyshire County Council and the Peak Park Planning Board, now the Peak District National Park. In the forty years since then it has become an excellent example of what can be done with imagination and commitment. 17 miles of the route of the Railway, from High Peak Junction at Cromford to Dowlow, has been converted to the High Peak Trail, available to walkers, cyclists (as part of the National Cycle Network) and horse riders. At Middleton the engine has been restored to working order, now operated by compressed air, and is demonstrated at regular intervals between Easter and October, with regular maintenance.[2] Inside the engine house various items are on display, while outside at the top of the incline there is a small exhibition, including a LMS wagon. A visitor centre has been built here, together with toilets, facilities for cycle hire and a car park. The former engineman's house is now the base for the countryside rangers who supervise the whole route, while the former reservoir is now the cottage's garden. A selection of historical booklets about the Railway and the Engine are available, together with a plan of the

latter on which Fig.28 in chapter 6 is based. At Middleton Bottom the rope tensioning apparatus has been restored (without a rope), while at Sheep Pasture Top the shell of the engine house survives. At High Peak Junction the railway's workshops are preserved and open to visitors. Nearby is a small display of railway vehicles, while the water tank used to fill the tenders remains, still overflowing with water from the spring. The rope tensioning apparatus at the bottom of the incline is preserved, while just up beyond the former A6 road bridge the catch pit can still be seen. To the west the Trail goes through Hopton Tunnel, and at Hopton Top the railway cottages survive.

10-3. The Middleton Engine House and its engine were built by the Butterley Company in 1829. Here the left hand cylinder, which is 25in in diameter with a 60in stroke, can be seen, together with its valve chest, again on 30th August 2010. For the layout of this engine, see Fig.28. The cylinder's condenser is located beneath the floor, as is the air pump. The handle in the foreground is the regulator for this cylinder; there is a similar handle for the other cylinder, the engine being driven from a standing position. The engine is maintained in excellent and immaculate condition.

In the North East Frank Atkinson (b.1924), later to be the founder of what is now Beamish, the Living Museum of the North, persuaded the National Coal Board to donate to him the Warden Law Engine on the Hetton Railway in Durham after it closed in 1959. Dr. Atkinson was an advocate of 'unselective collection' – 'you give it, we'll collect it'; if an item was of historical importance to the history of north-east England, it should be preserved. So in 1961 the engine house was

10-4. In this view from the oiling gallery, another taken on 30th August 2010, the idler wheel with its two grooves can be seen in the centre with the flywheel below it, flanked by the two beams. At ground floor level in the bottom left corner is the writing desk for the engineman and, behind the idler wheel, is the seat for the brakeman.

dismantled, followed by the engine itself, the single cylinder beam engine built by Thomas Murray in 1836. Eventually everything found its way to Beamish, opened in 1970. Sadly, it has remained dismantled; the cylinder is inside the Regional Museum Store, other parts lie around outside. Whether everything survives now is uncertain. Equally sadly, development projects at museums like Beamish depend for their progress on grant aid from outside bodies, on a strong business case and high scores for educational value and public interest. The reconstruction of the Warden Law Engine and its engine house hardly registers on the scale. Fifty years after it was dismantled no one has any firm idea when work on restoring and re-erecting it might begin.

One of the stationary engines on the Canterbury & Whitstable Railway was the 25 h.p. Tyler Hill Engine, built by Robert Stephenson & Co of Newcastle upon Tyne in 1828. It was removed in 1846, but incredibly parts of it survive. Their history after that date is uncertain (see photo 10-6), but at one time they were owned by British Railways. Exactly which parts survive is uncertain, as some are stored at Canterbury's Heritage Museum and some are stored elsewhere. The railway's 0-4-0 locomotive INVICTA is on display at the Heritage Museum. It is hoped that one day everything can be displayed in a new museum at Whitstable.

10-5. This view, again taken on 30th August 2010, shows part of the right-hand wall of the Engine House, with on the left the indicators installed in later years to show the catch points at the bank head were set correctly, and to their right the three-position telegraph, with 'G' (Go) and 'S' (Stop) visible (see 3-21 for its twin at the foot of the incline).

10-6. The vertical-cylinder and the flywheel from the Tyler Hill Engine on the Canterbury & Whitstable Railway, seen here stored in the open at Canterbury on 16th February 2006.

10-7. The Weatherhill Engine as displayed at the old Railway Museum at Queen Street in York on 1st August 1974, shortly before dismantling. The steel supporting frame and the cut flywheel can be seen.

This brings this account to the two railway stationary engines displayed in the Great Hall of the National Railway Museum at York since its opening in 1975. The larger of these is the Weatherhill Engine, which operated the higher of the two inclines taking the Stanhope & Tyne Railway out of Stanhope in County Durham. It was replaced by a new hauler in 1919, but was left in place by the North Eastern Railway, undoubtedly because it was felt to be an historic piece of machinery. In 1924 it was actually brought back into use for several weeks when its replacement needed major repairs; a locomotive was sent to act as a stationary boiler. When the London & North Eastern Railway opened its Railway Museum at Queen Street in York in 1931, the Weatherhill Engine was dismantled and then re-erected in it. It came of course without its building, whose walls had been an integral part of the design of the engine, so that a steel frame had to be erected to support the ends of the two beams and the crankshaft, with its crank pin and flywheel. Suitable space for it in the museum was limited, so to make it fit the drums were removed, together with much of the top half of the flywheel. The reader is asked to compare the sketches of it made by the NER in 1919, illustrated in Fig.29 in chapter 6, the picture of it in the old Queen Street Museum at York, taken in 1974 (10-7) and a picture of it in the Great Hall 'today' (10-8). It will be immediately obvious that there are major and significant differences between the three illustrations.

10-8. The Weatherhill Engine as displayed in the Great Hall of the National Railway Museum at York on 22nd September 2010.

10-9. The cylinder, 29in by 60in, and valve chest manufactured by Thomas Murray of Chester-le-Street in Durham, probably in 1838, and fitted to the Weatherhill Engine after its original cylinder exploded in the 1880s, as recorded on 1st February 2011.

Work to create the new National Railway Museum at Leeman Road stretched the resources of the Science Museum staff in London to the limit. It was decided at a senior level at a fairly early stage that both the Weatherhill and Swannington Engines should be operational in their new home, to be achieved by hiding away an electric motor fitted with a wheel which in turn would rotate the flywheel. As the flywheels on both engines had been cut, new flywheels had to be cast. But whereas the Swannington Engine was to be fixed to the floor, the Weatherhill Engine would need to be supported. No detailed schedule of work was drawn up; it proved difficult to find firms to tender for the work, and the difference in the tenders submitted was tens of thousands of pounds, while all the time the opening date for the new museum drew nearer. Nevertheless, the 'refurbished' engines were installed on time. Three years later the NRM asked the contractors to draw up a list of the work they had done so that there would be a record of it.

Comparing even the 1974 and 2010 pictures, it will be obvious that the biggest difference is the provision of a massive welded steel 'A' frame to support the central crankshaft, with the side walls supporting the ends of the beams. This feature, still less any welded steel, was not of course part of the original engine, as the 1919 drawings show; but unfortunately its provision in 1975 led subsequent interpreters of the engine to describe as 'built to Phineas Crowther's Patent of 1800', which is completely untrue.

10-10. Mr.Malcolm Young was generously allowed to go up to the 'operating platform' after hours on 1st February 2011 to photograph items otherwise inaccessible to the public. This shows the crankshaft, square like the original, with (from right to left) the crank pin, the flywheel and the central drive pinion.

10-11. The nicely-decorated handwheel used to slew the front drum out of gear when required, on 1st February 2011. Curiously, this wheel is not shown on the NER drawings of 1919.

10-12. The gearing and slewing rod from this handwheel to the drum bearing, now fixed permanently in position, 1st February 2011.

In summary, the Engine as now exhibited has (a) an A frame which the original did not have; (b) an additional steel frame at the rear of the engine; (c) a second hand cylinder and valve chest, fitted in the 1880s; (d) second hand gear wheels (fitted by the North Eastern Railway); (e) no drums; (f) a new, though similar, crankshaft, made in 1975; (g) a new flywheel, cast in 1975; (h) an access platform which is not at the height of the platform shown in 1919; (j) a floor level (within the railed area) which is lower than the original and has some of the original driver's controls missing, together with other less obvious differences – for example, the bearings which once allowed the drums to be slewed to take them out of gear are now fixed, although curiously the hand wheels which did this and can still be seen (although they are not explained) do not appear on the 1919 drawings!

Clearly all this raises major issues of interpretation which need to be resolved, and then the information for visitors needs to be revised accordingly.

The Swannington Engine from Leicestershire also found its way to the Queen Street museum in York after it ceased work in 1951. It too was removed from its engine house, although here the building was not an integral part of its design. It also lost its drum, and despite being a horizontal engine and lacking the extreme height of the Weatherhill Engine (see 5-30 and 6-6), it too had its flywheel cut. Again the Science Museum wanted to see this engine demonstrated to the public, and so it too had to have a new flywheel cast and to be fitted with a small electric motor to rotate the flywheel. However, while the NRM records show the original flywheel measuring 9ft 4in in diameter, the flywheel made in 1974 measures approximately 15ft 4in in diameter. The reason for this difference is not known. The differences of detail are fewer than with its neighbour, but there is an argument that they should be included in the material interpreting it to the public. The two engines are usually demonstrated daily during mid-morning and mid-afternoon.

Meanwhile the Swannington Heritage Trust has done an excellent job publicising information about the industrial history of its area and undertaking exploratory and renovation work. This has included excavating the foundations of the engine house and restoring the route of the incline.

Up to the early 1970s what had been preserved of rope haulages had either been engine houses or the engines from inside them. The most successful has been the Middleton Engine, at least partly because the engine was retained inside its engine house; engines dismantled and removed elsewhere have suffered the vagaries of fate. But then came a much more ambitious scheme – to preserve a section of rope haulage on the Bowes Railway in County Durham, which would be demonstrated to the public; to acquire a full range of the railway's wooden wagons, as part of its history and because they would be needed for the demonstrations; and to include with the scheme the railway's engineering and wagon shops, both for their historical importance and to provide the maintenance facilities for the scheme.

This scheme arose from the enthusiasm of members of Tyne & Wear County Council, created in April 1974. Only a few months later came the announcement of the closure of Kibblesworth Colliery (see chapter 9), now within the new Tyne & Wear area, and with it the closure of the Railway's five remaining inclines. Dr. Stafford Linsley, a lecturer at Newcastle University, persuaded the members of the new Council's Environment Improvement Committee that a railway of such national significance, with its associations with George Stephenson, should be professionally filmed before it closed. Thus it was that Amber Films of Newcastle upon Tyne made the film 'The Bowes Line', recording 'a day' in the life of the line.[3]

But then the councillors thought that if the line was so important that it ought to be filmed, ought it not to be preserved? And if so, what management model would be best to achieve this? The Council realised that a voluntary organisation, registered as a charity, would be much more able to obtain grant aid than the council. So the Council set up the Tyne & Wear Industrial Monuments Trust, a registered charity, and backed it with the council's administrative services, from planning, the secretariat and the treasurer's department. The Council then acquired the section of the Bowes Railway between the bridge over the former Pelaw Main Railway just west of Black Fell bank head, Black Fell Engine House, the Blackham's Hill West and East Inclines and the Blackham's Hill Engine and the bank head of the self-acting Springwell Incline, together with its bank head, brake cabin and return wheel. All this was then leased it to the Trust. Dr. Linsley became chairman of the Trustees, who then set up the Bowes Railway Project Committee, a body composed jointly of Trustees and volunteers who wanted to support the scheme, with your author as chairman. He noted that virtually all of the now-preserved section had formed part of the Springwell Colliery Railway and that 1976 was the 150th anniversary of its opening; he further noted that the Duchess of York had visited the railway in 1936 as the daughter of the 14th Earl of Strathmore, then chairman of John Bowes & Partners Ltd, and suggested that she be invited to visit again, forty years later, to open the preservation scheme. To everyone's astonishment Queen Elizabeth the Queen Mother accepted. On

15th July 1976 she arrived at Blackham's Hill by helicopter and after the formalities, presentations[4] and a buffet lunch outside the engine house, she travelled by a hastily-assembled steam-hauled royal colliery train, complete with colliery band, down to Springwell to depart by car.

The rope inclines could be demonstrated because the gradient of the Blackham's Hill East Incline was only 1 in 70. This would allow a locomotive to take a set of twelve wagons up to Pelaw Main Junction, where it could run round and then push them into the East Incline bank head, ready for the rope haulage to begin, and then bring the set back to Springwell at the end of the day.

Major problems soon began. The County Council had acquired the railway; but the workshops at Springwell were leasehold and were acquired by a property development company who intended to replace them with a large housing development. The Council pointed out that the developer's land was divided by a freehold railway that it did not intend to sell, and that it would oppose a planning application for housing development. The developer then demanded over £½ million to sell his land, which he reduced eventually to well under half that. The preservation scheme was lucky to have powerful backers. In addition, the whole of the preserved section, with its buildings and wagons, was recognised by English Heritage as a Scheduled Ancient Monument, giving it protection in law.

But other major problems rapidly appeared, tackling them being greatly helped by there being a registered charity run by hard-working volunteers preserving a unique historic railway. New ropes were needed for both inclines, kindly given at cost by the rope manufacturers Latch & Batchelor Ltd at Hay Mills, near Birmingham; the railway's power supply came into its substation at 20,000 volts, reduced to 3,000 for the Blackham's Hill Engine; when the supply was reduced to 11,000 volts, 11,000-3,000 transformers were needed, acquired with help from the Science Museum; then after numerous failures a new electricity cable had to be laid up to the engine house. The Railway Inspectorate had never heard of the Bowes Railway, but it was quickly visited by the well-known Major Peter Olver, who proved very supportive, not least in helping and approving the methods of operating the rope haulage and the official training of volunteers; the only toilet on site was one cubicle and a 10ft urinal, and the Tourist Board refused grant aid until the annual visitor numbers reached 20,000. The volunteers were committed, but many lacked both the knowledge and the skilled trades needed to maintain the railway.

But there were successes too. The last surviving Bowes Railway steam locomotive, an 0-4-0ST, was obtained in 1976. Three years later this was joined by one of the small 'Planet' diesels that had worked Pelaw Main traffic into Springwell (see chapter 9) and then by another 0-4-0ST. Because Blackham's Hill had no road access suitable for visitors, it was essential to provide a passenger service between Springwell and Blackham's Hill, and this was opened in 1979 using a colliery brake van, with small passenger platforms being completed in 1981. To prevent conflicting movements between a rope hauled train and a passenger train, electric interlocking was installed between the two locations. At Springwell a wooden signal box housed a lever frame containing a lever which, with the one-engine-in-steam staff locked into it, locked the exit point from the yard, while at Blackham's Hill a ground frame had a similar lever, locked by a key with the rope coupling pin attached, locking the catch point at Blackham's Hill East bank head. Thus the passenger train could run up to Blackham's Hill, run round at Pelaw Main Junction, push back into Blackham's Hill and then return to Springwell while the rope haulage ran two sets on the Blackham's Hill West Incline. When the passenger train had returned to Springwell and been locked out of section, a set could be run part way down the Blackham's Hill East Incline while the loco ran round at Springwell and more passengers arrived.

Everything brought to the railway, such as brake vans for the passenger service, extra wagons, the water crane and its tank, were painted in Chelsea blue, to show visitors that these items were not original to the Railway. All of the Railway's original wagons were restored with absolute attention to historical accuracy, even to using the exact paint, colours and different NCB liveries and replicating signwriting errors in the letters and numbers on the wagons. This meant that when the public visited the site, they saw a colliery railway looking and operating exactly as it was in 1963.

In 1979 the Springwell workshops became the home for Locomotion Enterprises (1975) Ltd, led by Mike Satow, which had previously built the replica of the Stockton & Darlington Railway's *Locomotion* and who had gained the contract to build replicas of Robert Stephenson's *Rocket* and Braithwaite & Eriksson's *Novelty*, together with replicas of two carriages, for the re-enactment of the Rainhill Trials in 1980. Then in 1981 the Bowes Railway Project Committee was converted into the Bowes Railway Co Ltd, a company limited by guarantee and also a registered charity.

The biggest help for the Railway came from the development of a scheme by the Manpower Services Commission to help the long-term unemployed. This developed into one of the MSC's biggest schemes, helped by the availability of men from the mining industry and by the fact that key workers who were essential to the employment of other men could be kept on for

10-13. A set of six descending the top section of the Blackham's Hill West Incline on the Bowes Railway on 7th June 1987, with the Black Fell Engine House in the distance. The land on the right then being cleared now houses two bungalows, a livery stables and other buildings, with a tarmac access road right to the new gates.

10-14. A set approaching Blackham's Hill West bank foot/Black Fell on 4th July 1982. The complete incline can be seen, with the Mount Level Crossing and its crossing-keeper's cabin half way up. The crossing-keeper not only operated the three gates here but was part of the bell code system for the West Incline. The siding coming off to the left had served the Black Fell boilers until 1950.

10-15. The return wheel pit for the East rope at Blackham's Hill stripped for repair on 12th July 1981. New brickwork was built and then a latticed steel frame put on top to carry the weight of the wagons. Finally the steel work was covered with new decking, with removable planks for easy access. The whole job took about three weeks.

longer than twelve months. The scheme thus allowed the Railway to employ a railway manager and two assistant managers, one in charge of the workshops and one in charge of outdoor work, together with a range of skilled and unskilled staff. It was essential to coordinate the work of the volunteers with that of the MSC staff, but over time all the workshop machinery was overhauled and brought back into working order, including the wheel lathe, and skilled trades employed, not least a wagonwright to tackle the biggest of the wagon repairs. The volunteers located a derelict steel-framed building which the MSC men dismantled and then rebuilt at Springwell to house toilets, a café and a ticket office. The rebuilding of the return wheel pit at Blackham's Hill was carried out, together with many other smaller projects.

The development of the workshops resulted in enquiries asking if they could undertake work for other similar organisations; in the 1980s this was long before the infrastructure that supports the railway heritage industry today had been developed. From this the project management began to consider the situation. As the quality of repairs improved, so there was less work from the Railway to keep the Engineering Shops working full time. Equally the MSC scheme would eventually come to an end. Perhaps if outside work could be taken on, then the profit from it might pay for work

from the Railway and also make it possible for the Railway to employ a handful of skilled men full time, thus helping to ensure the continuation of the engineering skills needed. The work would also help other heritage sites that did not have facilities like those at Springwell. But the County Council vetoed the idea; it was not permissible, it said, for a private organisation, even a charity, to make itself a profit from council-owned property. The opportunity to attain financial viability and continue traditional engineering skills was destroyed.

So those elsewhere who had work they wanted doing were refused, and not long afterwards the Manpower Services scheme ended and all its workers left. Then in 1986 the Government abolished Tyne & Wear County Council, dividing its responsibilities between the five metropolitan districts. The boundary between Sunderland and Gateshead districts ran through the Railway at Blackham's Hill, so the line east of Blackham's Hill and the workshops passed to Sunderland, while west of Blackham's Hill passed to Gateshead, with each council appointing a director to the Bowes Railway Company's board.

From the beginning of the scheme the two Blackham's Hill inclines had been operated alternately, compared with simultaneously in NCB days. To demonstrate the haulages to the public,

10-16. *The rope being detached from the set arriving at Blackham's Hill from the West Incline on 7th June 1987 (compare with 9-31). The pit for the return wheel for the East rope lies beneath the decking in front of the leading wagon, with the rope going underground in the foreground and emerging between the two tracks where the roller can be seen. On the far side the next set of six awaits its turn to descend the incline once the rope has been attached.*

10-17. *A set of twelve arrives in Springwell Yard on 21st June 1992 – the preserved rope haulage in full operation. Various designs of wagon are in good order and display original Bowes liveries. No.22, 0-4-0ST Andrew Barclay 2274 of 1949, an original Bowes Railway locomotive, stands awaiting passengers at the platform (since replaced by a large aluminium structure). The large stone building in the background is the Wagon Shop; the bell push to rap the set away back up the incline was on the corner of this building.*

10-18. Looking down the Fitting Shop in the Engineering Shops at Springwell in August 1983. All the machinery was fully operational, including the wheel lathe at the far end. The belt-driven machinery painted blue was donated by a location at Ealing in London. As this picture was taken on a weekday, all the men were employed under the Manpower Services Commission scheme.

10-19. 10-ton wagon No.572, a Bowes Railway 'Ordinary' design, undergoing a Heavy General Repair in the Wagon Shops in August 1983, the work partly done by an MSC wagonwright and his mate and by volunteers. A new headstock, stanchions, cornerplate and planking can be seen at the end nearest the camera.

two sets of six were lowered and raised on the West Incline, and then the set of twelve was lowered down the East Incline. In practice, this was rarely lower than Pelaw Main Junction. In preservation the wagons did not of course carry any coal, and the rope haulage volunteers were nervous that the set, dragging the rope after it, might not gain sufficient speed to go over the Springwell Road level crossing and into Springwell Yard. The gates would have to be opened and the catch point above them closed before the set left the bank head, and if the set stalled, the gates might have to remain against road traffic for up to 10 minutes, leaving drivers wondering what was going on.

The wagon repairs volunteers decided to do their best to help. Only those with oil axle boxes would be put into the operating set, including the Bowes steel wagons acquired since 1976. These axleboxes would be stripped down and thoroughly overhauled and cleaned, the pads freshened up and the baths filled with new oil. All the springs would be checked, and changed where required to give a balance of +/-½in from vertical. At last the set was ready to be tried, all the operating staff were trained and ready, and to everyone's excitement it worked! Visitors at Springwell could now see a rope haulage set of twelve come into and leave the Yard.

This achieved, minds now turned to what seemed the final stage. From the platform at Blackham's Hill the trackbed of the former Pelaw Main branch went on to Wrekenton for about ¾ mile. Examination showed that there was room to accommodate the footpath that had developed and that there was sufficient land at Wrekenton to instal a run-round loop. If the track was re-instated, the scheme could offer a steam-hauled round passenger trip of about 2½ miles. Moreover, if electric interlocking was installed at Pelaw Main Junction to make it possible to lock the passenger train out on the branch, then the East Incline set could be run into Springwell Yard and back out again while the passenger train went to Wrekenton, the loco ran round and the train was hauled back to Blackham's Hill to drop passengers off and collect those who wished to travel back to Springwell.

Previously the train guard had worked the points at Pelaw Main Junction, but if the Wrekenton scheme was implemented, someone would need to be there permanently during an operating day and to give both him and the equipment proper protection a small building would be needed. There was enough room to build this without encroaching on the Scheduled Ancient Monument.

10-20. The Black Fell Engine House from the south on 21st May 2010. Since then more damage and dereliction has occurred, and the trees and bushes on the left have grown to 20ft or more and completely taken over that area. All rollers and rail chairs in the area would appear to have been stolen. The area and the building are owned by Gateshead Borough Council.

It never happened. The chairman was voted off the board completely in 1991 and left the following year. Although the track to Wrekenton was eventually installed, the passenger trains that went there were never coordinated with the rope haulage; indeed, those now in charge had little interest in the rope haulage. Little money was given for its maintenance and then in 1999 a householder's new retaining wall collapsed across the West Incline. Gateshead Council showed little interest in resolving the problem. Faced with this, the rope haulage personnel lost heart and left. After 1999 the two inclines ceased to be operated.

Never since the preservation scheme began in 1976 has the Black Fell Engine House had a security fence round it, so that generations of thieves and vandals have been able to break in and steal the metal or smash everything, leaving it beyond display or repair. Some of the track and all of the West Incline rollers have disappeared. No maintenance has been done and so the incline's route and the bank head at Black Fell have become covered with bushes and trees. Gateshead Council refused to support the scheme after 2009 and stopped its grant aid. The annual maintenance programme on the Blackham's Hill electric hauler

10-21. Looking up the Blackham's Hill West Incline from near the bank foot on 21st May 2010.

10-22. Looking down the bottom section of the Blackham's Hill West Incline from the Mount Level Crossing at Eighton Banks on 21st May 2010, with the Black Fell Engine House in the distance. Two years later the three crossing gates are still present, but the crossing cabin, although padlocked, has a hole in the roof.

10-23. The top section of the Blackham's Hill West Incline from just below the bank head on 21st May 2010. Compare with picture 9-30. This section is also owned by Gateshead Borough Council.

10-24. Blackham's Hill from just below the East Incline bank head, with the kip on the left, on 21st May 2010. From Blackham's Hill eastward is owned by Sunderland City Council.

has long been abandoned and the engine left to decay in its building. Outside vegetation has spread over the kip and the electric interlocking system between Blackham's Hill and Springwell has also been abandoned. It would cost now a huge sum to overhaul the hauler, to re-instate the West Incline haulage and repair the East Incline haulage - which in any case could not be operated because all the qualified operating staff, who are the only people allowed in law to train new volunteers, have long gone. In 2010 the volunteer who was in charge of the rope haulage for the whole time that it was operated, forlornly wrote a booklet entitled *Bowes Railway Rope Haulage : A guide*, setting down all the procedures for maintaining the ropes and equipment and the hauler, and all the rules and procedures for operating the haulages, so that at least there was a final record for posterity.

The new management wanted to see the site developed differently. The company acquired various equipment from the National Coal Board, including an overhead crane made in 1883 and the Koepe winder from Murton Colliery. Examples of underground diesel and battery locomotives were acquired for exhibition, and people were allowed to bring their own wagons and locomotives to the site. A large new car park and a stronger security fence, both long needed, were installed at Springwell. To be able to say that there was still rope haulage, the small direct haulage that had been used to fly-shunt wagons into the Wagon Shop was overhauled and is now demonstrated when required, albeit without qualified volunteers. The Wagon Shop itself slowly rose to the top of English Heritage's list of buildings in North East

England severely at risk, eventually becoming so dangerous that people were banned from entering it.[5] Vehicle repairs were concentrated on making replica tubs and chaldron wagons for sale, and although some work has been done to the Railway's basic fleet, the correct colours and liveries have been abandoned, including the use of Chelsea blue to denote non-Bowes items. Six of the historic wagons were destroyed in an arson attack in 2011. All of the Railway's own volunteers have left, for various reasons, and to operate the Railway in 2010-11 volunteers have come from various other heritage sites in North-East England. The same sites have also loaned locomotives to provide additional attractions on Bowes open days, and hired a Bowes 0-4-0ST for themselves to provide the company with much-needed income.

The view of Sunderland Council's staff is that everything that is done on the Bowes Railway is the responsibility of the Bowes Railway Company. A Sunderland councillor was appointed chairman in 2011, but resigned after only five months, with the previous chairman resuming post until a new chairman took office. The company's website still (2013) proclaims that the Railway 'is the world's only surviving standard gauge operational preserved rope haulage system', despite the two Blackham's Hill inclines not having operated since 1999.

The Bowes Railway scheme is of national, even international, importance, and much hard work and investment saw the rope haulage preservation and operation achieved – and then allowed to disappear. Much discussion has taken place 'behind the scenes', even at national level, but so far (2012) no way forward has been found.

Another preservation scheme which has also sadly deteriorated the longer it has continued centres on the summit of the **Sao Paulo Railway inclines at Paranapiacaba in Brazil.** Given the inclusion of both incline systems in chapter 8, using entirely British-built equipment and 'loco brakes', the preservation scheme justifies including here. The village of Paranapiacaba itself was built to house the workers on the Railway. In 2000 it was included in World Monuments Watch and since then investment has restored some of the major buildings in the village. The Serra Nova inclines ceased commercial use in 1982, with the remaining traffic they carried passing to the new line and its electric locomotives; but Paranapiacaba, at the summit of the inclines, was served by an electric suburban service from Luz Station in Sao Paulo, and a preservation scheme developed. Surviving at Paranapiacaba was the two-cylinder horizontal stationary engine at the summit of the Serra Velha inclines, opened in 1867, an engine built by William Fairbairn of Manchester. This had ceased work in 1970, but was restored in 1984-5. Nearby at the summit of the Serra Nova system was the very impressive 1,000 h.p. triple expansion engine built jointly by Joseph Foster & Sons Ltd of Preston and Yates & Thom Ltd of Blackburn. This was completed in October 1898, commenced work in 1901 and was rebuilt in 1930; a detailed description can be found in chapter 8. Its oil-

fired boilers were available in full working order. At the 1982 closure nineteen of the twenty oil-fired 'loco brakes' also survived, at their shed at Paranapiacaba.

The initial preservation scheme retained the 5th incline in full working order and used loco brakes to operate a passenger service down to the interchange point, or 'patamar', with the former 4th incline. The scheme was opened on 30th October 1986. It would seem that this ceased in 1990 when the rope was condemned and not replaced. This left the stationary engine as a static exhibit. It was then superbly restored, retaining the old rope. Amongst vehicles brought to Paranapiacaba was the 0-6-0ST loco supplied by Sharp Stewart (works no. 1846) for the opening of the line in 1867. Other examples of the Sao Paulo Railway's historic vehicles were brought there to be stored in the sidings. Two museums were developed on the site, one for vehicles and larger artefacts, based around the former steam boiler house for the 5th Incline Engine, and the other in the former manager's house for smaller exhibits .

During the 1990s the site was opened to the public on an apparently regular basis. But after that, from the occasional reports of British visitors, it would seem that over time less and less was open to the

10-25. Loco brake 20 (RS 4035/1930) on a passenger train in 1987, during the first period of preservation. This appears to be taken at the 4th interchange ('patamar'), so the train would have descended from Paranapiacaba gripping the rope. The gauge is 5ft 3ins. Note the angled sheaves to accommodate the rope on the curves. Note that two people are sitting on the rope.

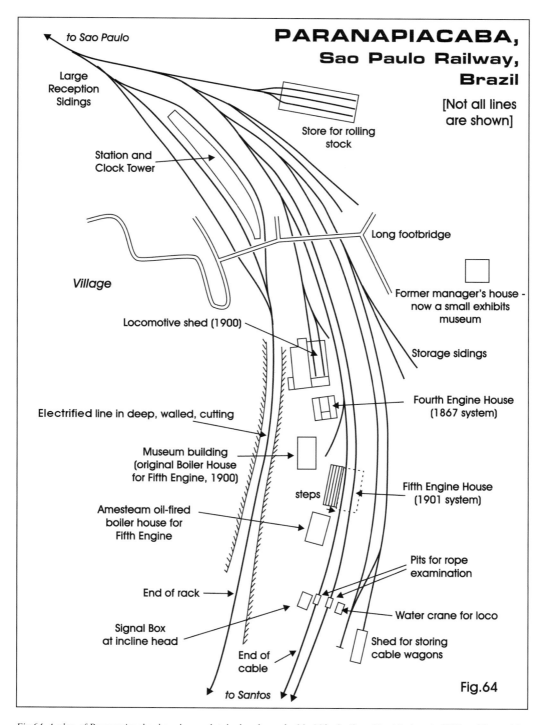

to Sao Paulo

PARANAPIACABA,
Sao Paulo Railway,
Brazil

[Not all lines
are shown]

Large
Reception
Sidings

Store for rolling
stock

Station and
Clock Tower

Long footbridge

Village

Former manager's house -
now a small exhibits
museum

Locomotive shed (1900)

Storage sidings

Electrified line in deep, walled, cutting

Fourth Engine House
(1867 system)

Museum building
(original Boiler House
for Fifth Engine, 1900)

steps

Fifth Engine House
(1901 system)

Amesteam oil-fired
boiler house for
Fifth Engine

Pits for rope
examination

End of rack

Water crane for loco

Signal Box
at incline head

Shed for storing
cable wagons

End of
cable

Fig.64

to Santos

Fig.64. A plan of Paranapiacaba, based on a sketch plan drawn by Mr. Mike Swift on his visit there in 1996 and by studying
Mr. Bruno Sanches' photographs in 2007.

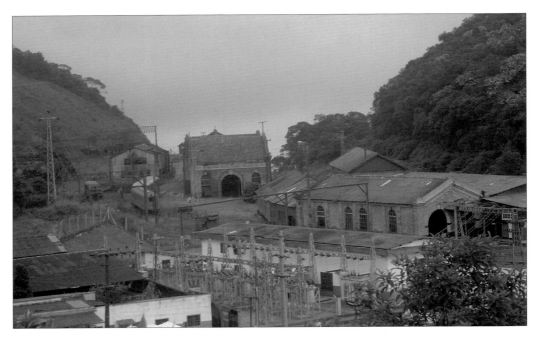

10-26. A general view of Paranapiacaba on 1st January 2003. The grey building left of centre covers the American oil-fired boilers installed in the 1950s for the 5th incline engine. In the centre of the picture, with the horizontal yellow name stone, is the former boiler house (1901) of the 5th incline engine; this now houses a museum. On the far right is the two-road steam loco shed of 1900, while behind it is the 4th incline engine house of the Serra Velha system of 1866.

10-27. Another view looking towards Santos, from the footbridge over the electrified lines on 1st December 2007. Here the loco shed is on the far left, the engine house for the 1866 engine is in the middle, then the former boiler house for the 1898 engine, now a museum, and finally the back of the building covering the 1898 engine. This is underground and entered on the opposite side down a flight of long steps.

10-28. The 4th Incline stationary engine at the summit of the Serra Velha Inclines on 1st December 2007. It was built by William Fairbairn & Co of Manchester in 1866. Note the band brake on the flywheel and on the side wall the semaphore signal with its bell, giving the signals to the engineman to begin hauling.

10-29. The same engine from the rear, this time more visibly a twin-cylinder horizontal engine. The general layout of the engine can be seen, together with the driver's position on the raised platform and his indicators. This view too was taken on 1st December 2007. Out through the door can be seen the brake-van in 10-30.

10-30. On the Serra Velha system one of these brake vehicles was used on the uphill end of every set. They were permanently attached to the rope, which can be seen here. The so-called 'clip brake', to be wound down on to the rails in an emergency, can be seen mounted centrally between the wheels. These vehicles were built by the Ashbury Company of Manchester and were originally open but were later covered in.

10-31. The historic two six-wheeled wagons used for carrying ropes, in the open, but now derelict, corrugated iron shed in which they were housed, at Paranapiacaba on 1st December 2007. Both wagons have grease axle boxes and multi-leaf laminated springs, which would suggest that they date from before the First World War and possibly much earlier.

10-32. The driver's seat, controls and instruments on the 5th Incline Engine of these inclines (Serra Nova), built in 1898 according to information on it. The box and bell on the right housed the electronic system, telling the driver to begin hauling. This replaced the original semaphore signal for this purpose (see 10-33).

10-33. Looking straight ahead, the hauler driver saw this on the far wall – a semaphore signal. This was pulled by the signalman at No.5 Patamar when the haulage system was ready for the haulermen to haul. Both pictures were taken on 1st December 2007.

10-34. Looking back along the left hand side of the magnificent 1,000 h.p. steam winding engine at Paranapiacaba built in Britain to operate the 5th Incline endless haulage on the Serra Nova system, which it did for 81 years. The driver's position can be seen on the elevated platform at the back.

public, and the permanent staff there were withdrawn to save money, leaving the buildings locked up; so that when visited in March 2010, people found that only the Sharp Stewart 0-6-0ST of 1867, burning wood and hauling a nicely-restored coach, was available, working over a distance of about one kilometre between the station and the No.5 patamar.

On 1st December 2007 a Brazilian party spent all afternoon photographing everything at Paranapiacaba, and in 3½ hours Bruno Sanches took 316 photographs, a marvellous record of how everything looked on that day. He was fortunate to visit before access to the buildings was withdrawn. Photographs 10-26 to 10-36 are selected from this wonderful record.

In 2011 no fewer than thirteen of the loco brakes were still extant, as follows:

Number	Builder	Works number	Year built	Status in 2011
2	Kerr Stuart	662	1899	Preserved at Luz Station depot, Sao Paulo
3 #	Robert Stephenson	3065	1902	Preserved at Memorial do Imigrante, Sao Paulo
4	Kerr Stuart	664	1899	Preserved at Memorial do Imigrante, Sao Paulo
7	Kerr Stuart	671 *	1900	Depot at Paranapiacaba in working order
8	Kerr Stuart	668	1900	Yard at Paranapiacaba awaiting scrap
9	Kerr Stuart	669	1900	Preserved at Museum at Tubarao, Santa Catarina state
11	Kerr Stuart	667 *	1900	Preserved at Memorial do Imigrante, Sao Paulo
14	Robert Stephenson	3066	1902	Depot at Paranapiacaba in working order
16	Robert Stephenson	3068	1902	Preserved at CPTM Station, Jundiai
17	Robert Stephenson	3112	1903	Depot at Paranapiacaba in working order
18	Robert Stephenson	3113	1903	Yard at Paranapiacaba awaiting scrap
19	Robert Stephenson	4034	1930	Yard at Paranapiacaba awaiting scrap
20	Robert Stephenson	4035	1930	Depot at Paranapiacaba in working order

originally numbered 13   * these two locomotives have swapped their original works plates

However, none of those in working order at Paranapiacaba could be steamed as the volunteers could not afford to buy the fuel oil needed, and they appeared not to have been steamed for some time.

By 2011 the station itself was fenced off and only a tourist passenger service was operated there, on an occasional basis. The two stationary engines survived, but their buildings and the former director's house, now a museum housing small exhibits (see Fig.64), were all locked up, the yard was grassed over and many of the vehicles there were derelict. The No.5 patamar was also overgrown.

10-35. The back of the loco shed on 1st December 2007 with loco brake 17, RS 3112/1903, and next to it 14, RS 3066/1902, both said to be in working order in 2011, although they had not been steamed for some time, as fuel oil is very expensive to buy.

10-36. The three derelict loco brakes, 8 KS 668/1900, 18 RS 3113/1903 and 19 RS 4034/1930, in the yard at Paranapiacaba on 1st December 2007. Bruno Sanches did not know which was which.

10-37. The now excavated and preserved area around the summit of the Denniston Incline, where the storage bins (hoppers) and the incline's drumhouse were located, on 14th October 2010.

10-38. Looking down the top section of the upper Denniston Incline, with the kips flanking the fulls road, now holding a restored 'Q' class wagon, on 14th October 2010.

Thousands of miles away some worthwhile preservation has taken place at Denniston on New Zealand's South Island, where the famous Denniston Incline closed in 1967 (see chapter 8). An earthquake the following year destroyed part of the route, but the road to Denniston and beyond remained open. Early in the twentieth century about 2,000 people lived there, but a century later this has dwindled to two homes permanently occupied and about 50 other people. However, in 1990 the Institution of Professional Engineers New Zealand marked the incline's importance as part of New Zealand's engineering heritage by placing a plaque at the bank head, and this stirred local people to form a society entitled 'The Friends of the Hill' to research, preserve and interpret Denniston's history. This in turn led in 2007 to the formation of the Denniston Heritage Charitable Trust, supported by and with representatives from national government, local government, local businesses and local people. The Trust has continued the work, and now promotes tourism to the area with 'The Denniston Experience'. The foundations of buildings at the bank head have been exposed and a wagon has been installed there. It is also now possible to visit one of the former mines and make an interactive visit underground. As with all these preserved sites, those interested in learning more should visit their websites.

10-39. Rarely in Britain is anything related to rope haulage preserved through private initiative. The restoration and preservation of one of the eight water balance inclines at the Penrhyn Quarries at Bethesda in North Wales, owned since 2007 by Welsh Slate Ltd, is to be highly commended. However, it continues to be a working quarry, and public access is limited. This picture was taken in July 2003.

On the opposite side of the world from New Zealand, a local initiative in London has a similar ambition, although in very different circumstances. Chapter 5 recounted the brief history of the Camden Incline on the London & Birmingham Railway, replaced by locomotive working in 1844 and its equipment subsequently disposed of. But the engine house vaults were beneath the track, and so were simply bricked up and abandoned when they were no longer wanted.

Camden is a very historic part of north London. Besides the railway, with the historic portals of the Primrose Hill Tunnel, there is the Regent's Canal, with its Camden Lock, a great deal of Victorian architecture and Camden Market. As in New Zealand, feeling grew amongst local residents that this rich heritage was gradually being lost, and should not only be preserved but conserved and interpreted. A Camden Civic Society already existed and a local residents' association; in 2006 they were joined by the Camden Railway Heritage Trust. The Trust drew up a list of items of railway interest, and top of this was the stationary engine vaults, a vast area measuring about 170ft long by 135ft wide.

The West Coast Main Line from Euston to Birmingham and beyond still passes over the vaults, but 150 years after these were closed, Health & Safety regulations today require that Network Rail must undertake a structural survey of them every six years. As the vaults are partially flooded, they have to be pumped out before this can be done. When the survey was carried out between mid-December 2006 and January 2007, representatives of the Camden Railway Heritage Trust were invited to inspect the vaults for themselves and were subsequently able to visit again. The vaults have been upgraded to Grade II*, and other work has been done, including the production of a railway heritage trail in Camden, all aimed at raising awareness in the local community. The main issues to be resolved are the cause of the flooding, the use(s) to which the vaults could be put and the sources of financial support to undertake the work, all major problems when money is tight and support from local and national government tends to be lacking. Again, those wishing to learn more should visit the Trust's excellent website, crht1837.org.

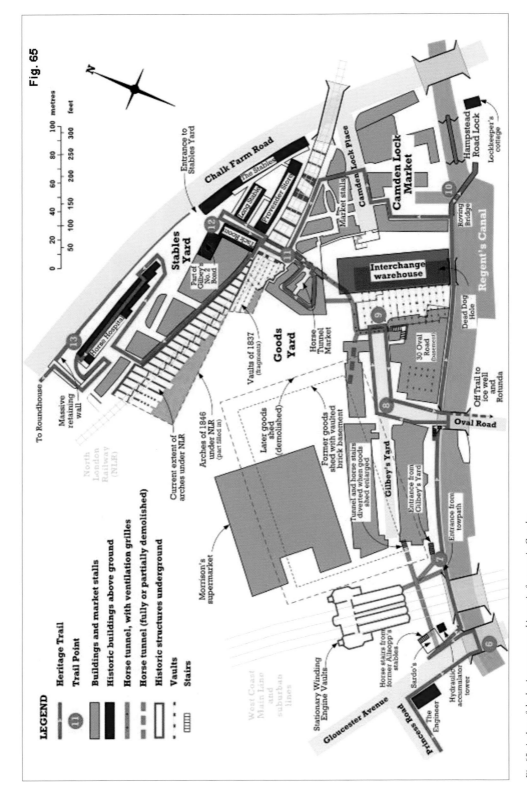

Fig.65. A plan of the heritage area and its main features in Camden.

Engine Room looking at Openings to Central Vault

10-40. The Engine Room, looking at the openings to the Sheave Rooms and the central vault in January 2007. The apex of the red V on the diagram indicates the point from which the picture was taken. Look at the quality of the brickwork and imagine the many thousands of bricks that were used for the whole vaults.

Engine Room looking at Openings to Sheave Rooms and Central Vault

10-41. The Engine Room, looking at the openings to the sheave rooms and the central vault, in January 2007. It should be remembered that the 'top half' of the diagram shows the area intended for use by the Great Western Railway but that GWR equipment was never installed and this side remained empty.

Outer Boiler Room towards Chimney

10-42. *The Outer Boiler Room, looking towards the chimney for this side in January 2007. The depth of the flooding can clearly be seen on the brickwork.*

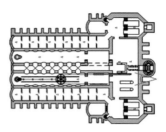

Sheave Room with Opening to Rope Tensioning Vault and Well

10-43. The sheave room, with the opening to the vault housing the rope tensioning carriage, and beyond it the well, January 2007. The sheer length of the vault is exceptional. The 'luminous spots' are other members of the party.

The final unique and fascinating example of preservation in Britain demonstrates what can be achieved with determination and persistence, even though it is a complete reconstruction of a long-vanished haulage. This can be seen at what is now the Cambridge Museum of Technology.

In 1894 Cambridge Corporation opened the Chedders Lane Sewage Pumping Station alongside the River Cam, housing two large engines built by Hathorn, Davey & Co of Leeds. These were supplied with steam from three boilers burning household rubbish. In 1923 a fourth boiler was added, built by Babcock & Wilcox Ltd of Renfrew in Scotland; this was a water-tube boiler, fired by coke. In 1926 the council installed a 1ft 7in gauge direct haulage system to carry away ash and clinker from these boilers. This incorporated a horizontal single cylindered engine built by Manlove, Alliott & Co Ltd of Nottingham, a firm better known for manufacturing laundry equipment. This drove a drum through reduction spur gearing. The ash

and clinker was carried in side-tipping tubs to a simple discharging point in former brickworks pits; the tipping point was moved as required. By the late 1950s the pits were full and the system was abandoned and subsequently cut up for scrap. In August 1968 the works, now owned by Cambridge City Council and administered through its Refuse & Sanitary Committee, was closed and replaced by electric pumps.

The Cambridge Society for Industrial Archaeology pressed upon the Council the historical importance of the site, but it took two years for the Pumping Station to be listed as a Scheduled Industrial Monument and to be opened as a museum. The Society was subsequently converted into the Cambridge Museum of Technology Trust, a registered charity. About fourteen years later the Trust obtained the freehold of the site. Other equipment has been acquired to enhance the museum, which is run by the Trust's Friends and volunteers, supported by a small annual grant from the City Council.

10-44. *The engine house and its direct haulage at the Cambridge Museum of Technology on 30th June 2011. The building was completed in 2010; as built in 1994 it had only a roof and a concrete floor, with open sides. The system demonstrates yet another use for rope haulage -the removal of ash waste from steam boilers. The downhill end of the haulage can be seen in the background.*

10-45. *The stationary engine, built about 1908; its history is given in the text. The main steam pipe, fitted with its regulator, is lagged, with the main pinion wheel on the far side. Note the wooden spool on the end of the drum shaft; its string goes up to an indicator which shows the position of the tubs on the haulage.*

10-46. The Babcock & Wilcox boiler of 1923, still supplying steam to the various stationary engines on the site, on 30th June 2011.

10-47. The three tubs, filled with ash from the present boiler, are hauled slowly up to the top of the haulage, where the return wheel is located, on 30th June 2011.

In the 1980s a group of volunteers led by Mr. Alan Denney decided that it would add to the site if the small ash haulage system could be re-constituted. Through his membership of the International Stationary Steam Engine Society, Mr. Denney discovered that a number of small steam engines were for disposal following the closure in October 1986 of Tilmanstone Colliery in Kent. One was what was known in the coal industry as a 'jack engine' – a small stationary engine installed near to a colliery shaft for winding materials and equipment to avoid using the main shaft hauler. Appreciating the museum's plans, the National Coal Board generously donated this engine to the museum, together with the considerable length of rope on its drum, provided the group dismantled and removed it. This engine had been built by John H. Wilson & Co Ltd of Liverpool and was purchased new, probably about 1908 during the sinking of the colliery. It was very similar to the numerous small steam winches that the firm produced for ships. Some 2ft 0in gauge track was acquired from the London Brick Company's brickworks at Warboys elsewhere in Cambridgeshire after it closed in 1985. Some 2ft gauge tubs were created by putting 1ft 6in gauge side-tipping bodies on to 2ft guage frames acquired from Specialist Plant Associates at Eaton Socon near St. Neots. However, the frame of one of the original tubs was discovered, and is now displayed near the haulage. The site of the old engine and the route to the brickworks pits now lies underneath a modern housing estate, but it was still possible within the site to construct a new route from the original 'ash tunnel' of the old boilers, about 250yds on a varying gradient averaging about 1 in 10. The new system was first demonstrated in 1994. For the direct haulage, the rope goes out to the far end of the run and around a pulley to come back down to what is now (2012) a set of three tubs. For quite some time the engine had just a roof over it, but in 2010 the museum was able to complete the engine house with walls and windows, and a nice parquet floor. As with the other working stationary engines at the museum, steam is supplied at about 80 p.s.i., still from the 1923 boiler, and so ash and clinker from this boiler can still be carried in the tubs. This excellent re-constructed system is normally operated, with the other engines on the site, on bank holidays.

****

Thus rope-operated haulage was developed at the very beginning of wooden waggonways in Britain in the early seventeenth century, and spread as waggonways themselves spread in the eighteenth century. Then as the First Industrial Revolution developed, industrialists in the first decades of the nineteenth century were constantly making more and more demands on waggonways and then railways, that they should cross increasingly-difficult terrain and that they should handle heavier loads and more traffic and at greater speed. The industrialists themselves responded to these demands with new inventions, processes and machine engineering, whilst the civil engineers responded with new railways. Locomotive development was part of the response, but so too was chain and then rope haulage. So although *Rocket* won the Rainhill Trials of 1829, the next decade saw increasingly-sophisticated rope haulage systems adopted on railways the length of the country, even for the carriage of passengers. But they stretched technology to its limit, and as locomotives became more powerful and reliable, rope haulages began, slowly, to disappear. Nevertheless, new rope

inclines continued to be built to carry mineral traffic, and in their narrow gauge form were seen as the answer to many transport problems, often for the transport of raw materials, across a wide range of industries. So standard gauge inclines on mineral lines and numerous narrow gauge haulages continued in use into the twentieth century, often until the industries that supported them closed down; the last commercially-operated standard gauge incline in Britain did not close until 1986, eighteen years after the end of steam locomotives on British Railways.

Often inadequately recorded and poorly understood, chain and rope haulages tended to become the forgotten element in railway history. It is hoped that this record will stimulate new research to give them the place they deserve.

1 Older stationary engines than those described here are preserved, notably in the Science Museum in London and at Crofton in Wiltshire on the Kennet & Avon Canal, where a Boulton & Watt Engine from 1809 is kept in working order; however, none of these are railway in origin.

2 Nearby on the Cromford Canal the Leawood Pumphouse is similarly demonstrated. This vertical-cylindered beam engine was built in 1849.

3 Unfortunately, in the fashion of documentary films of the time, the railwaymen are the only people who speak, and there is no commentary, so that those who are unfamiliar with the line do not know the changing locations. It is still available as a DVD.

4 Including five former NCB employees who had 252 years' service on the Railway between them.

5 Towards the end of 2012 the Bowes Railway received a six-figure grant from English Heritage towards the cost of a full repair of the Wagon Shop building, and in January 2013 this was followed by a grant of £341,000 from the Heritage Lottery Fund. Much of the latter will fund the employment of a training and outreach officer and an education officer and go towards work with rail training company Intertrain, which trains entrants to the rail industry. Money will also be spent on restoring the buildings at Springwell Bank Head. However, there would seem to be no mention of the main rope haulage or any work to restore the Blackham's Hill Engine or the two rope inclines. New discussions with Gateshead Council about the West Incline and the Black Fell Engine House began in 2012.

Indexes

Note: in giving locations in Wales, the former county names have been used

1 Haulages

2 Railways

3 Stationary engines (? indicates that the name of the engine is unknown)

4 Manufacturers of stationary engines

5 Passenger services on haulages

6 People